The Ecology of Insect Populations
in theory and practice

THE ECOLOGY OF INSECT POPULATIONS
in theory and practice

L. R. CLARK, P. W. GEIER
C.S.I.R.O., Division of Entomology, Australia
R. D. HUGHES
Australian National University
R. F. MORRIS
Department of Forestry, Canada

METHUEN & CO LTD
11 NEW FETTER LANE . LONDON EC4

First published 1967
Reprinted 1968
1·2
SBN 416 29320 4
© *L. R. Clark, P. W. Geier, R. D. Hughes*
and R. F. Morris, 1967
Printed in Great Britain
by Ebenezer Baylis and Son Limited
The Trinity Press, Worcester, and London

Distribution in the U.S.A.
by Barnes & Noble Inc.

Preface

This book is an attempt at taking stock of what is understood at present about the population dynamics of insects and the ecological aspects of pest control. It is small, and sets out only to outline the development of ecological principles and their application. Much additional reading will be necessary for those who wish to obtain a detailed knowledge of insect ecology.

The decision to write the book was made a few years ago during the course of an exercise undertaken by three of us to clarify and define our ideas. Except for R. F. Morris of the Department of Forestry, Canada, we are (or have been) members of the staff of the Division of Entomology, C.S.I.R.O., Australia, and were appointed by A. J. Nicholson when he was Chief of that Division. We all gladly acknowledge the part that his ideas have played in the development of our approach to ecological theory and practice.

In the process of defining our views, it has been necessary to appraise and criticize the work of others, and Nicholson has received his share of criticism. However, his contributions provided the theoretical basis on which we worked, and we regard our efforts as an extension of the investigations carried out by him during the past forty years. Our way of generalizing about the determination of insect numbers differs from that of Nicholson in orientation and scope, but it is essentially a development of his original concepts in a simple form which we have found useful for practical purposes. In our approach, we have been influenced also by the work of other ecologists, especially C. S. Elton, A. G. Tansley, M. E. Solomon, H. G. Andrewartha, L. C. Birch, A. Milne, C. B. Huffaker, and D. Chitty.

In various ways, many people have aided us in the preparation of the book. First of all, we thank our C.S.I.R.O. colleagues, P. B. Carne and D. P. Clark, who participated in many of our discussions, and provided us with much of the information given in Chapter 4 on *Perga affinis affinis* and *Phaulacridium vittatum* from the results of work being written up for publication. We are grateful for the helpful comments made on one or more chapters by M. E. Solomon, C. B. Huffaker, Yosiaki Itô, H. Klomp, K. Bakker, W. G. Wellington, and C. S. Holling. We wish to thank D. F. Waterhouse, present Chief of the C.S.I.R.O. Division of Entomology, for his support of our work. L. Marshall and C. Lourandos of that Division helped with the illustrations.

vii

PREFACE

The following journals kindly gave us permission to use material published in them: *American Naturalist* – excerpts from the papers of L. C. Birch (1960) and D. Pimentel (1961) published in volumes 94 and 95; *Annual Review of Entomology* – excerpts from the papers of M. E. Solomon (1957), A. J. Nicholson (1958), and H. G. Andrewartha and L. C. Birch (1960) published in volumes 2, 3 and 5; *Australian Journal of Zoology* – excerpts from the papers of A. J. Nicholson (1954a, b) and L. R. Clark (1964c), and the reproduction of figures (7, 8, 9, 10, 11, 22, 34, 35, 36 and 37) and tables (7, 12, 13) from the papers of P. W. Geier (1963a, 1964), A. J. Nicholson (1954a, b), and L. R. Clark (1962, 1963d, 1964c); *Canadian Entomologist* and *Memoirs of the Entomological Society of Canada* – excerpts, figures (31, 32, 33), and tables (1, 2, 11) from the papers of A. Milne (1957a), R. F. Morris (1957, 1963), C. R. MacLellan (1959, 1962, 1963), M. M. Neilson and R. F. Morris (1964), and K. E. Watt (1963a); *Canadian Journal of Zoology* – excerpts from the papers of W. G. Wellington (1957, 1960) and D. Chitty (1960); *Cold Spring Harbor Symposia on Quantitative Biology* – excerpts from the papers of A. J. Nicholson (1957), A. Milne (1957b), H. G. Andrewartha (1957), and L. C. Birch (1957) published in volume 22, and the reproduction of figures (23, 24) from A. J. Nicholson's paper; *Ecology* – excerpts from the papers of A. G. Tansley (1935) and F. E. Smith (1961); *Hilgardia* – reproduction of figures (25, 26, 27) from the papers of S. E. Flanders and M. E. Badgley (1963), C. B. Huffaker (1958a), and C. B. Huffaker, K. P. Shea and S. G. Herman (1963); and *Journal of Theoretical Biology* published by Academic Press Inc. – excerpts from the papers of H. G. Andrewartha and T. O. Browning (1961), and A. Milne (1962).

We thank also the following publishers for permission to quote copyright material from books: Chapman and Hall – for an excerpt reprinted from *Biological Control of Insect Pests and Weeds* (ed. P. DeBach) which was published in 1964; George Allen and Unwin – for excerpts reprinted from *The Ascent of Life* by T. A. Goudge, published in 1961; John Murray – for excerpts reprinted from *The Origin of Species* by Charles Darwin, published in 1859; Sidgwick and Jackson – for excerpts reprinted from *Animal Ecology* by C. S. Elton, published in 1927; and The University of Chicago Press – for excerpts reprinted from *The Distribution and Abundance of Animals* by H. G. Andrewartha and L. C. Birch, published in 1954.

Finally, we would like to express our gratitude to the authors who were agreeable to letting us quote as seemed necessary from their published work, and for permission to use their figures or tables. We have done our best in the difficult matter of using statements out of context to describe

the observations and ideas of others, and hope that the authors concerned
will feel that they have been treated fairly.

Canberra,   L.R.C.
January 1966   P.W.G.

Contents

CONTENTS

4 THE FUNCTIONING OF LIFE SYSTEMS

5 THE STUDY OF NATURAL POPULATIONS

CONTENTS

6 THE ECOLOGY OF PEST CONTROL

CHAPTER I

Population and environment

I.I INTRODUCTION

In nature, insect species exist and evolve as components of 'communities' of plants and animals in particular habitats. Some insect species, including many plant feeders, exist only in one type of community; others, including many predators, exist as members of a number of community types which may differ greatly in floral and faunal composition. All insect species have a limited distribution range; and, characteristically, insect numbers fluctuate to a greater or lesser extent both in time and in space.

Anyone like ourselves who, for economic reasons, attempts to investigate and explain the numbers of an insect species has to appreciate these realities and their attendant complexities. He has to learn how to think clearly about the elements, events, and processes involved in the determination of insect numbers in order to plan an investigation adequately, and to provide a comprehensive and balanced interpretation of the results. For clarity of thought, it is necessary to define two basic concepts.

The concepts of primary importance to the investigator concerned with either the local or overall abundance of an insect species are those denoted by the words 'population' and 'environment'. Both are words in general use – 'population' referring originally to the group of people inhabiting a particular area – and 'environment' referring to the region, surroundings, or circumstances in which anything exists. The ecological meanings attached to these words can affect the way in which investigations are conducted, the manner in which results are interpreted, and the degree of understanding that is achieved. Because quantitative field studies on the dynamics of specific populations are a recent development in ecology, it is not surprising that leading theorists have different ideas of population and environment, and have disagreed vigorously in their opinions.

I.2 CURRENT CONCEPTS OF POPULATION AND ENVIRONMENT

Let us consider the views of a philosopher, T. A. Goudge, who is interested in evolution, and those of some leading ecological theorists, as expressed in the following extracts.

Goudge (1961):

Population. . . . the term 'population' applies to any collection of individual organisms which is such that it persists . . . through a finite though vaguely delimited span of time in a vaguely delimited region of space . . .; it is a type of open system which interacts with the environment and is analysable into various sub-systems such as demes. . . .

Further, since a population is an open system, we may speak of it as an 'entity' or a 'whole', provided we do not allow ourselves to think that we are referring to something which has an independent status apart from individual organisms and their interrelationships.

Environment. The complexity is so great, indeed, that an exhaustive description of it cannot be given; or, at any rate, cannot be other than an ideal limit to which description may try to approximate. It will be sufficient . . . to mention certain large-scale aspects and to ignore details. Thus 'the environment' of a particular local population includes: (*i*) the purely physical or abiotic *milieu* in which the population exists, including its geographical location, the prevailing climatic conditions, terrain, etc.; (*ii*) the organic or biotic *milieu*, including the non-living organic matter and all the other local populations of plants and animals in that region. For each individual member of the population, the 'environment' includes, in addition to (*i*) and (*ii*), the other members of the population . . .

Nicholson (1957):

Population. . . . a group of interacting and interbreeding individuals which normally has no contact with other groups of the same species. That is to say it is a discrete dynamic unit of a species population . . . a population is something more than a concept. It has a similar objective reality to a family, or a tribe, or a nation.

Environment. . . . an 'environment' is not an entity in its own right; instead it is the complement of some particular entity which needs to be specified before the term has any meaning. . . . when discussing the environment of an individual, I distinguish between 'the population', or the 'other individuals', and '*the environment*', this word being used to refer to the totality of external factors which influence a population . . .

Andrewartha and Birch (1954):

Population. . . . a group of individuals each having an environment which resembles those of its neighbors but differs from theirs if only because the environment of an individual includes its neighbors but not itself.

Andrewartha (1961):

Environment. . . . the environment of an animal is everything that may influence its chance to survive and multiply.

Milne (1962, 1957b):

Population. . . . the number of individuals of a particular species existing in a particular place. Population, of course, changes in time.

Environment. . . . the effective environment must be defined with respect to the individual because the population is itself an environmental factor having effect on the individual according to density. . . . The effective environment is everything else in the universe *which affects the fulfilment of the organism.*

Solomon (1949):

Population. . . . a number of organisms of the same species forming a more or less frequently interconnected group, separated more or less clearly from other groups of the species.

Environment. . . . for the most part we are faced with an intricately combined action by population and environment together. Hence any idea that the environment can be clearly distinguished from the population on a functional basis is illusory . . . *the population functions in relation to a whole which includes itself.* It is therefore better to think of the population as an integral part of the ecosystem. If we wish to consider the population as an entity in relation to its ecological setting, that setting should be the ecosystem, rather than an imaginary 'ecosystem minus the population', called the environment. This is not to say that the environment concept should not be used, but rather that we should remember its defects and be ready to replace it whenever necessary.

The generalized descriptions of population and environment provided by Goudge are careful attempts at logical definition, and may be adopted therefore as a basis for consideration of the pragmatic definitions of the ecological theorists. To these definitions must be added further description in order to show how the different ecological theorists think basically about the functioning of populations and their environments in the determination of abundance. Concepts of population and environment should be applicable generally. They should be of value not only in studies on the population dynamics of single species, but also in the investigation of integrated groups of populations in plant-animal communities.

Unlike the other theorists mentioned, Nicholson (1954b, 1957, 1958) has chosen to treat populations quite emphatically as entities. In his view, populations, granted the environmental resources necessary for continuity, function as systems which, *per medium* of such 'mechanisms' as intraspecific competition, 'adjust' ('regulate' or 'govern') their numbers 'in relation to their own properties and those of their environments' (see section 3.21). Some populations can be termed 'self-adjusting' in the sense that interactions between their members are instrumental in preventing increase to self-destroying numbers. However, conceptual difficulties arise in applying the idea of self-adjustment to populations whose growth is normally limited by the density-related action of natural enemies – the effects of which always depend to a considerable extent on conditions other than the population density of the prey species.

B

3

For this reason, and because the idea of self-adjustment on the part of a population requires even more qualification when one takes into account the coexistence and interdependence of populations in plant-animal communities, Nicholson's concept of populations as self-adjusting systems is unsatisfactory as a generalization.

Andrewartha and Birch recognize that some populations may have evolved self-adjusting mechanisms (incorporating, in certain cases, reversible genotypic changes) but, in the words of Andrewartha (1959), they regard such mechanisms as 'a small and very particular part of the general ecological theory of environment'. Unlike Nicholson, they consider that the numbers of natural populations are frequently determined without the operation of such mechanisms (see section 3.22). According to them, populations are groups of individuals, each of which has a somewhat different environment – because they have chosen to define environment in relation to the individual animal.

Their approach, with its emphasis on environmental components, involves some dichotomy of thought. On the one hand, the population is regarded as the object of study – in terms of specific properties, density, dispersion, birth rate, death rate, and even self-adjustment of numbers – and, on the other, the environment is considered only in terms of an individual animal. The awkwardness of the dichotomy is not eliminated by the device of describing the influence of environment in statistical terms, i.e. as the probability of survival and reproduction of an average individual.

On the basis of Goudge's definition, the Andrewartha-Birch concept of environment is unnecessarily restrictive. After all, a population is as much an ecological as an evolutionary unit (see Andrewartha and Birch 1954) – the same elements, events, and processes being involved in the determination of numbers as in evolution. Moreover, if 'a science of community ecology may eventually be built on the base provided by population ecology' (Andrewartha 1961), the concept 'environment of an individual' could not be maintained exclusively.

Milne (1957a, 1957b, 1962) largely accepts the Andrewartha-Birch restriction, but formulates his idea of the role of populations in a somewhat different way (see section 3.23). He attaches more importance to the influence of population density, e.g. in conditioning the action of some natural enemies, and considers intraspecific competition to be the 'ultimate controlling factor for [population] increase'. Milne's need to write not only about environment in relation to the individual, but also at length about 'environmental capacity', a concept which has meaning only in relation to a population, exemplifies the inadequacy of the restricted definition.

Of the definitions listed, only that of Solomon (1949) *emphasizes* explicitly the inseparable existence of population and environment. After considering the circumstances in which population numbers are determined in nature, he wrote: 'The most realistic view, though not invariably the most useful, is one which embraces the whole complex of population and environment'; and went on to introduce the well-known idea of *ecosystem* proposed by Tansley (1935) to describe, in the functional sense, natural complexes of plant and animal populations and the particular sets of physical conditions under which they exist. Ecosystems are, or tend to become, stable states of existence in which the population numbers of the component species fluctuate within circumscribed limits.

Because of the 'all-embracing' and 'subtle' nature of that concept (Andrewartha and Birch 1954), and the idea that it 'can not lead far in the problem of natural control' (Milne 1957b), the approach advocated by Solomon was rejected by the other theorists, and not developed further by its author. As a result, progress in the philosophy of ecology has been retarded considerably because Solomon's approach is the only one which:

(*i*) expresses a full appreciation of the fact that a population and its environment, however delimited and defined, are complementary elements in a *system*, and interact in the ecological events and processes which are involved in the determination of population numbers; and

(*ii*) links the study of specific populations with the study of communities and, hence, ecology with evolution.

1.3 THE LIFE SYSTEM CONCEPT

The approach advocated by Solomon can be used in the study of the dynamics of specific populations simply by regarding that part of an ecosystem which determines the existence, abundance, and evolution of a particular population as the 'life system' of that population. Thus a life system is composed of a subject population and its effective environment which includes the totality of external agencies influencing the population, including man (in practice, those biotic and abiotic agencies whose influence can be observed and, preferably, measured). As Goudge has said, for each member of a population, the environment also includes the other members.

The components of a life system are depicted in figure 1. The inherited properties of the subject species, in the form of an array of genotypes, mould matter and energy supplied by environmental resources into phenotypes – the individuals of the species. The inherited ability of individuals to survive and multiply and the conditions for existence provided by the effective environment, namely 'supplies' of *all* kinds and limited repressive action by inimical agencies, enable them to form a population with group (statistical) characteristics which result from their collective existence. Basically, the persistence and abundance of a population are the outcome of interactions between the inherited properties of individuals and the intrinsic attributes of the effective environment. In other words, the intrinsic qualities of the subject species and those of its environment are the *co-determinants* of population numbers. These co-determinants define the actual reproductive ability of individuals, and the extent to which immigration adds to the population; they also define the extent to which individuals are removed prematurely by mortality and emigration.

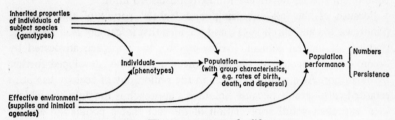

FIGURE I. The components of a life system.

The idea of life system has none of the apparent exclusiveness or bias of some other concepts of population and environment. It imposes no restrictions *a priori* on thought about *how* population numbers are held within observed limits, and, by associating the study of single species with the study of communities, it draws attention to the essential unity of ecology. It is as flexible in application as the idea of ecosystem (see section 3.12). The spatial delimitation of a life system depends simply on spatial delimitation of the population to be studied – a matter mainly of purpose and convenience. For example, the idea can be used to include all local populations of a species that are linked to some degree by dispersal or by migration, or for a single local population. When a species exists in the form of isolated populations, it has as many life systems as it has populations.

Although something of a truism, the idea of life system can serve to provide beginners with useful orientation in the task of understanding the value of viewpoints and concepts in population ecology, and experienced workers with the sometimes-needed reminder that a population and its environment are interdependent elements which function together as a system. We found the idea more useful than the available alternatives when thinking and writing about the ecological and evolutionary aspects of pest control.

CHAPTER II

Numerical change in insect populations

2.1 INTRODUCTION

In common with the majority of other organisms, the body temperature of insects is largely determined by the temperature of their surroundings. Within the range of ambient temperatures to which insects are naturally exposed, the rates of their physiological processes vary directly with temperature. Thus, in many places, the seasonal, cyclical, and other variations of weather exert a profound influence on the *rates* of change of insect numbers. However, in considering the relationships between the physiological processes of the individuals in a population of an insect species and the other organisms which are involved in the numerical changes of the population, it can be assumed that the life functions of *all* biotic components of the life system react to variations of temperature in essentially the same way. Consequently, it is possible to consider the rates of those processes on a physiological time-scale (e.g. calculated as the product of time and effective temperature, see Hughes 1962, 1963), and thereby to eliminate much of the variation caused directly by changes in temperature. The following introductory discussion is based on such a concept of 'physiological time' in order to simplify initially the problem of change in insect numbers.

If the size of an insect population in an area is estimated at frequent intervals, e.g. by sampling, a graph can be drawn showing the variation of numbers with time. Such graphs are usually called population curves. They can, for example, be used to depict, for many successive generations, the population numbers of a particular developmental stage which is easy to sample in the field (see section 5.7). More detailed population curves show estimates of the total number of individuals, or of population density, as it varies within a generation. Such curves usually reflect the influence of seasonal conditions on population numbers.

When the seasonal population curves for different species of insect are compared, it is found that there are only a few basic patterns of short-term temporal change. These patterns are characteristic of the life histories of the species concerned.

7

The annual cycle of an insect species may consist of a single generation. Since numerical increase for an insect species can result only from egg laying (or larviposition), the pattern of numerical increase depends upon the duration of the oviposition period relative to the time taken by the rest of the life cycle (figure 2). If the oviposition period is relatively short, an early asymmetrical peak of numbers is usually observed. If the oviposition period is longer in comparison, the peak of numbers is less pronounced and more symmetrical. When the oviposition period is very long, no marked peak of numbers occurs and a smooth population curve is obtained.

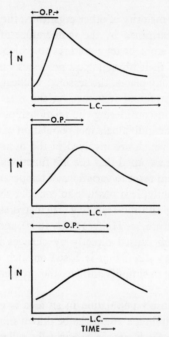

I GURE 2. Patterns of numerical change when the duration of the oviposition period changes relative to the whole life cycle.

A relatively short oviposition period frequently results in a preponderance of one developmental stage at any particular time. In each developmental stage, the pattern of numbers in time tends to be similar in form to that for the whole population curve. However, because of normal variation in the time taken to complete a developmental stage, the time taken by the whole population to complete successive stages increases, and the overlap between stages becomes more pronounced. (Figure 3A shows an example when the mean duration of stages is taken as constant.)

8

When the season favourable for development is long, two or more generations of a species may occur each year. Successive generations often show different patterns of numerical change. A well-defined break of diapause at the end of winter, or after a period of summer drought, is often followed by a short period of concentrated oviposition, and numbers in the first generation may rise rapidly to an early asymmetrical peak. Because of

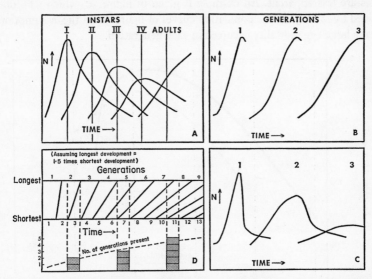

FIGURE 3. A. Normal variation of development of individuals increases the time the whole population spends in successive nymphal instars and increases the overlap between instars.

B. Showing the lengthening of oviposition periods in successive generations caused by normal variation of development times of individuals.

C. Showing how the effect of an age-specific mortality in the egg stage is increasingly obscured in the numerical pattern of successive generations because of the prolongation of the oviposition period.

D. Normal variation in the development time of individuals of a continuously-reproducing species will lead to increasing overlap of successive generations until individuals of many generations are present and indistinguishable.

normal variation in the time taken to complete development during the first generation, the oviposition period of the second generation tends to be longer than that of the first, showing a more symmetrical peak of numbers. For the same reason, the population curve for a third successive generation tends to be flatter than that of the second generation (figure 3B).

The mode of decline from the peak of insect numbers after oviposition can be expected to vary with the mortality to which a population is subjected. If the mortality affects only one developmental stage of the insect, i.e. is markedly 'age-specific', this will be indicated clearly by the population curve of species which have a relatively short oviposition period. When the oviposition period is long relative to the time taken to complete subsequent development, individuals belonging to different developmental stages are present at the same time and, consequently, age-specific mortalities are less apparent. An example is given in figure 3C, which was obtained by modifying the population curves of figure 3B on the assumption that a large egg mortality occurred in each generation.

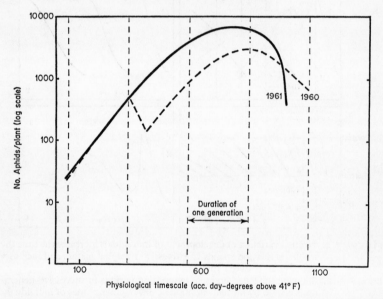

FIGURE 4. Population curves of the cabbage aphid *B. brassicae*, in which overlapping generations cause numerical trends longer than the average duration of one generation, i.e. 250 day-degrees above 41°F. (Modified from Hughes 1963.)

Up to now, we have considered species in which the successive generations are either distinct, i.e. completely separated in time, or overlapping but represented by individuals of distinctly different age. If the favourable season is very long, more than three generations may occur. The process by which normal variation in developmental time prolongs the presence of successive developmental stages within a generation also extends the time during which successive generations are represented, so that they overlap increasingly (figure 3D).

In such circumstances, individuals of two or more generations may be reproducing at the same time and successive generations become indistinguishable. Patterns of oviposition and age-specific mortality within a particular generation are mingled with those of other generations, and both reproduction and mortality proceed at 'average' rates. The complete overlapping of generations is therefore characterized by the absence of short-term change in population numbers. Numbers tend to rise and fall over periods longer than the time taken to complete a generation. The relatively slow numerical changes are analogous to those shown by human populations. The aphids of temperate regions show marked overlapping of generations and numerical fluctuations of this type (e.g. see figure 4 and Hughes 1963).

2.2 A GENERALIZED DESCRIPTION OF NUMERICAL CHANGE

Change in the shape of a population curve over any length of time depends only on the changing relation between births and deaths. The peaked curves in figures 2 and 3C result from an initial period when births greatly exceed deaths, followed by a period during which the reverse obtains. When the oviposition period is relatively long, more deaths occur during the period of population increase and the resulting curve tends to be flatter and more symmetrical. Finally, in the situation in which successive generations overlap, young continue to be produced as other individuals die, and any excess of births over deaths and *vice versa* results in slow changes in population numbers.

In order to discuss the species characteristics (i.e. the observable manifestations of inherent properties), and the environmental influences which cause the fluctuations typical of population numbers, it is useful to generalize about population change. A general description of population change can be obtained by imagining a population curve divided into very short time segments which can be defined precisely in terms of the number of insects present initially and the rate of numerical change. The rate of change will, of course, be the difference between the numbers of births and deaths which occur during the interval.

Each segment of the curve can be defined mathematically by the equation:

$$N_t = N_o e^{(b-d)t} \tag{1}$$

where t is a very short interval of time;

N_t the number of insects after time t;

N_o the number of insects at the beginning of the interval;

b the birth rate during time t;

d the death rate during time t; and

e   is a constant which, for convenience, is taken as the base of Napierian logarithms.

This demographic equation is basic to most theoretical discussions of population dynamics in the literature, although the equation itself may be presented in different mathematical forms. The exponential term $e^{(b-d)t}$ is sometimes written e^r, the difference term r being called the natural rate of increase of the population. By dealing only with very short time segments, equations of this form can be used to describe any type of population curve, i.e. their use does not imply that a curve has any particular form.

In practice, studies of insect numbers usually have to be restricted to 'sub-populations' of a species within limited areas. In such areas, population numbers are affected by the movement of individuals to and from them. For this reason, the general equation for population change has to be modified to incorporate the effects of such movements. The equation now becomes:

$$N_t = N_o e^{(b-d)t} - E_t + I_t \qquad (2)$$

where E_t represents the number of individuals that leave an area in time t, and

I_t the number which enter it.

Changes in the shape of the population curve result from any influences changing the values of the terms on the right hand side of equation (2).

It is important at this stage to recall the simplifying assumptions made at the beginning of this chapter because certain environmental components may affect the course of a numerical response to any other influence. The dependence on temperature of numerical changes is of major importance. The response to a favourable influence can only occur at a rate governed by the ambient temperature. Weather, with its seasonal and perhaps shorter cycles, is clearly an environmental component whose attributes affect the *rate* of numerical change directly, and numerical change itself, through the interaction of temperature-dependent and temperature-independent events. Again, the numerical response of a subject population to any short-term change of environmental influences cannot always be direct. This is because adaptation has resulted in 'programming' of the species' sequence of physiological processes (i.e. life cycle) to fit in with the basic seasonal fluctuations of the environment.

Before considering the influences which affect the rates of birth, death, and movement, the significance of the initial number of insects in the equation must be made clear. N_o represents the combined numbers of the different age-groups of individuals present in the population. In insect populations, these groups could be: eggs; the different larval or nymphal stages; pupae; immature adults; reproducing females and males; and post-reproductive adults; some or all of which might be present at any particular time. N_o obviously depends on the history of population change, and this dependence can be shown to account partly for the proportions of the initial numbers formed by different age-groups.

The species characteristics and environmental influences which affect population numbers find their expression in the birth rate, the death rate, and the rates of movement into and out of an area. For each rate, however, the interactions between their co-determinants differ quantitatively. The birth rate of a population is determined primarily by the characteristics of the subject species, and environmental influences play a modifying role. Conversely, the death rate is determined primarily by environmental influences with species characteristics in the modifying role. In the determination of dispersal rates, species characteristics and environmental influences interact with different effects on individuals, causing some to move out of an area and others to remain there. In the outcome of movement, neither species characteristics nor environmental influences can be said, in general, to play a dominant role.

A comprehensive catalogue of all the influences affecting birth rates, death rates and movement would be a long and tedious document. The following abbreviated discussion has been included to bring out certain general features of the multiplicity of influences which should be looked for in any study of an insect population. To give a practical theme, examples derived from studies of a single kind of insect, namely the tsetse flies, will be used where possible to present a naturally-integrated sequence. Most entomologists are familiar with the unusual life history pattern of *Glossina* spp. The extensive studies made on these flies have been reviewed by Jackson (1949), Buxton (1955), and recently, from the point of view of population ecology, by Glasgow (1963).

2.3 INFLUENCES AFFECTING THE BIRTH RATE

The birth rate of a population can best be defined from the amount that the initial number of individuals would be increased during the short time interval t in the absence of any mortality or movement to and from an area. When the terms for these factors are removed from equation (2), the change in numbers results from multiplying N_o by e^{bt}. From such a term the value of b can be defined precisely by the use of exponential tables.

If the time interval is short enough, the birth rate will approximate closely to the fraction by which the population could have increased during time t by the production of offspring, i.e. to Y_t/N_o. The usefulness of this approximation is seen in the normal expression of human birth rates in terms of 'numbers of live offspring per 1,000 of population'. It is helpful to set out the fraction Y_t/N_o fully in order to see how species characteristics and environmental influences may affect the birth rate of a population:

$Y_t/N_o =$ *total number of offspring produced during time t/ (no. eggs +*
no. larvae + no. pupae + no. immature females + no. repro-
ducing females + no. post-reproductive females + no. males).

Clearly, the number of influences affecting the birth rate during a short time t will be related to the number of age-groups present in the population at the time.

To illustrate the point, tsetse fly populations are made up largely of two free-living cohorts – puparia, and reproductive adults. *Glossina* spp. are ovoviviparous and the larvae, which are deposited at a late stage of development, dig into the ground and pupate. Normally, no post-reproductive adults are present, both sexes being fertile as long as they live. In such a population, the birth rate would be affected by:

(*i*) *The average fecundity of the females* – i.e. the potential number of young they could produce in the time. Tsetse flies are able to produce about twelve young per female, i.e. about two per month (Jackson 1949). The potential reproductive ability of a species is of primary importance in the study of population dynamics.

(*ii*) *The average fertility of the females* – i.e. the realized production of offspring resulting from the modification of fecundity either by physiological factors or by fertilization success, where that is necessary.

Environmental influences such as weather and the available food supply may limit the number of offspring left per female not only by their effects on longevity (see section 2.4) but also by restricting egg production and oviposition in other ways. For example, the temperature range within which reproduction can occur is often much narrower than the range over which other activities remain normal (see Pospelov 1926, Wigglesworth 1950). Both for plant-feeding and other insects, the quality and quantity of the food supply may exert a marked effect on the number of eggs laid per female. For instance, egg production in the Colorado beetle *Leptinotarsa* varies according to the species of potato on which the larvae are reared (Trouvelot and Grison 1935).

With female tsetse flies, three large blood meals are required for the development of each larva to full size (Mellanby 1937), and fertility will be low unless the supply of blood is adequate. When the numbers of tsetse attacking a host are very high, a form of reciprocal interference acting *via* irritation of the host species results in reduced fertility (Glasgow 1963).

There is usually a clear relationship between the size of a female insect and the number of eggs which it can develop (Waloff 1958). This size-fecundity relationship probably operates through the size of the foodstore accumulated during development and converted later to egg yolk. Shortage of food may therefore decrease fecundity. Again, if a prolonged resting-stage, such as a diapause, occurs between the time of food accumulation and that of egg-maturation, the length of the diapause period will be reflected in the fertility of females (Waloff *et al.* 1948). The use of foodstores to produce mature eggs sometimes reduces the chances of survival of females if they fail to find sufficient food. Under these circumstances some of the eggs may be resorbed to provide nourishment, and the fertility of the females will be lower.

In many species of insect, one impregnation is sufficient for a female for as long as she is capable of reproduction: in other species, however, one batch of eggs is laid at a time and mating must precede each oviposition, e.g. *Thermobia domestica* (Sweetman 1938).

In the case of tsetse flies, one impregnation, usually at the time of her first blood meal, enables a female to produce her full complement of young. The habit of swarming around moving animals exhibited by newly-emerged males makes impregnation of the females virtually certain at all but exceptionally low population densities (Glasgow 1963).

(*iii*) *The sex ratio* – i.e. the proportion of females in the population. In most species, including tsetse flies, approximately half of the individuals born are females, but there are numerous well-known exceptions, e.g. among the parasitic Hymenoptera. In many parasitic species, facultative parthenogenesis occurs, the unfertilized eggs giving rise to males (arrhenotoky). The sex ratio, and therefore the birth rate, vary with the conditions that affect mating or fertilization, e.g. population density and the prevailing weather. In certain ichneumonids and encyrtids, the sex of the offspring is related directly or indirectly to the size of the host insect attacked, male parasites being more numerous than females in the emergences from the smaller hosts and *vice versa* in the case of the larger hosts (e.g. see Seyrig 1935, Clark 1962).

Male tsetse flies have a considerably shorter adult life than females which results in a sex ratio favouring the females of roughly 2 : 1 (Jackson 1944). This may well be a very important adaptation for maximizing the birth rate (Glasgow 1963). It is interesting to note that the different behaviour patterns of male and female tsetse flies cause the swarms which irritate host animals to be largely composed of males. It has been observed, however, that the number of males is generally directly proportional to the population density in an area (Glasgow 1963).

Other influences. The birth rate of a population is affected by the presence of non-reproducing females. In the determination of the relative numbers of reproducing and non-reproducing females, a multiplicity of influences and processes become involved in variations of the birth rate.

15

In most species, the mortality of females increases sharply after the completion of oviposition, e.g. *Erioischia brassicae* (figure 5), but environmental conditions may affect the longevity of post-reproductive individuals considerably. An example of this is seen in the cabbage aphid *Brevicoryne brassicae*, post-reproductive females of which live proportionally much longer at 7°C than at higher temperatures (Bonnemaison 1951).

The proportion of reproducing females in a population depends on four factors. The first is the length of the oviposition period compared with the

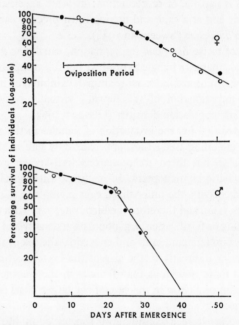

FIGURE 5. Patterns of mortality in two caged populations (o and ●) of the anthomyiid fly *Erioischia brassicae* showing the change in mortality rate after the reproductive phase is completed.

rest of the life cycle. The longer the oviposition period, the higher will be the proportion of reproducing females. Secondly, the birth rate itself will affect the proportion, for where the rate is high the proportion of immature individuals will tend to be higher compared with the number of reproducing females, and the number of post-reproductives will tend to be lower. Thirdly, Cole (1954) has shown that any influences that shift forward the modal point of oviposition in a generation cause an increase in the birth rate. Thus shortening of the development period, or of the reproductive period (if there is no decrease in fertility), increases the birth rate. On the other hand, the facultative occurrence of a stage of arrested development in the life cycle has the effect of reducing the birth rate of a population. Many environmental influences may be involved in determining the length of the developmental and oviposition periods of female insects. Of such influences, weather conditions and food are probably the most important.

Finally, environmental influences can affect the proportion of reproducing females directly by causing age-specific mortality immediately before oviposition begins.

2.4 INFLUENCES AFFECTING THE DEATH RATE

The death rate of a population can be defined in a similar way to the birth rate as the amount by which initial numbers would be reduced during a short interval of time in the absence of births and of movements to and from an area. When the terms for these factors are removed from equation (2), the change in numbers results from multiplying N_o by e^{-dt}. Exponential tables can be used to determine d, but a good approximation is given by dividing the total number of deaths during a short time interval t by the total number of insects present initially.

Since death can occur at any stage in the life cycle of an insect, the species characteristics and environmental influences which affect the relative numbers in each age-group are often of primary importance in determining the effect of a particular mortality on the death rate of a population. Only if the mortality is not age-specific will its influence on the death rate be independent of the age-structure of the population. Any age-specific mortality will affect the death rate to an extent dependent upon the proportion of the population represented by the age-group concerned. The various causes of mortality should therefore be considered as to whether they are selective or indiscriminate in action. In addition to affecting the death rate in a different way from indiscriminate destruction, selective mortality may also affect the proportion of reproducing females in a population, and hence the birth rate.

Much has been written about the causes of mortality in insects and the reader should consult such well-known texts as those of Allee *et al.* (1949) and Andrewartha and Birch (1954) for detailed accounts of the many environmental influences, species characteristics, and interactions involved. Bakker's (1964) classification of the interactions that occur within life systems is also helpful. Among other things, he draws attention to the need to distinguish between the direct determinants of death, e.g. starvation, and the causal influences that lead to death, e.g. food shortage in an area and such processes as inter- or intra-specific competition for food.

The causes of mortality may be outlined as follows:

(*i*) *Ageing*. The percentage of individuals in a natural population which die from 'old age' is usually small, but varies from one species to another. In populations where the reproductive rate is low (for any reason) the numbers in older age groups will be relatively high, and senility may become an important component of total mortality. The age-structure of tsetse fly populations shown by Saunders (1962) indicates that tsetse may frequently die of old age.

(*ii*) *Low vitality*. Many environmental agencies which cause mortality, first weaken an insect and later kill it. Some may weaken an insect and thereby render it more liable to destruction by other agencies. In such cases, it is often useful to ascribe the death of an insect to low vitality. In tsetse flies, lower vitality may be involved in the shorter life of the males. In some insect species, changes in the average vitality of individuals occur from generation to generation, e.g. *Malacosoma pluviale* (Wellington 1960). Such changes may be inherent and may be regarded therefore as species characteristics.

(*iii*) *Accidents*. Accidental death is quite common among insects – especially death caused by malfunctions of the moulting process. Similarly, failure to expand fully the imaginal wings usually has fatal consequences.

Death often comes to a predator or parasite through the mechanical effects of the defence mechanism of its prey or host. The mechanisms most commonly fatal involve the ejection of a sticky fluid by the prey species, which often causes glueing-together of the wings or mouthparts of predators. As for the tsetse flies, irritated host animals use their tails to swat them (Glasgow 1963)!

(*iv*) *Physico-chemical conditions*. Extremes of temperature are usually fatal to insects. The mortalities caused are often selective, because one or more of the developmental stages of many insect species have a much higher tolerance than the others. Adults and pupae of tsetse fly occurring in relatively unfavourable sites, e.g. places where there is little shade, are killed rapidly by high temperatures during hot dry periods. However, it is unusual for temperature to cause catastrophic mortality because most species are well-adapted to the variations of physical conditions in their normal habitats.

Pollution and anoxia are quite common causes of death in populations of aquatic insects, especially in species which respire through gills. An interesting example of asphyxiation in a terrestrial form is provided by the lettuce root aphid *Pemphigus bursarius* which forms galls on poplars. Predatory anthocorid bugs enter open galls and feed on a few of the aphids therein. The aphids which are not attacked die from the fumigant effect of chemicals produced by the stink-glands of the bugs (Dunn 1960).

(v) Natural enemies. The species that either prey upon insects or parasitize them are usually classified as predators, parasites and pathogens. However, as is usual with such classifications, it is difficult to define the borderline between each category.

Predators. Insects form part or all of the diet of a vast number of animal species including vertebrates. Fishes, amphibia, and reptiles all utilize insects as a major source of food, some species being adapted anatomically to this end, e.g. the archer fishes and chameleons. Among the birds, there are numerous groups with highly-specialized insectivorous habits. Mammals predacious on insects include bats and the Insectivora.

Among the insects themselves, 'the habit of feeding upon other insects is found in all the major orders . . .' (Clausen 1940). In many instances, predacious insects are free-living in all stages except the egg. Characteristically, individual predators need to consume a number of prey individuals in order to reach maturity. They kill and consume prey either immediately or within a short space of time, and consequently acts of predation may rarely be observed. Some species feed indiscriminately upon all developmental stages of their prey; others cause selective mortalities. Solomon (1949) introduced the idea of 'functional' response to describe changes in the number of prey killed per predator, and 'numerical' response to describe changes in the numbers of a predator species induced by changes in the density of prey.

Among the many predators which attack tsetse flies (e.g. birds, dragonflies, robberflies, bembicine wasps), are web-spinning spiders the effects of which have been estimated quantitatively. Glasgow (1963) reports that *Hersilia* sp. caused 17% mortality per week in a population of *Glossina swynnertoni*.

Parasites. The parasites of insects include those insect species (frequently regarded as a special kind of predator) whose larvae feed internally or externally upon single host individuals and eventually kill them. Certain nematode worms are also classified as parasites of insects.

Three orders of insects contain many species adapted to the parasitic mode of life, namely Hymenoptera, Diptera, and Strepsiptera, and the reader is referred to Clausen (1940) for a detailed account of their biology. Like most insect species, tsetse flies are attacked by a number of species of parasitic insect, particularly by Mutillidae (Hymenoptera) and Bombyliidae (Diptera) (Chorley 1929).

Characteristically, parasitic insects cause age-specific mortalities. There is always a time lag before they kill their hosts, and the latter continue to participate for a time in normal activities, e.g. the consumption of food or the utilization of protective cover, and in competition for such resources.

C   19

Much theoretical work has been done on host-parasitic interactions e.g. by Nicholson (1933), Nicholson and Bailey (1935). Experimentalists who have worked on the problem include Burnett (1949, 1951, 1958a, b), Flanders (1958a, b), and Utida (1955). Other ecologists have studied the problem in the course of their work on the dynamics of natural populations, e.g. Morris (1959), Miller (1959, 1960), and Clark (1964a).

Relatively little work has been undertaken on the influence of nematode parasites on insect populations, the available information being summarized by Welch (1963). In general, the effects of parasitism by nematodes are not obvious until after a long period of infestation. Two families of nematodes are known to kill their hosts – Mermithidae and Neoaplectanidae. The former kill their hosts at the time of emergence; host destruction by the latter involves the action of pathogenic microbial agents. Mermithids and other nematodes limit the reproductive ability of their hosts and so may affect the birth rate, e.g. Crisp (1959) found that the number of eggs in gravid adults of *Sigara scotti* parasitized by mermithids was only about one-third of that in unparasitized individuals.

Pathogens. Mortality resulting from disease has been traced to viruses, bacteria, protozoa, and fungi. Perhaps the chief distinguishing feature of pathogens is the shortness of the time taken by them to develop and kill their hosts relative to the length of the host life cycle. Consequently, the mortality induced is frequently not age-specific. In some insect species, however, individuals become increasingly immune to infection with age, and the adults are often resistant although they may transmit pathogens, e.g. viruses, to their offspring.

Epizootics occur most frequently at times of high host density, but they may develop at relatively low densities if the pathogen, e.g. a virus, has been widely dispersed in large quantities after a previous epizootic. Frequently the occurrence of epizootics depends not only upon host density but also upon the prevailing weather conditions. Some fungi are known to attack their hosts under favourable weather conditions irrespective of host density (see Tanada 1963). Such conditions as the virulence of a pathogen, the viability of host insects, and their spatial distribution are also contributory influences.

The effect exerted by some viruses on population numbers increases if the host insects are subjected to environmental stress, e.g. induced by food quality or shortage (see Vago 1953, Tanada 1963).

(*vi*) *Shortage of food.* Starvation is frequently the direct cause of death to individual insects after accidental loss of their food supply or separation from it. Sometimes, it is the cause of decrease in population numbers. The temporary shortage or absence of food (or water) is often a selective cause of mortality because the older stages of insects tend to accumulate food reserves.

Food is a consumable resource and, as insects eat, the amount remaining is reduced unless the supply is accumulating (e.g. by plant growth) at a rate which exceeds that of consumption or spoilage. Starvation can therefore be induced in a population by increase in its numbers or biomass. For example, during outbreaks of the psyllid *Cardiaspina albitextura*, population numbers may increase to a level at which the food supply is inadequate for the number of late instar nymphs present, and some die from starvation. Many of the adults which emerge subsequently, fail to find sufficient food and die without reproducing (section 4.29).

Starvation also occurs if environmental influences reduce the food supply below the level at which there is enough for all individuals present. A good example of a decline in the available food supply, induced independently of insect numbers, is provided by the cabbage aphid, *Brevicoryne brassicae* (Hughes 1963). This aphid often forms large colonies on the flowering heads of brassica plants. The flowering heads provide a very favourable supply of food until a rapid translocation of materials occurs to the maturing seeds.

Cannibalism has frequently been observed in insect species, especially at times of overcrowding or when food is in short supply. Cannibalism also commonly occurs when individuals suffer accidental injury or when they are temporarily incapacitated by moulting. Two of the best-known insects in which cannibalism occurs are the flour beetle *Tribolium confusum* (Chapman 1928) and the codling moth *Cydia pomonella* (Geier 1963a).

The presence of the food material normally eaten by an insect species does not necessarily mean that this material is available for consumption. Behavioural or morphological characteristics may limit the actual supply of food available, and many individuals may starve either in the 'midst' of food or not far from it. The beetle *Chrysomela gemellata*, which feeds on the weed *Hypericum perforatum*, colonizes areas with few or no trees present. Because of its behaviour responses, this beetle is unable to remain within forests. Most of the large quantity of *H. perforatum* within the forests adjoining treeless areas is therefore unavailable as food (Clark 1953). In tsetse species, the reverse holds in that behavioural mechanisms keep the flies within easy reach of the shade of high bush. The flies do not normally feed on animals which live in open grassland, although they would provide suitable and abundant hosts.

(*vii*) *Shelter*. Many insect species utilize kinds of protective shelter to avoid exposure either to unfavourable weather conditions or to natural enemies. For example during the hot season, both tsetse adults and pupae are liable to be killed by the normal upward variations in air temperature. However, behavioural mechanisms ensure that the flies respond photo-negatively, which causes them to remain within dense bush during the heat of the day. Penetration of the marginal areas adjoining bush, e.g. tussock grassland, is greatest during the cool wet season (Glasgow and Duffy 1961). Mature larvae of the codling moth *Cydia pomonella* require sheltered sites on their host trees in which to construct their cocoons, e.g. cracks and crevices in the wood, and thick scales of exfoliating bark. If such cocooning sites are in short supply, less favourable sites will be selected, but the rate of successful establishment decreases both with the quality and quantity of the available shelter. The amount of adequate cocoon shelter within an orchard sets an upper limit to the number of larvae that can survive to pupation (Geier 1963a).

The need for some kind of protective shelter to ameliorate environmental conditions is a particular case of the requirement of all insect species for favourable 'living-space' in which to carry out the activities essential for population persistence. When insect numbers become very high relative to the amount of living space available, forms of reciprocal interference occur between or within species which frequently lead to mortality. For example, after the larvae of the pasture scarab *Aphodius howitti* have reached the stage of constructing individual burrows, they show signs of 'great irritation' if they come into contact with one another when foraging on the ground surface for food, and 'slash aggressively' with their man-dibles. At times of high population density, many larvae are wounded and die either as a result of desiccation, predation by birds, or infection by soil organisms (Carne 1956). The possibility of overcrowding and the need for individuals to find more favourable living-space brings us to the question of movement in populations.

2.5 MOVEMENT AS A CAUSE OF NUMERICAL CHANGE

It is impossible to design adequately a study of the population numbers of an insect species without some knowledge of the 'mobility' of its members. This is particularly important if different developmental stages of a species live in different places. Frequently, however, a detailed analysis of move-ment and displacement is unnecessary because, even though movement into and out of an area may cause a high rate of population 'turnover', the numbers of individuals present may not change greatly. In other cases, important numerical changes result from movement, and intensive analyses are required.

Movement into and out of areas selected for the study of particular populations, i.e. 'immigration' and 'emigration', can be classified broadly into three types: '*spread*', '*dispersal*', and '*migration*'. To some extent, spread occurs in all insect species. It involves no specialized adaptations to ensure displacement, and is due simply to the movement of individuals in the course of searching for food and other requisites. Spread is restricted to areas in which the environmental conditions are favourable for a species. It is an important phenomenon because it leads to displacement within the area occupied by a population and results in more or less random mating. For tsetse flies, spread has been estimated to proceed at the rate of about 200 yards per week, and is sufficient apparently to prevent genetic differentiation within the elongate, but continuous tsetse belts (Glasgow 1963).

Dispersal may be defined as a form of movement which leads to the removal of a variable percentage of individuals from an area to other places, irrespective of the favourableness of the latter. In the course of such movement, it is usual for some individuals to find new sites favourable for survival and reproduction (*effective dispersal*), and for other individuals to be unsuccessful and perish. No evidence for this sort of movement has been observed in tsetse flies – which may explain gaps in the distribution of some species.

Migration is the term used here to describe the movement of individuals from one breeding area to another, or from a breeding area to an area favourable for some other phase of existence (aestivation or hibernation) and back again (e.g. Common 1954). The term is also used to describe mass movements which lead to the removal and premature mortality of individuals which constitute a population surplus.

The prolonged movement of individuals involved in the dispersal of some species and in the migration of others requires specific adaptations of one sort or another (see Johnson 1960). It is usual for such movement to occur only during one developmental stage in the life cycle of a species, e.g. the sexually immature adult. Frequently, some form of physiological polymorphism is involved in the determination of which individuals in a population disperse (or migrate). In this facultative determination of the proportion of individuals that leave an area, a variety of environmental influences may play a part, e.g. weather, or the quality or quantity of food available.

Most insect species appear to have evolved some form of dispersal or migration which serves either to increase the chances of survival, or to make survival possible. In some instances, these forms of displacement minimize the possibility or the effects of crowding and consequent over-exploitation of environmental resources: in other instances, they enable populations to escape from the annual occurrence of intolerable climatic conditions (and so serve the same purpose as diapause in many other species). For example, the cabbage aphid *Brevicoryne brassicae* depends for its persistence on the 'planktonic' dispersal of alatae over extensive areas which enables sequential colonization of the succession of short-lived plants which provide its food supply (section 4.24). The monarch butterfly *Danais plexippus* depends on migration for its existence (Urquhart 1960).

Because of the complexity of the behavioural mechanisms and other influences involved in dispersal and migration, workers who investigate the effects of movement frequently find it best to restrict their attention to *displacement* and *effective dispersal*. For example, Rainey's (1964) study of the displacements of swarms of the desert locust, *Schistocerca gregaria*, led to the conclusion that such displacements are determined to a very large extent by low-level wind fields. Swarms are transported sooner or later into zones of convergence. In zones of convergent wind-flow, swarms are likely to encounter frontal conditions and rain, and hence to find suitable breeding areas. Despite its capacity for sustained power output (Weis-Fogh 1956), this locust is frequently transported by wind like an aphid.

2.6 DISCUSSION

At the beginning of this chapter, certain simplifying assumptions were made which led to a systematic discussion of the proximate influences which affect numerical change in populations. These influences, namely species characteristics and environmental agencies, bring about the ecological events which are all that we can actually observe of the functioning of life systems.

We observe in subject populations various 'demographic' occurrences, e.g. matings, births, deaths, and movements; we observe also other events which either affect the existence of individuals directly, e.g. attack by natural enemies, or modify the supplies (food, shelter, moisture, heat, etc.) which permit the existence of individuals. The latter events affect the magnitude, extent, frequency, or duration of the demographic occurrences observed. Because our interest is focused on populations, we find it useful to think of demographic occurrences as *primary* events, and those which affect or qualify them as *secondary* events.

Ecological events, whether 'primary' or 'secondary' in the sense that we are using the terms, are the manifestation of the processes (see Solomon 1949, 1957) involved proximately in the determination of population numbers. The task of the ecologist who studies particular populations is to identify the principal processes involved in numerical fluctuation and stabilization, to evaluate their modes of action and effects, and to provide syntheses (models) which describe their collective operations. From such syntheses, generalizations can be made about the proximate determination of numbers and population persistence. Generalizations of this kind form the subject of the next two chapters.

CHAPTER III

Current theories to explain insect numbers

3.1 THE DEVELOPMENT OF ECOLOGICAL THOUGHT

3.11 Evolution and ecology

Darwin's *Origin of Species*, published in 1859, provides a useful starting point for a consideration of ecology which Haeckel defined in 1886 as the science treating of the reciprocal relations of organisms and the external world (in Warming 1909). The basic theme of ecology is well expressed in Darwin's own words:

There is no exception to the rule that every organic being increases at so high a rate, that, if not destroyed, the earth would be covered by the progeny of a single pair. . . . A struggle for existence inevitably follows. . . . Owing to this struggle, variations, however slight and from whatever cause proceeding, if they be in any way profitable to the individuals of a species, in their infinitely complex relations to other organic beings and to their physical condition of life, will tend to the preservation of such individuals, and will generally be inherited by the offspring. . . . Not that under nature the relations will ever be as simple as this. Battle within battle must be continually recurring with varying success; and yet in the long-run the forces are so nicely balanced, that the face of nature remains for long periods of time uniform, though assuredly the merest trifle would give the victory to one organic being over another. . . . Nothing is easier than to admit in words the truth of the universal struggle for life, or more difficult – at least I have found it so – than constantly to bear this conclusion in mind. Yet unless it be thoroughly engrained in the mind, the whole economy of nature, with every fact on distribution, rarity, abundance, extinction, and variation, will be dimly seen or quite misunderstood.

While Darwin's insight provided a general scheme of ecological thinking, Moebius (1877) is usually singled out as one of the earliest practitioners in ecology for his study of the natural economy of oyster-beds. To Moebius we owe the concept of 'Lebensgemeinden' or 'Lebensgemeinschaften', i.e. ' . . . communities of living beings, organizations of species and individuals which, in accordance with prevailing physical conditions of life, exist in a state of interdependence, and maintain their kind in a given place through reproduction'.

26

Ever since, the idea of 'life communities' has been the common basis of all ecological work. The bond created by the concept is stronger and deeper than might be suggested by the plurality of approaches and the frequent dissents apparent in ecological literature. In fact, most differences in ecology arise ultimately from the diversity of ways in which 'life communities' can be considered.

In its applied form, ecology is the key to the management of nature. It is not surprising therefore that practical workers have played an outstanding role in its development as a science.

3.12 The early evolutionary approach

For the early ecologists, 'life communities' were aggregates of organisms whose association they could explain in Darwinian terms of 'environmental fitness' and of 'struggle for existence'. Those authors endeavoured to describe such ecological entities as they could recognize by broad evolutionary criteria, and to define patterns of change, or succession. Quite naturally, botanists led the field in those days, and Warming (1909) was prominent among them. His views are expressed in the following quotations:

Living beings forming a community have their lives linked and interwoven into one common existence. . . . The term 'community' implies a diversity but at the same time a certain organized uniformity in the units. . . . The non-living (physical, chemical) . . . factors . . . do not suffice to impart a full comprehension of the . . . production of communities in the vegetable kingdom . . . another factor – the *competition* among species of plants [is so important] that many species are excluded from great areas on the Earth, not by direct interference on the part of non-living factors, but by the indirect interference involved in competition for food with other stronger species. Another factor, *animal-life*, also has a powerful influence upon the kind and the economy of vegetation . . . plants possess a peculiar inherent force or faculty by the exercise of which they *directly adapt themselves* to new conditions . . ., [and] become fitted for *existence in accordance* with their new surroundings . . . between external influences and the utility of variation there is a definite connexion, which is of obscure nature (*self-regulation* or *direct adaptation, epharmosis*).

Progress in ecology can be gauged precisely by the degree of understanding gained of that 'obscure connexion'.

Warming was followed by a series of authors, some zoologists (e.g. Shelford 1911, 1913) and some botanists (e.g. Clements 1916), whose descriptive, essentially non-quantitative work represents a consolidation of earlier thinking on communities. Their conceptual models led them to define 'biocoenosis' as a collective of living beings forming an evolutionary unit, or 'biome', connected functionally with the non-living components, or 'abiotic' conditions, of the environment. These conditions were determined by the properties of a physical, quasi-geographical entity, the 'biotope' (Dahl 1908) whose extent coincided with that of the 'biocoenosis' (Friederichs 1927). Hence, the 'life community' came to be regarded by certain authors (e.g. Phillips 1934–35) as a biological organism in its own right, i.e. in Friederichs' (translated) words 'a system which maintains itself in being through self-regulation. The regulatory function of the 'biocoenosis' consists mainly in keeping species in harmony with each other'.

Those extreme views provoked a penetrating critique by Tansley (1935) who wrote:

Animal ecologists in their field of work constantly find it necessary to speak of *different* animal communities living in or on a given plant community, and this is a much more natural conception, formed in the proper empirical manner as a direct description of experience, than the 'biotic community'. ... For these reasons also, the practical necessity in field work of separating and independently studying the animal communities of a 'biome', and for some purposes the necessity of regarding them as external factors acting on the plant community – I cannot accept the concept of the *biotic* community. ... This refusal is however far from meaning that I do not realize that various 'biomes', the whole webs of life adjusted to particular complexes of environmental factors, are real 'wholes', often highly integrated wholes, which are the living nuclei of *systems* in the sense of the physicist. Only I do not think they are properly described as 'organisms' ... I prefer to regard them, together with the whole of the effective physical factors involved, simply as '*systems*'. ... It is the systems so formed which, from the point of view of the ecologist, are the basic units of nature on the face of the earth. Our natural human prejudices force us to consider the organisms (in the sense of the biologist) as the most important parts of these systems, but certainly the inorganic 'factors' are also parts – there could be no systems without them, and there is constant interchange of the most various kinds within each system, not only between the organisms but between the organic and the inorganic. These *ecosystems*, as we may call them, are of the most various kinds and sizes. They form one category of the multitudinous physical systems of the universe, which range from the universe as a whole down to the atom. The whole method of science ... is to isolate systems mentally for the purposes of study, so that the series of *isolates* we make become the actual objects of our study. ... Actually the systems we isolate mentally are not only included as parts of larger ones, but they also overlap, interlock and interact with one another. The isolation is partly artificial, but is the only possible way in which we can proceed.

The early community ecologists and their direct successors tended, quite understandably, to abide by the broader concepts of 'life community'. From Warming to Phillips, there are signs of a growing reluctance to consider units smaller than 'whole biocoenoses' as if for fear of overlooking some 'holistic' quality characteristic of complex ecological situations. Although founded on principles which are essentially sound, the contribution of those authors was limited by the very unwieldiness of the natural units chosen by them for study.

3.13 The functional approach

The next advance was made by animal ecologists. It achieved two things. First, it provided a conceptual link between the processes of evolution recognized by Darwin and the proximate determination of the numbers of individuals in specific populations. Secondly, it introduced the experimental method into animal ecology.

When discussing the possibility of reducing the injuriousness of pests by introducing species which prey on them, Howard and Fiske (1911) wrote as follows:

... it is necessary that among the factors which work together in restricting the multiplication of the species there shall be at least one, if not more, which is what is here termed facultative (for want of a better name) and which, by exerting a restraining influence which is relatively more effective when other conditions favour undue increase, serves to prevent it. There are a very large number and a great variety of factors of more or less importance in effecting the control of defoliating caterpillars, and to attempt to catalogue them would be futile, but however closely they may be scrutinized very few will be found to fall into the class with parasitism, which in the majority of instances, though not in all, is truly 'facultative'. . . . A natural balance can only be maintained through the operation of facultative agencies which effect the destruction of a greater proportionate number of individuals as the insect in question increases in abundance.

The particular emphasis placed by Howard and Fiske on the role of natural enemies in the control or regulation of animal numbers was obviously motivated by the subject under discussion, i.e. the relative injuriousness of two forest defoliators, *Porthetria dispar* and *Euproctis chrysorrhea*, in the palaearctic region (where they were heavily preyed upon by many parasitic species) and in North America (where they had been introduced without their full range of natural enemies). The 'facultative' quality which the authors recognized in the action of certain causes of death, and which, they claimed, constitutes an essential element in the numerical determination of populations, is attached explicitly to 'processes', to 'functional relationships', and *not* to the material conditions, objects, or beings whereby facultative actions happen to be effected. This is a distinction of fundamental importance which has tended to be overlooked – with regrettable consequences, especially since Howard and Fiske's prudent word 'facultative' came to be supplanted by Smith's (1935) term 'density-dependent'. The following quotation reveals the last author's failure to make the point clear:

Of the *density-dependent* factors, it is believed that entomophagous insects would have to be ranked at the head of the list in general, although in certain specific cases infectious and contagious diseases would precede them. The quantity of food also operates as a *density-dependent* factor. Certain spatial requirements of the insect for the fulfillment of which the number of spaces is limited, such as situations protective against either enemies or the rigours of the climate, or nesting sites, also have the characteristics of *density-dependent* factors in relation to population density since they cause competition; that is to say, they cause the mortality rate to increase with increasing density of the insect and to decrease with decreasing density.

The problems of predator-prey relationships, which arose in part from the 'biological control' of insects and in part from the economy of 'exploited populations', were distinctly numerical. They were generally recognized as such soon after World War I, and were considered in the light of mathematical formulations elaborated by a series of authors following the early lead of Verhulst (1839), e.g. Lotka (1920, 1925), Thompson (1922a and b, 1923), Pearl (1925), and Volterra (1926). Experimental ecology evolved naturally as a means both of providing the data for mathematical formulation, and of testing deductive models *in vivo*. It was introduced by workers like Gause (e.g. 1932, 1936, 1937) and Holdaway (1932), and strongly developed by later authors (e.g. Park 1933 *et seq.*, Nicholson 1950, 1957, Huffaker 1958a, Burnett 1960, etc.).

The following quotations from Elton (1927) are indicative of the advances made in functional ecology at the time:

. . . we shall point out that practically no animal population remains the same for any great length of time, and that the numbers of most species are subject to violent fluctuations. . . . The chief cause of fluctuations in animal numbers is the instability of the environment. The climate of most countries is always varying. . . . The variations in climate affect animals and plants enormously, and since these latter are in intimate contact with other species, there are produced further disturbances which may radiate outwards to a great distance in the community . . . as soon as a food animal sinks below a certain degree of abundance its enemies either starve or turn their attention to some other source of food. . . . In fact, if several important key-industry species become suddenly very abundant or very scarce, the whole food-cycle may undergo considerable changes, if only temporarily. The various automatic balanced systems which exist will tend to bring the numbers . . . back in the long run to their original state. . . . The regulation of numbers of most animals would appear, therefore, to take place along the following lines. Each species has certain hereditary powers of increase, which are more or less fixed in amount for any particular conditions. It is usually also kept down in numbers by factors which affect breeding, *e.g.* lack of breeding-sites, etc. It is further controlled by its enemies, and if these fail, by starvation. But the latter condition is seldom reached. There are a few species which seem to regulate their numbers almost entirely by limiting reproduction. . . .

It is noteworthy that, by the late 1920's, Elton, Nicholson (see section 3.21), and earlier authors had provided most of the stock-in-trade of original concepts with which ecological theorists were to busy themselves for the next three decades.

3.14 Modern trends

After Elton (1927) several distinct, but related, lines of thought can be recognized as immediate offshoots of the work of the early authors. These are: 'physical factor ecology'; 'production ecology'; 'biocoenology'; and 'population ecology' in the strict sense, meaning the study of events and processes which determine the distribution, abundance, and persistence of specific populations. The development of population ecology will be discussed separately, for it bears more directly on the subject of this chapter.

Physical factor ecology evolved in the 1920's and 1930's as a reaction against the undue emphasis which had been placed on the self-regulatory properties of 'biomes', or 'biocoenoses' *sensu* Friederichs (1927). Its tenets were expressed as follows by Bodenheimer (1930, in Smith 1935):

> The previous generation was dominated by the ideas of the struggle for existence, of competition for food, of balance in nature, and of regulation of the normal number of individuals of an insect species by its parasites. During recent years it is coming more and more to be recognized that it is the abiotic factors, principally climate, that regulate the numbers of individuals.

It soon became obvious, and not last to Bodenheimer himself (1938, p. 111), that this extreme view was a gross oversimplification and inadequate in that it failed to account for the adaptiveness of organisms to change, and for the ability of individuals to interact with all components of their environment, 'biotic' and 'abiotic'. However, the students of physical factors in ecology (e.g. Shelford 1927, Uvarov 1931) made a useful contribution, if only by forcing others to interpret more critically the role of climate and weather in the determination of abundance.

Production ecology, inspired in part by Elton (1927), has proved to be more durable. Its object is the study of the more complex 'life communities', or 'biomes', considered as trophic associations, or food-cycles. Elton appears to have regarded the existence of trophic associations as a condition of numerical regulation, stating that ' . . . in a general way, the food-cycle

31

mechanism is in itself a fairly good arrangement for regulating the numbers of animals . . .'. Thus, by definition, production ecology is concerned essentially with the dynamic structure of the system whereby regulation is effected, rather than with the actual operation of the regulatory processes on individuals within populations. Its name results from an increasing preoccupation with the supply, or production of food, and, ultimately, with the flow, or exploitation, of energy within trophic cycles. It has tended to diverge from population ecology by extending its scope to the organic structure (e.g. Lindeman 1942, Odum 1957, Hairston 1959), the physiological economy (e.g. Juday 1940, Odum 1957, Teal 1957, Slobodkin and Richman 1961), and the physical energetics of 'living systems' (e.g. Odum and Pinkerton 1955, Odum and Smalley 1959, Patten 1959, Golley 1960, Odum 1960, Slobodkin 1960, Engelman 1961). Although population ecology and production ecology thus defined have little common ground at present, future developments in the latter are likely to affect population ecology to an increasing degree, especially in regard to understanding the influence of long-term evolutionary processes on the determination of numbers.

The gap created by the divergence of population and production ecology has not become a no-man's land. It was explored by a series of workers who have attempted to reconcile the broad evolutionary approach of the early community ecologists with the findings of their more functionally-minded successors. They are the 'synecologists' or 'biocoenologists' of the German school originated by Friederichs (1927), and their associates. The purpose of 'biocoenology' is to derive, from the study of complex associations, an understanding of the numerical determination of species. Actually, 'synecology' has resulted mainly in definitions and descriptions of particular association systems, based on Darwinian principles (e.g. Gisin 1943, Macfadyen 1952, Tischler 1955, Schwenke 1955, Kontkanen 1957, Balogh 1958). The searching criticism which Peus (1954) has made of the 'biocoenological' approach suggests that it lacks acuity as an analytical method, that it is not convenient for experimental investigations of numerical regulation, and therefore that it tends to preclude inductive synthesis.

Special mention must be made of ecologists who, although related to the 'biocoenologists' by their premises and methods, have pursued a different aim, i.e. that of investigating the diversity of life forms in ecological associations. Two key concepts proposed by Elton (1927) dominate much of this work. The first is 'niche', expressing the functional role played by a life form in a community; the second is 'pyramid of numbers', or the numerical relationship between life forms in different niches. Contributions in this field include mathematical models describing relative frequencies of species (e.g. Williams 1953), analyses of the adaption of life forms to niches (e.g. MacArthur 1958, MacArthur and MacArthur 1961), and studies on the phylogeny of 'life communities' (e.g. Preston 1962). Such workers have added considerably to our understanding of evolutionary processes, but they have not dealt directly with the immediate problems that confront population ecologists.

3.2 CURRENT THEORIES IN POPULATION ECOLOGY

Population ecology has been defined by Andrewartha (1961) as 'the laws governing the numbers of animals in relation to the areas that they inhabit.
. . . Population ecology takes into account (amongst other things) the relationships of animals to their food, and to other sorts of animals that eat the same sort of food, or prey on them or are related to them in some other way'. The term applies to the same field of inquiry as 'population dynamics' as defined by Nicholson (1954b):

> The branch of biology concerned with the forces (that is to say, the measurable influences) which govern movement of matter through populations, from the environment and back again. Only by reaching an understanding of these forces can we expect to account for the distribution and densities, and for the changes in the distribution and densities, of populations which are observed in nature.

During the last thirty years many workers have contributed to our present knowledge of population ecology (e.g. Franz 1950; Gause 1937, etc.; Morris 1963, etc.; T. Park 1948, etc.; and Utida 1957, etc.). Some ecologists have made valuable contributions in their efforts to clarify current knowledge by critical reviews and assessments. A number of leading workers have put forward theories to explain the abundance and distribution of species. Outstanding among the analytical reviews are those of Bakker (1964), Klomp (1964), Solomon (1957, 1964), and Wilbert (1962). The theorists include Nicholson (e.g. 1933, 1958), Andrewartha and Birch (e.g. 1954, 1960), Bodenheimer (1938), Chitty (1957, 1960), Huffaker (e.g. 1958b), Klomp (1958, 1962), Milne (1957a, b, 1962), Pimentel (1961), Smith (1935), Solomon (1949), Thompson (e.g. 1939, 1956), and Wynne-Edwards (1962).

For convenience, the main theoretical contributions can be considered in four groups: (i) those of workers who think that density-related processes of the sort first termed 'facultative' (see Howard and Fiske 1911) and later 'density-dependent' (see Smith 1935, Solomon 1949, 1957) play a key role in the determination of population numbers by operating as stabilizing (regulating) mechanisms; (ii) those of workers who regard such processes as being, in general, of minor or secondary importance, and consider that they play no part in determining the abundance of some species; (*iii*) those of workers who have sought a middle course between these views; and (*iv*) those of workers who emphasize the influence of 'the genetic factor' in the determination of population numbers (see Birch 1960).

As examples of the different viewpoints, the theories of Nicholson, Andrewartha and Birch, Milne, Chitty, and Pimentel will now be examined. In considering these conceptual models, it should be borne in mind that, in spite of the large amount of ecological literature, relatively few field studies on natural populations have been carried out with appropriate planning, in sufficient quantitative detail, and over a long enough period to provide the sort of information from which a balanced perspective can be obtained. Because of the inherent complexity of such studies, and because of shortages of personnel and finance, many ecologists have turned to laboratory work for the elucidation of principles. Such investigations are essentially supplementary in character and not a valid substitute for the study of natural populations. They can, however, provide guidance in the planning of field work as well as assistance in interpretation.

3.21 Nicholson's theory

Nicholson's views on the determination of insect numbers, which constitute the most extensive development of ideas of the kind put forward earlier by Woodworth (1908) and Howard and Fiske (1911), were first outlined in 1927 in a paper on mimicry. Nicholson has subsequently restated and amplified his views in numerous articles, the most important of which were published in 1933, 1954a, b, 1957, and 1958. He has used primarily (and legitimately) the deductive approach, a method more familiar to mathematicians and physicists than to biologists. After World War II, he undertook a series of laboratory studies on population dynamics with the sheep blowfly *Lucilia cuprina* (section 4.25). By this means, he was able to demonstrate that many of his original conclusions applied under experimental conditions. He has found considerable support for his basic ideas in the data obtained by others on natural populations, and today most animal ecologists recognize the didactic value of his work.

Nicholson treats populations essentially as entities – integrated groups with characteristics 'which are more than the sum of those of the constituent individuals' (Nicholson 1957). His main concern has been with the properties, structure, and functioning of populations, and especially with mechanisms which help to keep them in being, i.e. with the *stabilization* of numbers. His basic proposition is that populations exist in a state of balance in their environments as a result of density-related opposition to indefinite population growth.

Nicholson (1954b) presented a classification of the environmental elements, i.e. 'requisites', necessary for the growth and multiplication of organisms. He described as *'density factors'* the functional relations which exist between requisites, other environmental elements, e.g. natural enemies, and also the biological characteristics of the subject species – and the population numbers of that species. He divided those relations into several categories, two of which need mention here:

(*i*) *Density-legislative factors* – those whose effect upon population density is not altered by changes in the numbers of the population. He recognized that such 'non-reactive' factors have an important influence upon population numbers, which he described as 'purely legislative' or 'rule-making', as distinct from 'governing' or 'rule-enforcing'.

(*ii*) *Density-governing factors* – those which respond to change in population density by intensifying their opposition to population growth as numbers increase, eventually preventing further growth, and by relaxing their opposition as numbers decrease. Density-governing factors react either promptly or with a time lag in the stabilization of population numbers.

Nicholson substituted 'non-reactive' and 'density-governing' for the widely used terms 'density-independent' and 'density-dependent', partly because of the descriptive inadequacies of the latter and partly because of some confusion that has arisen in their usage (Nicholson 1954b, 1957). He recognized that the term 'density-dependent' should apply not to environmental elements as such, but only to the particular relation which they actually bear to population numbers, and stated:

For example, the rate of supply of food, and the space available to the animals are often uninfluenced by population density, and the severity of attack by enemies may be determined by some other factor which limits their numbers. . . . Thus 'density-dependence' and 'density-independence' are terms which designate the kind of influence exercised by a factor upon a population under a given set of circumstances, and they should not be associated directly with particular attributes of particular environmental elements. The same factor may be density-dependent in one situation and density-independent in another, even within the same species population. (Nicholson 1957, pp. 154–55.)

Nicholson gave his view of density-dependence with even greater clarity in the discussion which followed Andrewartha's contribution at the 1957 Cold Spring Harbor Symposium on Quantitative Biology (Andrewartha 1957, p. 235). Referring to the limitation of populations by food supply, Nicholson said:

D

The supply of food is density-dependent only when it is determined by the activities of the animals, as happens with predators and phytophagous animals which control the abundance of their prey or food plants. When the quantity supplied is independent of the animals . . . it is by definition *density-independent*. . . . It is not the quantity of food supplied but the *availability* of food to competing individuals which is density-dependent.

Such is the essence of the idea of density-dependence.

Nicholson's theory can be summarized as follows:

Populations are self-governing systems. They regulate their densities in relation to their own properties and those of their environments. This they do by depleting and impairing essential things to the threshold of favourability, or by maintaining reactive inimical factors, such as the attack of natural enemies, at the limit of tolerance.

The mechanism of density governance is almost always intraspecific competition, either amongst the animals for a critically important requisite, or amongst natural enemies for which the animals concerned are requisites.

Governing reaction induced by density change holds populations in a state of balance in their environments. The characteristic of balance is sustained and effective compensatory reaction which maintains populations in being in spite of even violent changes in the environment, and which adjusts their densities in general conformity with prevailing conditions.

Far from being a stationary state, balance is commonly a state of oscillation about the level of the equilibrium density which is for ever changing with environmental conditions.

Destructive factors do not add to mortality when they continue to operate over long periods, but merely cause a redistribution of mortality, for the intensity of competition automatically relaxes sufficiently to make room for the destruction they cause. Such compensatory reaction causes the effect of destructive factors upon density to be much less when balance is reattained than that which they produce when they first operate.

Although population densities can be governed only by factors which react to density change, factors which are uninfluenced by density may produce profound effects upon density. This they do by modifying the properties of the animals, or those of their environments, so influencing the level at which governing reaction adjusts population densities. . . . (Nicholson 1954b, p. 10.)

Nicholson's way of thinking is illustrated further by the following quotation from his 1958 paper (pp. 108–9):

When there is a gradient from inherently favourable to unfavourable conditions, the mechanism described permits a species to persist indefinitely in all favourable places; and it causes the intensity of induced resistance to fall towards zero as the limits of favourability are approached. Consequently, near the fringes of distribution, density-governing reaction must be slight and inconspicuous.

Individuals of most populations tend to diffuse out of favourable places into the surrounding country and many species can maintain themselves permanently in fringing zones where favourability is below the threshold level – the inability of the resident animals to replace themselves by reproduction being offset by the continual immigration from neighbouring favourable places. Note that, although density-governing reaction may not occur in these fringing zones, it is ultimately responsible for the limitation of density there. This is because the number of immigrants is a function of the size of the population in the favourable place from which these emigrated, which itself is adjusted by density-governing reaction.

Nicholson's outstanding contribution has been criticized in a variety of ways. As we see it, the limitations in his work relate mainly to his particular way of envisaging, emphasizing, and describing ecological phenomena, and arise both from the scanty consideration that he gave to populations in their natural setting, i.e. as they coexist in ecosystems, and from his preoccupation with the density-related processes which can operate as stabilizing (governing) mechanisms, e.g. intraspecific competition. The following quotation provides an example of the way in which Nicholson has applied his concept of balance, as derived from theoretical and laboratory models, to natural populations. When referring to the influence of climatic variability on populations, he wrote (1954b, pp. 44–45):

Although true equilibrium is impossible under fluctuating conditions, there is at each moment a density level which, if it were attained by the population, and if the environmental conditions prevailing at that moment were to persist, would cause the environmental forces opposing density change, including those induced by the population, to exactly counterbalance the properties of the population favouring multiplication. Consequently, it can be said that the level of equilibrium density fluctuates in association with environmental fluctuations, through the effects these have upon the properties of animals and those of their requisites. Reactions tending to cause increase or decrease are produced respectively when a population is below or above the equilibrium density appropriate to the conditions prevailing at each moment. . . .
The situation is complicated by the fact that any marked climatic changes produce very noticeable direct effects upon population densities . . . .
If the fluctuating conditions are definitely unfavourable at times, a population progressively decreases during those times, but at the intermittent favourable periods the population tends to adjust itself to the prevailing conditions. This determines the density at the beginning of each unfavourable period and therefore also the general level from which the population falls during these periods. Density governance is merely relaxed from time to time and subsequently resumed, and it remains the influence which adjusts population densities in relation to environmental favourability.

This exposition on balance raises several questions concerning the meaning and value of some statements in Nicholson's theory. Firstly, is it useful to approach the study of natural populations with an idea of balance which involves a large number of unmeasurable equilibrium densities? How meaningful is the concept of an equilibrium level in the case of a population like that mentioned above 'which tends to adjust itself to the prevailing conditions' during 'intermittent favourable periods'? What in fact determines its density at the beginning of each unfavourable period? And finally, what is the precise meaning of the proposition (Nicholson 1954b, p. 10): Adjustment of population density 'in general conformity with the prevailing conditions'?

Nicholson's particular orientation to population problems has resulted, not infrequently, in forms of generalization which are not easy to grasp even for workers who recognize the value of distinguishing between stabilizing mechanisms and other ecological processes. He is right in describing intraspecific competition as a mechanism of that kind in the situations envisaged and studied by him. However, to go a step further and to describe populations in general as being 'self-adjusting' ('self-governing' or 'self-regulating') systems is not useful for practical purposes. In effect, by concentrating so much of his attention on density-related 'subtractive' processes, Nicholson has appeared to underrate the role of other influences in the determination of population numbers. This has provoked most of the largely-invalid criticism which has been levelled at his work.

In our view, if Nicholson had stated his theory:

(i) by treating populations *together* with their environments more explicitly as the functional systems whereby abundance is determined;

(ii) by dealing first and more systematically with the 'legislative' or 'rule-making' influences which characterize life systems;

(iii) by dealing secondly with the variety of density-related stabilizing mechanisms which help to keep populations in being;

(iv) by emphasizing the differences as well as the similarities between intraspecific competition and density-stabilizing destruction by natural enemies; and

(v) if he had stated in greater detail his acceptance of the possibility that stabilizing mechanisms may operate only intermittently in some life systems: it is likely that few population ecologists would have found much to question seriously, and that more use would have been made of his fund of ideas.

3.22 The theory of Andrewartha and Birch

The theory of Andrewartha and Birch (1954, pp. 660–1) is stated briefly by them as follows:

The numbers of animals in a natural population may be limited in three ways: (*a*) by shortage of material resources, such as food, places in which to make nests, etc.; (*b*) by inaccessibility of these material resources relative to the animals' capacities for dispersal and searching; and (*c*) by shortage of time when the rate of increase *r* is positive. Of these three ways, the first is probably the least, and the last is probably the most, important in nature. Concerning *c*, the fluctuations in the value of *r* may be caused by weather, predators, or any other component of environment which influences the rate of increase.

In putting forward this theory, they 'rejected the traditional subdivision of environment into physical and biotic factors and "density-dependent" and "density-independent" factors on the grounds that these were neither a precise nor a useful framework within which to discuss problems of population ecology' (Andrewartha and Birch 1960, p. 219). Andrewartha (1961, p. 183) wrote:

Of course, the fact that we have to reject the extreme models that have been built on the idea of density-dependent factors does not necessarily mean that we cannot make use of Howard and Fiske's original idea that environment may be divided into density-dependent and density-independent factors. . . . In particular the reciprocal relationship which exists between the density of a population and the amount of some expendable resource that is in short supply . . . has often been described in terms of density-dependent factors. . . . But the idea of density-dependent factors cannot be fitted into the model of environment that I described. . . . This model of environment has been proved to be generally useful and there seems little merit in discarding it in favour of a narrower model which can at best explain only a small part of the variability that may be observed in natural populations.

It is made clear by these authors that they consider there are many instances in which the numbers of animals are determined without the operation of stabilizing mechanisms; that in other cases the part played by such mechanisms accounts for so little of the numerical variability that it is unimportant; and finally that, even when stabilizing mechanisms account for much variability, it is more meaningful to think of situations in terms of absolute and relative shortages of resources (i.e. of population requisites), etc., than of reciprocal density-resource relationships and such processes as intraspecific competition. To Andrewartha and Birch, density-related processes and stabilizing mechanisms are of secondary importance.

The adequacy of the Andrewartha-Birch theory to explain insect numbers can best be examined by considering first their interpretations of the abundance of the two insect species on which they did most of their ecological field work, namely *Austroicetes cruciata* (a swarm-forming grasshopper) and *Thrips imaginis* (the apple blossom thrips).

For *A. cruciata*, their general conclusion was 'that the distribution and abundance of *A. cruciata* are determined largely by weather; there is no evidence for 'density-dependent factors.' For *T. imaginis*, they concluded:

All the variation in maximal numbers from year to year may therefore be attributed to causes that are not related to density: not only did we fail to find a 'density-dependent' factor, but we also showed that there was no room for one.

The evidence with respect to what determined the numbers during the season of minimal abundance is not quite so definite. It was shown beyond doubt that food never acted as a 'density-dependent factor' and with reasonable certainty that no other 'density-dependent factor' was operating. It was suggested, by analogy with what is known of the influence of weather on maximal numbers, that weather also determined minimal numbers in a way that was essentially independent of density. (Andrewartha and Birch 1954, pp. 581–82.)

It is possible to explain the observations made on these two species in ways which fit the observed facts more completely than the interpretations of Andrewartha and Birch.

3.221 *Austroicetes cruciata*

Andrewartha (1939, p. 102–3) stated:

In South Australia the active stages of the grasshopper are present from August to November. There is only one generation each year. Eggs are laid in October–November, and remain dormant until the following Spring. During August or early September the young hoppers emerge.

In the early stages the hoppers tend to congregate on patches of suitable food. Grasses and legumes, notably spear grass, barley grass, and trefoil are preferred. At first there is normally plenty of the favoured food plants. As the season advances these either dry up or are consumed, and the grasshoppers either feed on less favoured plants which are still green (e.g. Salvation Jane) or migrate to adjacent crops and pastures.

A sequence of favourable years resulted in an outbreak of *A. cruciata* which continued from 1935 to 1939. During this period:

. . . the swarms were too obvious to need counting; the individual swarms did not seem to increase in density, nor did the boundaries of the area affected by swarms expand, but there was a perceptible increase from 1935 to 1939 in the proportion of this area occupied by the swarms. (Andrewartha and Birch 1954, p. 585.)

In 1940 the nymphs emerged mostly during the first week of September. There was very little food available, due to the lack of rain in the winter.

The spring rainfall was insufficient:

. . . to maintain vigorous growth of spear grass, and the grasshopper numbers were reduced as a result of starvation. . . . On 3rd September hoppers were present in plague numbers in most situations examined; in one or two local situations there was evidence that death from starvation had already occurred on a large scale. On 3rd October the hoppers were found in plague numbers in only a few favoured local situations; it was noticeable that their development had been unusually slow. By 29th October the grass-hoppers had practically disappeared; only two small situations were found where they were numerous. By 18th November they had disappeared almost completely. (Birch and Andrewartha 1941, pp. 95–96.)

However, in spite of the very unfavourable conditions, some grasshoppers survived and reproduced.

When, after severe droughts, conditions again become favourable to *A. cruciata*, multiplication by the species begins in the isolated places where survival occurred. By dispersal from these places, both before and after reaching maximal levels of abundance, the areas in which the species had been eliminated are repopulated. At least some of the 'drought refuges' (or their immediate surroundings) are favourable to *A. cruciata* at times of average or above average rainfall. When conditions favour increase in *A. cruciata* numbers for a few years, swarms are likely to be produced first in or near drought refuges.

On the subject of swarm formation Andrewartha (1939, p. 103) has written:

Although the young hoppers crowd on certain patches of food they show, at first, no definite tendency to be gregarious. Later during the fourth and fifth instars (when they are nearly mature) the hoppers may mass together into bands and migrate over short distances. At no stage are the bands so dense as those formed by the locust,* nor is the urge to migrate so well developed. Indeed, in certain seasons, when food in the vicinity of the hatching areas is particularly abundant, the gregarious and migratory habits may fail to develop.

The adults are only weakly gregarious; they tend to form loose swarms.

In the same paper, when referring to the movement of the grasshoppers from their breeding grounds to crops, Andrewartha stated (p. 102):

They do not normally move from their breeding grounds until the favoured food plants (e.g., spear grass, barley grass, and trefoil) have either been consumed or have dried off. When the grasshoppers are numerous the food on the breeding ground is consumed more quickly; in an early season

* The Australian plague locust *Chortoicetes terminifera*.

the plants on the breeding ground may dry off sooner; both these factors make for an early invasion of crops. The converse, viz., a late season, or few grasshoppers, makes for a late invasion of the crops.

When the hoppers reach the adult, or winged stage, the range of their movement is extended. They may come from several miles away to feed upon patches of green crop.

It is a well-known fact that, as in the case of other plague species of Acrididae, swarms of *A. cruciata* do not develop until the population density becomes high (e.g. Clark 1947). Swarm formation and subsequent mass emigration in *A. cruciata* constitute a density-related process in which it is likely that both numbers per unit area and numbers relative to food supply play a part. Mass migration from breeding grounds at times of high abundance is a process which affects the chance of survival of individual grasshoppers. For various reasons, e.g. because they were insufficiently 'gregarized', some grasshoppers stay at the breeding grounds where some food frequently remains after mass migration has occurred. Their chance of survival to the reproductive stage is usually increased by emigration of the majority. Emigration also increases the chances of individuals to survive by enabling many grasshoppers to find new sources of food at a time when the supply in the breeding ground is decreasing rapidly. There is no doubt that swarming at times of high abundance plays a significant part in determining the numbers of *A. cruciata* and its ability to persist in the South Australian 'grasshopper belt'.

Birch (1957) when discussing the food shortage to which *A. cruciata* is usually subjected towards the end of the spring, stated: 'The small amount of green food that is left at the end of the spring is related not to the number of grasshoppers but to the onset of the hot dry summer'. Although he recognized that 'more grasshoppers will eat more food' he concluded that: 'Because grasshoppers find so little of the food that remains with the approach of summer the chance of a grasshopper finding food is independent of the number searching for it.'

This interpretation cannot apply to situations in which the number of grasshoppers was excessive for the amount of food that they could find. As quoted above, Andrewartha (1939) recognized two elements in the food shortage which occurs towards the end of spring – the numbers of grasshoppers present, and seasonal pasture conditions. In a later paper (Andrewartha 1943, p. 315), he mentioned a third element:

In a good year there may be so much vegetation that, even though the grasshoppers are numerous, there still remains plenty of food for the sheep, but in a dry year their competition with the sheep may greatly increase the shortage of feed. . . . If the sheep don't eat the feed the grasshoppers will.

42

It can be assumed therefore that, when the supply of green feed in an area became inadequate for the number of grasshoppers present, because of weather conditions, sheep grazing, etc., the chance of a grasshopper surviving to the reproductive stage would often have been limited substantially by the presence of other individuals of the same kind. 'With the approach of summer', intraspecific competition for food would have occurred over a range of grasshopper densities, its intensity and outcome being determined by the stage of development reached by the insect, and by its numbers relative to the available food supply.

It is clear that, although weather undoubtedly played a major role in the determination of changes in the numbers of *A. cruciata* and the levels of abundance reached, density-related processes, namely mass emigration and intraspecific competition, were also involved. These processes tended to adjust numbers locally to the available supply of food. However, because the supply of food provided for *A. cruciata* by vegetation fluctuated in a way that was largely independent of the numbers of the grasshopper, these processes could not prevent violent and irregular fluctuations in the abundance of the species both in time and in space. Moreover, intraspecific competition for a dwindling food supply frequently resulted in the local elimination of *A. cruciata*. It is readily understandable that Andrewartha and Birch were led to conclude that there was no evidence for density-dependent factors (as defined by Smith 1935, see section 3.13).

3.222 *Thrips imaginis*

According to Andrewartha and Birch (1954), *Thrips imaginis* is a species in which breeding and development go on continuously although both the birth rate and the rate of survival decrease greatly during the hottest part of the summer and during the winter. Under warm conditions, a generation is completed in a few weeks, but the time taken during the winter is much longer. Nymphs and adults of *T. imaginis* are found in the flowers of roses, other garden plants, fruit trees, and weeds, but pupation occurs in litter around the bases of plants or just below the surface of the soil. In order to survive, the nymphs have to feed on pollen which is also important for egg production by adult females.

Using multiple regressions, Davidson and Andrewartha (1948b) related estimates of maximal population size attained each year to various measures of weather (affecting thrips development, etc., and their food supply), and concluded (p. 222) that 'the annual fluctuations in the maximum density attained by the population are controlled almost entirely by "density-independent" components of the environment'. Andrewartha and Birch (1954, p. 581) stated:

... altogether, 78 per cent of the variance was explained by four quantities which were calculated entirely from meteorological records.

This left virtually no chance of finding any other systematic cause for variation, because 22 per cent is a rather small residuum to be left as due to random sampling errors.

The Andrewartha-Birch interpretation of the *T. imaginis* data has been criticized by a number of workers including Kuenen (1958), Nicholson (1958, p. 110), and F. E. Smith (1961, p. 406), all of whom came to the same conclusion after examining the method of analysis. Nicholson wrote:

Unusual and very important evidence of population self-regulation is provided by the field data concerning *Thrips imaginis* Bagnall recorded by Davidson and Andrewartha ... and also by their statistical analysis of these.

Using correlation methods and the comparison of variances, Smith reanalyzed the results and concluded:

Direct analysis of the published data on the thrips population studied by Davidson and Andrewartha reveals a strong inverse correlation between population change and population size. A rapidly decreasing variance in population size is also shown to exist during the later portion of the spring population increase. Such evidence of density-dependence persists through the use of partial correlations using environmental factors known to be related to population size. The multiple regression model used by Davidson and Andrewartha is not appropriate for the interpretations they have made. They have in fact demonstrated the degree to which the population conforms to a predicted level, hence the degree to which the population is regulated. They have no evidence for a density-independent system.

It is apparent from the consideration of these ecological studies that the conclusions of Andrewartha and Birch (1954) concerning what we term 'stabilizing mechanisms' are not supported convincingly by the data obtained. The investigations concerned were not actually planned to identify such mechanisms and to evaluate the part played by them in the determination of numbers. This applies generally to the studies quoted in support of their theory.

3.223 *Shortages of material resources*

An important element in the generalizations of Andrewartha and Birch is their idea of absolute and relative shortages of food, which has been discussed in detail by Andrewartha and Browning (1961).

The essence of their interpretation of situations in which the supply of food limits the numbers of a species is put in the following words:

The powers of dispersal of the animal relative to those of its food seem largely to determine the density that the animals will maintain. When the powers of dispersal of the animal are small relative to those of its food much food will go undiscovered and the food will be abundant, whereas the animal may be abundant locally but will be very patchily distributed. But when the powers of dispersal of the animal are great relative to those of its food then both the animal and its food are likely to be rare and very patchily distributed. . . . (Andrewartha and Browning 1961, p. 89.)

This statement could be generalized for all situations of shortage involving either depletable or undepletable resources. It describes the determination of population density in terms of interactions between the inherent properties of a species and the intrinsic attributes of its environment. The 'effective amount'* of a resource and 'absolute' and 'relative' shortages of resources can all be thought of in the same terms, i.e. as outcomes of the interaction between the *co-determinants* of abundance (section 1.3). However, the population ecologist interested in the development of guiding principles and the economic entomologist who attempts to limit the numbers of a pest need to know, in terms of observable ecological events and processes, *how* shortages are caused, i.e. how population density, competition, behaviour, and other influences contribute towards bringing them about. In their interesting treatment of the problem of shortage in environmental resources Andrewartha and Browning did not proceed far enough with their analysis.

We cannot agree with Andrewartha and Browning (p. 85) that intraspecific competition, 'being chiefly relevant to the study of the evolution of the population, enters only indirectly into the scope of ecology'. Whenever intraspecific competition occurs, it is relevant as an ecological process – even though it may not be operating as a mechanism for stabilizing population numbers. Whether or not numerical stabilization is implemented by intraspecific competition depends *proximately* upon the conditions which other processes create, and *ultimately* upon the co-determinants of abundance.

3.224 *Discussion*
The theory of Andrewartha and Birch is a useful attempt to explain the distribution and abundance of insects (and other animals) with minimal reference to the part played by populations themselves, particularly by density. However, these authors have underrated the role of density-related subtractive processes. If their approach is followed, much that is relevant in the determination of numbers is likely to be overlooked.

* That part of a resource which is used by those individuals that get enough to reach maturity and to reproduce (see Andrewartha and Birch 1954).

To us, the principal contribution made by Andrewartha, Birch and Browning is that they have helped to put into perspective the part played by intraspecific competition and other density-related processes in the determination and stabilization of population numbers. We agree with them when they say 'density-dependent factors' and 'density-independent factors' do not form a precise framework for discussion of the problems of population ecology. However, as Nicholson maintains, it is necessary to distinguish between processes with subtractive effects that intensify with increase in population density – and can act, therefore, as stabilizing mechanisms – and processes with effects that do not change in this way.

3.23 Milne's theory

Milne has published three papers (1957a, 1957b, 1962), stating his views 'on the natural control of insect populations'. His synthesis incorporates what he considers to be of value in the opposing theories of other workers. Milne acknowledges three principal sources – the ideas of Thompson, Andrewartha and Birch, and Nicholson. The work of Thompson which was summarized effectively by Milne (1957a) is thought by him to lack 'fullness' (p. 195) because it underestimates the part played by density-related processes in the determination of population numbers. The Andrewartha-Birch theory is considered to be a truism (Milne 1957a, p. 209), a defect presumably of the work of Thompson also since his theory is regarded by Milne as being 'practically identical' with that of Andrewartha and Birch (Milne 1957b, p. 265). The gist of Milne's criticism of Nicholson's theory is that the latter overestimates the frequency with which such processes as intraspecific competition occur in nature, and the part played by natural enemies in the control of prey numbers.

As Milne admits, his own theory 'results largely from impregnation of the Thompson and Andrewartha-Birch theory with an element of the Nicholson theory . . .' (Milne 1957b, p. 266). He summarizes his theory as follows:

> For the most part, control of increase is due to the combined action of (a) density independent and (b) imperfectly density dependent environmental factors. In the comparatively rare cases where this combined action occasionally fails, increase to the point of collective suicide is prevented by competition between individuals of the population. Decrease of numbers to zero is prevented ultimately by density independent factors alone. For, unless the latter begin at the appropriate time to favour increase instead of decrease, the remnant of individuals left by the imperfectly density dependent factors must perish. (Milne 1957b, p. 265.)

This model is adduced from several conceptual premisses postulated and

46

defined by Milne, namely 'population' and 'environment' (section 1.2), 'natural control', 'ultimate capacity of a place for a species', 'environmental capacity of a place for a species', and 'environmental factors'.

According to Milne (1957a, p. 193):

> ... if a population is to remain in being, the highest densities must always be below the level resulting in collective suicide, and the lowest densities must always be above zero. Control simply means the arresting of increase and decrease short of these extinction levels.

Milne states that his 'definition of control is factual and not confounded with theory. . . .' To Nicholson (1933, 1954b), continued existence implies a state of balance between population and environment. To Milne, continued existence implies control by environment ('As I see it, the environment rules', 1957a, p. 209).

Milne's *ultimate* capacity of a place for a species' is:

> ... the maximum number of individuals that the place could carry without being rendered totally uninhabitable by utter exhaustion or destruction of resources (food and/or living-space in their various forms). . . . The *environmental* capacity of a place for a species is the maximum number of individuals that the species could maintain in the place. Obviously, environmental capacity cannot be greater than ultimate capacity; it could, conceivably, be equal to ultimate capacity but laboratory experiments with populations suggest that it is usually somewhat smaller. The two capacities are related, and both vary in time. . . . (Milne 1962, pp. 19–20.)

These capacities of places are ideal values in the relationship between species population and habitat. They determine the density levels at which Milne believes intraspecific competition operates to prevent increase to extinction (e.g. 1957b, figure 3).

Milne's 'environmental factors' are of three kinds: 'density-independent', 'imperfectly density-dependent', and 'perfectly density-dependent'. All share the ability to determine numerical changes in populations by direct action, either singly or in combination. They are defined as follows (Milne 1962):

A. Density-independent factors: (1) Physical circumstances, mainly, or basically, weather. (2) Actions of other species, such as their indiscriminate browsing, grazing, fouling and treading on vegetation, or casual predation and parasitism.

B. Imperfectly density-dependent factors: actions of other species competing for the same resources (interspecific competition), and of predators, parasites and pathogens in general.

C. The one and only perfectly density-dependent factor: competition (for food, space, etc.) within the population itself, i.e. intraspecific competition.

Milne's chief contribution is his classification of 'density-dependent factors' into 'perfect' and 'imperfect', and the question arises as to the value of this subdivision. He discussed his idea of imperfect density-dependence in terms of the influence of natural enemies upon population numbers. Milne wrote:

... the response of the parasite population to changes in host density can not be determined by that density alone. It is partly determined by other factors peculiar to the parasite itself or common to itself and host but affecting each to a different degree. ... There can be no exact and unfailing relation between population density and the action of enemies on the population. Enemies are at best only imperfectly density dependent in action. (Milne 1957b, pp. 258–9.)

On this basis, Milne insists that natural enemies alone are unable to control increase in the numbers of a prey species. Most population ecologists would agree with him once they had grasped his particular meaning. Milne's point, of course, cannot alter the fact that there are successful cases of biological control involving density-stabilizing interactions between predators and prey (i.e. control in the sense of Nicholson 1933), e.g. the well-known example of *Cactoblastis cactorum* which was liberated in Australia in 1925 for the control of prickly pear, *Opuntia* spp. (Dodd 1936).
Nicholson (1958, p. 109) wrote:

Before the introduction of *C. cactorum* prickly pear occupied millions of acres in Queensland, often in almost pure and impenetrable stands. After its release *C. cactorum* multiplied with extreme rapidity, soon reaching such densities locally that the whole of the prickly pear above ground was destroyed, and millions of partly fed larvae were seen to wander around and die of starvation. During the next two or three years there was some regrowth of prickly pear, for *C. cactorum* had almost ceased to exist; but this insect very quickly multiplied from its small residual numbers and destroyed the regrowth. This sequence of events continued over the whole infested area in Queensland. In a recent discussion, Mr. Dodd informed me the position for many years had been that, throughout the originally heavily invested areas, very small groups of prickly pear are seen only occasionally, and these are inevitably found before long by *C. cactorum* and destroyed, so exemplifying the type of 'spotty distribution' which has been shown to be a probable end result of the interaction between an effective specific parasite and a specific host. Occasionally, in areas which are far from any resident *C. cactorum*, patches of this weed may develop and infest several acres in the course of a few years. Sooner or later, however, these patches are inevitably found by *C. cactorum* and destroyed completely.

It is true to say that the action of *C. cactorum* does not have an 'exact and unfailing relation' with the numbers of *Opuntia* plants that develop, and that the weed is not controlled by *C. cactorum* alone. Climate and other influences, including the inherent properties of the interacting species, have made the observed outcome possible – just as they also made possible, in the case of *C. cactorum* itself, the control of increase in population numbers by the 'perfectly density-dependent factor' – intraspecific competition (for food).

Although Milne rightly distinguishes between the mode of action of intraspecific competition (*automatic*) and the action of density-reactive natural enemies (*probabilistic*), his idea that such processes should be classified as perfectly and imperfectly density-dependent is, in the long run, misleading. It is more useful instead to think in terms of whether or not observed density-related severity of predation or parasitism, or intraspecific competition, does in fact contribute significantly in the implementation of numerical stabilization under the particular conditions of a given life system. The fact that intraspecific competition is more or less automatic in action does not necessarily mean that it can prevent population increase to extinction: the fact that the density-related response of a particular predator to change in numbers of its prey is, to some degree, probabilistic in mode of action does not necessarily mean that it cannot serve as a reliable (if not infallible) density-stabilizing agent.

To sum up: although Milne has endeavoured with some success to achieve a helpful blending of ideas, his contribution has essentially the same kind of limitations as those of the theorists that he criticizes, namely over-emphasis or misplaced emphasis on some of the elements involved in the determination of abundance, due presumably to insufficient consideration of the life system as a whole.

3.24 Chitty's theory

In 1960 Chitty published a paper on 'population processes in the vole and their relevance to general theory'. His work is representative of the idea that populations are numerically 'self-regulating', through genetically-induced changes in the average vitality of individuals associated with changes in population density.

The possible influence of genetic factors on abundance has been considered by Birch (1960). Referring to oscillations in numbers shown by experimental populations of flour and grain beetles he wrote (pp. 16–17):

It is conceivable that such oscillations . . . could be due to selection favoring certain genotypes at high density and others at low density. As yet experiments have not been done to test this.
This hypothesis has been suggested as an explanation of outbreaks and declines of certain insect pests in Europe (Franz, 1950) and as a possible

explanation of the unsolved problem of four year cycles in the vole *Microtus agrestis* in Wales (Chitty, 1957).

Chitty's (1960) concept of self-regulation is best summarized in his own words:

No animal population continues to increase indefinitely, and the problem is to find out what prevents this. Increase among voles is halted by declines that recur fairly regularly, and can be identified by certain associated characteristics as belonging to a single class of events. . . . According to field evidence the individuals in a declining vole population are intrinsically less viable than their predecessors, and changes in the severity of their external mortality factors are insufficient to account for the increased probability of death. On the assumption that vole populations are a special instance of a general law, the hypothesis is set up that all species are capable of regulating their own population densities without destroying the renewable resources of their environment, or requiring enemies or bad weather to keep them from doing so. The existence of such a mechanism would not imply that it is always efficient, especially in situations to which a species is not adapted, or that species do not also occur in environments where the mechanism seldom, if ever, comes into effect. The hypothesis states that, under appropriate circumstances, indefinite increase in population density is prevented through a deterioration in the quality of the population. . . . Tests of this hypothesis are relevant to all theories about the factors limiting animal numbers, since the effects of most mortality factors depend upon properties of the organisms, and it cannot safely be assumed that so important an environmental variable as population density has no effect on the physiology of the individual or the genetics of the population. Contrary to the assumption often made, it is therefore a priori improbable that the action of the physical factors is independent of population density. It is therefore postulated that the *effects* of independent events, such as weather, become more severe as numbers rise and quality falls.

Wellington (1957, 1960, 1964), in a study of the western tent caterpillar, *Malacosoma pluviale,* found that colonies of that species contained different sorts of larvae which ranged from 'active' to very 'sluggish', and that the proportions of these types of individual differed between colonies, to which the terms 'active' and 'sluggish' could also be applied. In reference to an outbreak of this species on Vancouver Island he stated (1960, p. 289):

Within the outbreak, local infestations varied in age and intensity. A few were only in their first generation, and very light. Others, in their fourth year of residence, were much heavier. Noticeable differences in population quality accompanied these differences in age and abundance. . . . In newly infested localities, most colonies were very active. In older infestations, some were active but many were very sluggish – often too much so to survive. . . .
As infestations aged, even active colonies decreased in size and activity, but the year of minimal density was accompanied by increases in colony size

and vitality. . . . Examples from all sources indicated declining vitality while the population aged, followed by sudden recovery at or near minimal abundance when its least viable portion had been eliminated.

Wellington suggested that his observations provided support for Chitty's theory, as stated in 1960, but a more comprehensive interpretation is possible. It appears that, under favourable climatic conditions, the qualitative changes in populations of *M. pluviale* did not necessarily prevent increase in the number of colonies to a level at which density-induced food shortage, and density-related outbreaks of disease, helped to arrest population growth.* Wellington (1957, p. 308) wrote:

In 1955, a roadside survey of the outbreak located areas of heavy, medium, and light infestations in terms of numbers of tents per tree. Most trees were less than 7 m. high, so that larvae in the fourth instar frequently overlapped feeding areas if there were more than 10 tents per tree . . . areas that contained more than 10 tents per tree usually included many trees that had 20–50 tents each.

He added (page 315):

It is interesting that the new infestations of 1956 that were sparse enough to have only one colony per tree generally consisted of active colonies that constructed several tents and travelled over most of the crown during their larval period. Similarly, many trees that contained 20, 50, or even 70 tents supported only colonies that made compact tents and always fed close to them.

On the proper hosts, there is no doubt that less active colonies are much better suited for survival at moderate population densities, since they obtain food near home and do not mingle enough to spread disease among colonies. Nevertheless, since they often subsist on a minimal food supply even when they are not crowded, they suffer greatly from crowding that overlaps the limited feeding areas of adjacent colonies.

After referring to the occurrence of a heat wave, he dealt with related ecological events, including the 'upsurge' of a polyhedral virus. He wrote (p. 313):

In the field, disease that had been very sparsely distributed amongst even sluggish colonies suddenly became prominent, though its full effects were delayed until the larvae began to feed again.

When the heat wave broke, prepupational travel soon became general. . . . During the prepupational wandering, however, there was continual intermingling of diseased and healthy larvae. In addition, in more densely populated areas, active colonies of late fourth- and early fifth-instar larvae that starved during the heat wave foraged further than usual, with the result that

---

* Density-related predation and parasitism may also have been involved.

they often entered diseased colonies temporarily before returning to their own tents. Such mixing spread the disease not only among active mature larvae but also from sluggish third- to active fourth-instar larvae.

It appears from these statements that, sometimes at least, a complex density-stabilizing mechanism came into operation at high levels of abundance.

Progressive deterioration in the quality of individuals of *M. pluviale* in successive generations may have been of adaptive value in the original unmodified environment of the species if, for example, the dispersal of the more active adult moths was limited by the presence of a high density of host and other trees, in which case progressive qualitative deterioration would have been associated (normally or frequently) with relatively high numbers. The change in the properties of individuals may then have formed part of a stabilizing mechanism which minimized the chance of local population increase to extinction. At the time of Wellington's observations, however, the change in quality occurred both at high and at low levels of colony abundance and functioned, therefore, as an ecological process with an important but non-stabilizing influence on the numbers of the species. In the present much-modified environment of *M. pluviale*, progressive qualitative change in individuals would not, in fact, enable populations of the species to stabilize their own population densities 'without destroying the renewable resources of their environment, or requiring enemies or bad weather to keep them from doing so' (as postulated by Chitty's theory).

Milne (1962) has commented as follows on Chitty's (1960) theory and the contributions of others which appear to support it:

Certainly the series of papers cited shows that as population rises (after natural reduction) the average quality of individuals deteriorates, partly because of a limited increase in the proportion of individuals of weaker genotypes ('genetic shift') and partly because of a subsequent decrease in capability ('physiological impairment') of all genotypes. But in so far as they hold deterioration in quality responsible for control of increase . . . the authors are mistaken.

The 'genetic shift' in question is caused by the environment as a whole becoming so favourable that more of the weaker genotypes live and multiply (e.g. the types of a particular tent-caterpillar. . .). This 'shift' does not arrest population growth. It is merely a concomitant of growth, just as 'shift' in the opposite direction is a concomitant of decrease. . . .

Now let us look at the 'physiological impairment' which sooner or later manifests itself in addition as growth continues. . . . To hold this kind of deterioration responsible for control is as pointless as it would be to hold decline in rotating speed of road wheels responsible for stopping a motor car . . . .

In short, the notion of control by 'deterioration in quality' springs from failure to distinguish between (1) the variable properties of animals and (2) the effective environmental factors which work on these properties to bring about (cause) control.

What Chitty regards as 'self-regulation' on the part of vole and other populations is considered by Milne to be a natural or automatic concomitant of population increase and decrease due to environmental conditions. We have here two ways of interpreting the same phenomenon, one emphasizing endogenous population processes and the other environmental influences. Both were involved, and the need is to describe more adequately the density-stabilizing interactions which arrested population increase.

In the case of Chitty's voles, it appears that, when the population density became high, much intraspecific strife occurred. The qualitative changes that took place in vole populations formed together with intraspecific competition a complex mechanism for stabilizing population numbers (see section 4.27).

In the dim light of our present knowledge of reversible qualitative changes in populations, Chitty's hypothesis is better formulated as follows: The stabilizing mechanisms evolved within life systems which arrest numerical increase may incorporate qualitative changes in populations. These qualitative changes, which result in increased vulnerability to the action of inimical environmental agencies, may persist for several generations. We think that this statement agrees with Chitty's most recent formulation of his ideas (see Krebs 1964, figure 10; and Chitty 1965).

3.25 Pimentel's theory

On the basis of the proposition that 'population regulation has its foundation in the process of evolution', Pimentel (1961) revived the application of evolutionary principles to the problems of population dynamics by proposing a genetic mechanism for the determination of numbers. He summarized his views as follows:

That a genetic feed-back mechanism functions to regulate populations of herbivores, parasites, and predators is supported by evidence from the biomathematics of population dynamics and studies of natural populations. The mechanism functions as a feed-back system through the dynamics of density pressure, selective pressure, and genetic changes in interacting populations. In a herbivore-plant system, animal density influences selective pressure on plants; this selection influences genetic make-up of plant; and in turn, the genetic make-up of plant influences animal density. The actions and reactions of interacting populations in the food chain cycling in the genetic feed-back mechanism result in the evolution and regulation of animal populations.

Pimentel qualified his idea by saying:

I do not propose that the feed-back mechanism is the only means of population regulation, nor that this mechanism is independent of the 'competition' and 'environmental randomness' ideas. The three are interdependent, and I suspect that upon the introduction of a new animal type into a new ecosystem there is an evolution of regulation from both the 'competition' and 'environmental randomness' conditions to the feed-back mechanism. That is, before sufficient change takes place in the eating population and eaten population, the principal means of regulation is through 'competition' and 'environmental randomness'.

('Competition idea' means the views of Nicholson and his followers, and 'environmental randomness idea' means the views of Thompson and Andrewartha-Birch.)

Presumably, Pimentel was suggesting that the mutual evolution of those organisms which interact essentially as predators and prey would sometimes lead eventually to life systems which involved no density-related mechanisms of the sort described by Nicholson (1954b), and that the stabilization of numbers would result entirely from qualitative balance between the properties of the interacting organisms. His basic idea is a modern version of the thinking characteristic of the early community ecologists. The idea resembles that termed the 'environmental-fit hypothesis' by Nicholson (1958) who severely criticized Thompson's (1956) version of it. Pimentel's formulation has been challenged by Milne (1962). After discussing Pimentel's mathematical model, Milne wrote (p. 30):

Obviously, the model works successfully only if the hypothetical data are selected to that end. Furthermore, the model takes no account of the fact that there is hardly any food organism (if indeed any at all) that does not have several species attacking it. These species, because of their physiological and ecological differences, must exert differing and to some extent opposing selective pressures on the genotypes of the food organism.

In any naturally-evolved ecosystem, all populations tend to be well-adapted. Between some species and others that feed upon them, the adaptive counterbalancing of properties may well be such that numbers could be limited for many generations without the operation of density-related stabilizing mechanisms. However, it is unlikely that a situation of this kind could persist indefinitely because of the variable influence of weather and other environmental components which affect the numbers of eaters and eaten.

Although a high degree of mutual adaptation has been achieved tor interacting species, and further 'fitting together' will doubtless occur, it seems that the tendency of evolution is to modify and diversify density-related mechanisms of the kind described by Nicholson, and to result in the replacement of one type by another, rather than to make them redundant. Wynne-Edwards' (1962) theory to explain animal dispersion in terms of social behaviour states that, as a result of the evolution of 'conventional goals' of competition, such as territorial rights and social status, the populations of many animal species tend to limit their own numbers far below the starvation level and thus avoid the potentially disastrous consequences of unrestricted competition for food. Like the vertebrates in which Wynne-Edwards was mainly interested, many insect species have evolved density-related, physiological and behavioural mechanisms which minimize the chance of extinction by starvation.

For example, Clark (1949), when working on the locust *Chortoicetes terminifera*, observed that the formation of marching bands of young hoppers and mass emigration from feeding grounds occurred while there was still plenty of food available to the individuals present. Thus severe competition for food in the vicinity of hatching sites was avoided by the density-induced change from individualistic to gregarious behaviour. Mass emigration increased the chance of survival both for the individuals which remained behind, and for those that emigrated. Without mass migration, scarcely any individuals could have obtained enough food to reach the adult stage.

In the case of the cabbage aphid, *Brevicoryne brassicae*, the work of Hughes (section 4.24) indicates that, when food is brought into short supply by increase in the number of wingless forms, there occurs not only a density-induced reduction of the birth rate but also a density-induced increase in the production of winged forms which rapidly steps up the migration rate from an infested crop. For this species, density-adjusting interaction involves an increased production of the winged individuals which are essential for population persistence.

Pimentel's contribution serves to remind population ecologists that, although they are concerned primarily with the more immediate determinants of abundance, and observable actions and interactions within life systems, they need to take into consideration the evolutionary and genetical components of their subject.

3·3 CONCLUSIONS

We can summarize the contributions of the five population theorists by saying:

(*i*) Nicholson emphasizes the density-related 'subtractive' processes which act as stabilizing mechanisms within life systems, especially intra-specific competition, and builds his theory around them.

(*ii*) Andrewartha and Birch emphasize variations and differences in the *intrinsic* favourableness of environmental conditions, and consider that, in general, there is no need to look further for adequate explanations of population numbers.

(*iii*) Milne also emphasizes the influence of environmental conditions, but recognizes the particular significance of density-related subtractive processes in his account of natural control.

(*iv*) Chitty emphasizes the inherent properties of species, and suggests that, in general, there may be an inverse relationship between the average vitality of the individuals in a population and population density, which can act as a mechanism, or part thereof, for stabilizing numbers.

(*v*) Pimentel emphasizes mutual adaptation between the inherent properties of species and those of their food plants and natural enemies, and suggests that, in the course of evolution, density-stabilizing mechanisms of the sort described by Nicholson tend to be replaced by genetic feed-back processes between predator and prey species, which serve the same purpose.

It is a truism to say that the theories presented are simply different ways of regarding and evaluating the same things, conditioned by personal experience, preference, and aptitude; but mention of the fact is necessary because of the uncompromising way in which some leading theorists have adhered to their particular viewpoints.

Nicholson's contribution, which was discussed very briefly, is undoubtedly the most comprehensive and penetrating. The other theories are all valuable for the stimulation that they provide, especially those of Andrewartha-Birch and Milne. Their views help in developing the perspective needed for a well-balanced approach to the ecological problems of pest control.

At the present time, there is need for a generalized description of the ways in which insect abundance is determined, based on a concept such as 'life system' and incorporating: (*i*) all that is useful in the ideas of the theorists; and (*ii*) the latest information on natural populations, much of which was not available to them.

CHAPTER IV

The functioning of life systems

4.1 A WAY OF GENERALIZING ABOUT THE DETERMINATION OF INSECT NUMBERS

Insect species differ greatly in their characteristics as do the environments in which they live. Consequently, any attempt to generalize about the determination of insect numbers can serve only as a guide for the study of particular populations. From the ideas put forward by ecological theorists (notably Moebius (1877), Solomon (1949, 1957), Nicholson (1933, 1954a, b), Andrewartha and Birch (1954), Chitty (1960), Milne (1962), and Huffaker and Messenger (1964)), and from the results of recent population studies, it is possible to propose a way of generalizing about the determination of insect numbers. A comprehensive synthesis can be achieved by: (*i*) providing a unifying concept, namely 'life system', which incorporates all influences that may affect population numbers; and (*ii*) by describing, in terms of the general characteristics of life systems, the complex webs of interactions that determine the persistence and abundance of populations.

As indicated in chapter I, the spatial delimitation of a life system is mainly a matter of purpose and convenience. Like the term 'population', 'life system' implies continuity of existence and applies therefore to persistent, reproducing collectives of individuals. For practical purposes, the idea of life system can be applied to any natural collective of individuals which is known to have persisted for some generations as a result of reproduction. The idea is applicable also to reproducing collectives maintained under laboratory conditions.

4.11 The co-determinants of abundance

In nature, the numbers of any population are determined within an ecosystem (Solomon 1949, Tansley 1935), and held within circumscribed limits by interactions which involve both other populations and the physical conditions provided by the habitat (Bakker 1964). The part of an ecosystem which determines the existence of a particular population is called a life system – and is composed of the subject species and its effective environment (see figure 6). The latter consists of: (*i*) the resources (supplies of all kinds) required for population maintenance such as living space, food, and favourable physico-chemical conditions; and (*ii*) inimical agencies, both biotic and abiotic, which oppose the survival and reproduction of individuals of the subject species.

As stated in chapter I, the existence and numbers of a subject population are determined by the properties inherent in its members and the intrinsic attributes of its effective environment. These interacting *co-determinants* of abundance permit the existence of individuals (phenotypes) with certain observable *species characteristics*; enable them to form a population with

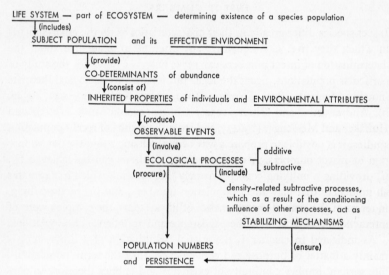

FIGURE 6. The elements involved in the functioning of a life system.

group characteristics additional to those of individuals; and decide population size (and quality). The co-determinants can be said to perform a dual role. Firstly, they control the life functions of individuals which lead to population increase by reproduction and immigration; secondly, they control the circumstances which lead to the limitation of numbers by premature mortality, restricted natality, and emigration.

4.12 The measurable expression of interactions between the co-determinants of abundance

4.121 *Ecological events*

The interactions between the co-determinants of abundance can be observed and measured only in the form of ecological events (section 2.6), namely:

(*i*) *Primary events*, such as births, deaths, and movements, which describe the basic demographic characteristics of the population, e.g. life cycle, annual generation sequence, etc., and express the inherited ability of individuals to survive and multiply.

(*ii*) *Secondary events* which qualify the magnitude, extent, frequency, or duration of primary events and influence populations in two ways:

(*a*) *By altering the supply of resources required for the existence of individuals.* The supply of resources may be increased or decreased in quantity or in quality. Events affecting supply may involve abiotic agencies; other organisms that either favour the subject species or compete with it; and competition or co-operation between individuals within the population.

(*b*) *By acting directly upon the existence of individuals.* Direct actions may be either harmful or beneficial. Events which affect individuals directly may involve: abiotic agencies, predators, parasites, or pathogens; hyperparasites; and the population density of the subject species.

4.122 *Ecological processes*

Observable events are the manifestation of processes which affect population numbers. These processes are essentially of two kinds:

(*i*) *Additive processes* which contribute towards the addition of individuals to the subject population by promoting survival and reproduction. They include, for example, the generation of environmental resources; the procurement and utilization of these resources by the subject species; the development, reproduction, and immigration of individuals; and limitation of the destructive action of natural enemies by other environmental agencies such as weather.

(*ii*) *Subtractive processes* which contribute towards removing individuals prematurely and towards limiting the production of offspring. Such processes include, for example, all forms of harmful and restrictive interaction between the individuals of the subject species (e.g. intraspecific competition and cannibalism); predation and parasitism; the action of unfavourable weather on the population; and interactions between environmental agencies which reduce the supply of resources such as food. It is usual for these processes either to restrict or to oppose additive processes, but in some instances a subtractive process may promote survival. For example, when the individuals of a subject species are competing for a greatly depleted supply of food, the occurrence of very heavy predation may result in a higher rate of survival than would otherwise be possible (see Clark 1963d).

The processes of life systems operate either independently of, or according to, population density in the following ways:

(*i*) *Density-independent processes.* Such processes exert effects that either remain almost constant, e.g. some forms of predation which destroy an almost constant percentage of individuals in successive generations (see LeRoux *et al.* 1963), or vary without relation to population density, e.g. the production of food (fruits) on apple trees in the life systems of the codling moth.

(*ii*) *Density-related processes.* Such processes may have either immediate or delayed effects (see Nicholson 1933, 1954b, and Solomon 1957). They may function over all or most of the density range of subject populations, or be restricted to part only of the range. The effects of some density-related processes increase as populations increase in size; the effects of others diminish. In some instances, the effects increase until the subject population reaches a certain size, and then diminish as the population continues to grow. The action of density-related subtractive processes such as intra-specific competition for food varies '*automatically*' according to the amount of the material resource available to individuals of the subject population, i.e. according to density relative to the supply of the resource. The sub-tractive action of some other processes, e.g. many forms of predation, may also increase with increase in population density – but less consistently, i.e. in a '*probabilistic*' manner. Their intensity of action is dependent, to a greater or lesser extent, upon conditions other than the numbers of the subject population, e.g. the prevailing weather or the available supply of alternative food (see Milne 1962).

Most of the attention paid to density-related processes has been con-centrated on those with subtractive effects that intensify as population numbers increase, i.e. the processes termed 'density-dependent', e.g. by Solomon (1957). Many ecologists agree with Solomon that:

> It is density-dependent processes which account for the regulation of populations. A regulator cannot operate as such unless it responds to some extent to changes in what is to be regulated. This idea is the same as that of 'feed-back' in cybernetics, though in the biological field there is no approach to precision except in certain laboratory experiments.

In other words, such processes can provide *stabilizing mechanisms* which oppose effectively the indefinite increase of population numbers. Whether they actually function as stabilizing mechanisms depends upon the con-ditions which other processes create within life systems.

4.13 The functioning of life systems

The primary contribution of a subject population to its life system is the generation of individuals. The population and the resources provided by the effective environment both participate in the generative function. They interact in additive processes which, if unopposed, would result in maximum realization of the inherited ability of individuals to survive and multiply. However, the additive processes are opposed by an array of subtractive processes, which, together with the former, define the actual reproductive ability of individuals, the population's age-schedule of mortality, and the actual rates of birth, death, immigration, and emigration. The numbers of a population fluctuate according to variations in the relation between the addition and premature loss of individuals.

4.131 *The fluctuation of population numbers*

The numbers of some insect populations fluctuate in an irregular manner between very wide limits as a result of variability in the supply of food and other resources. The apparent instability of numbers in such populations – characterized by the absence of a general level of abundance about which numbers fluctuate for long periods – has led some workers to describe the determination of insect abundance mainly in terms of the intrinsic variability of environmental conditions.

There are, however, other species whose population numbers have been observed to fluctuate regularly, for much or all of the time, about mean levels of abundance which do not change markedly. Some ecologists, e.g. Morris (1959), have ascertained that, for such species, processes of the sort described by Solomon (1957) as 'density-dependent' may influence numerical fluctuation to such an extent that their effects in one generation can be used to predict population numbers in the next. Those workers (e.g. Morris, ed. 1963) have found Nicholson's (1954b) concept of an equilibrium density useful when thinking about their work.

The two kinds of numerical fluctuation mentioned can be regarded as extremes – the first being exemplified by the grasshopper *Austroicetes cruciata* (section 3.221) – and the second by the black-headed budworm *Acleris variana* in New Brunswick (Morris 1959, Miller 1966). There is little doubt that the abundance of the two species depends both on density-related and density-independent processes. However, in the case of *A. cruciata*, weather exerts a dominating influence in the causation of population fluctuations; whereas numerical changes in *A. variana* appear to be dominated by the density-related effects of parasitism. Using Morris' (1959) 'key-factor' method of analysis, Miller (*in press*) developed a very effective equation for predicting the numbers of *A. variana*, based on parasitism and weather.

In his essay on the interpretation of mortality data, Morris (1957) generalized about the influence of subtractive processes upon numerical fluctuations, using the term 'mortality' to denote miscellaneous losses in a population resulting 'from direct mortality, from dispersal, or from reduced fecundity', and the terms 'intrinsic factor' for innate characteristics of species and 'extrinsic factor' for environmental agencies. He wrote:

To be able to interpret mortality with respect to its influence on population dynamics, we must first answer a number of basic questions: What is the significance of variation in degree of mortality and what causes it? Is the general level of mortality significant and are high mortalities necessarily any more important than low ones? Is the order of mortality in relation to preceding or following mortalities of any significance and how is this affected by contemporaneous mortalities?

After considering these questions, he concluded:

. . . variation is the important attribute of mortality, and that low but variable mortalities may therefore have more influence on population trend than high but relatively constant mortalities. Although density relationships are important, it is necessary to study the relation of mortality variations to other extrinsic and intrinsic factors in order to understand population dynamics. . . . Variations that occur at high levels of mortality may have an effect on population trend that is greater than or equal to the effect of similar variations at low levels of mortality, depending upon density relationships. Since most mortality factors appear to be density independent, however, it is essential in interpretation to keep in mind that variations at high levels are potentially more important. . . . The importance of the sequence in which different mortalities occur is also dependent upon density relationships and more specific conclusions can be reached only for individual situations where these relationships are understood. The magnitude of mortality contributed by contemporaneous factors is extremely important and serves to explain why it is possible for a low but variable mortality to act as the primary determiner of population trend.

To this statement on the causes of numerical fluctuation, it is necessary only to add that recent work undertaken mainly to predict population numbers from generation to generation (e.g. see LeRoux *et al.* 1963) confirms the view of Morris and shows that, for the species investigated, variations in the effects of one or a few ecological processes could account for most of the variability in population trend. When discussing the results of this work, the statistician Watt (1963a) concluded by saying:

. . . we do not need a tremendous amount of information about a great many variables to build quite revealing mathematical models for the population dynamics of these pests.

4.132 *The stabilization of population numbers*
The most characteristic feature about the numbers of a species is change. Yet there is also a stability in numbers which enables us to say that some species are rare and that other species are common. (Birch 1962.)

The available evidence on insect populations suggests that the numbers of many species are stabilized in the sense that they are prevented from increasing progressively with time by density-related subtractive processes. There is reason to believe that the numbers of other species are either changing to new general levels of abundance or gradually dwindling towards extinction – mainly as a result of man's progressive modification of environmental conditions and differences in adaptive ability. In other words, some life systems continue to be stable states of existence, whereas others may be either metastable states or unstable.

As a general working hypothesis, based on logical deduction and upon the empirical evidence obtained from recent field and laboratory studies, it can be assumed that population persistence depends upon:

(*i*) The influence exerted by environmental agencies **and** species characteristics, such as patterns of behaviour, whose 'permissive' and 'conditioning' effects★ determine when, where, and how the stabilization of population numbers is possible, and contribute towards setting the levels between which numbers may fluctuate. The permissive influence of such agencies and species characteristics is often taken for granted in publications dealing with numerical stabilization.

(*ii*) The operation of processes, related to population density by negative feed-back, which act, either probabilistically or automatically, as stabilizing mechanisms to limit numerical increase. Such mechanisms include the 'contest' and 'scramble' forms of intraspecific competition for depletable resources (see Nicholson 1954b); the action of certain predators, parasites, and pathogens; density-induced emigration; and forms of territorial behaviour. They may incorporate reversible qualitative changes in populations and genetic polymorphism.

Stabilizing mechanisms which involve interactions between the individuals of a subject species may be said to 'adjust' population numbers in relation to the supply of limiting resources; the other type of mechanism, e.g. density-related predation, may be said to 'contain' or hold them below certain limits.

The frequency and intensity with which stabilizing mechanisms operate

★ The idea of conditioning influences put forward here is similar to that of Huffaker and Messenger (1964, p. 79). They wrote: 'The category of general forces which occur and act without regard to density we term "conditioning forces" defined as, *environmental factors or agents which, uninfluenced by density, contribute to the setting or fixing of a framework of potential environmental capacity or affect interim population realization when capacity is not attained*. Thus, conditioning forces include not only the *direct* density-independent repressive actions but, as well, the *indirect* ways in which such density-uninfluenced forces operate in natural control . . .'. We include, as conditioning influences, density-related actions which do not serve as stabilizing mechanisms (see Clark 1963d and section 4.29).

in a life system depends upon the extent to which the innate ability of the population to increase is counteracted by the subtractive action of other ecological processes whose collective influence varies independently of population numbers. In some life systems, the overall effect of these opposing processes may be such that populations persist with only intermittent action by stabilizing mechanisms. In other life systems, stabilizing mechanisms may be operating most of the time. Moreover, both in the overall life system of a species which exists in a variety of contiguous environments, and in the particular life systems of a species which exists as a number of discrete populations, the frequency and intensity with which stabilizing mechanisms operate may differ greatly.

4.2 SOME NATURAL AND ARTIFICIAL LIFE SYSTEMS

Having considered in the abstract how population numbers and persistence are determined, we shall now describe, by way of illustration, a number of life systems that have been studied recently. These examples, which range from experimental laboratory models to complex natural systems, were chosen because the subject species concerned differ greatly in their characteristics, and involve very different environments. The investigations of these life systems differ also – in their purpose and in their scope. Like all other attempts to explain the abundance of insect species, they are far from being complete and some of the conclusions drawn will doubtless require modification in the light of further investigation. Only one field study has reached the stage at which a worthwhile attempt at predictive mathematical modelling was feasible (see chapter V). Collectively, however, the examples provide a substantial body of evidence in support of our way of generalizing and are presented for consideration as a whole.

We shall begin with codling moth in apple orchards in Nova Scotia and south-eastern Australia, and end with what is known at present of the complex life system of a species of psyllid in the latter region.

4.21 Two life systems of *Cydia pomonella* (Tortricidæ)

The codling moth is the oldest-known and most widely-distributed pest of deciduous fruit. It occurs today in almost every region of the world where apples and pears are grown, and can severely reduce marketable crops by spoiling the fruits in which its larvae feed.

Codling moth has been studied assiduously in a diversity of environments, mostly with a view to developing short-term means of crop protection. Those *ad hoc* investigations have not contributed much towards an understanding of the population ecology of the species, beyond revealing some of the characteristics which make for its adaptive versatility as a pest.

Following a broader approach, MacLellan (1958, 1959, 1960, 1962, 1963) and Geier (1961, 1963a, 1963b, 1964) have recently attempted to describe the determination of codling moth numbers under widely differing conditions in eastern Canada and south-eastern Australia, respectively. The findings of these authors illustrate the diversity of life systems in which the local populations of a broadly-distributed species can exist.

4.211 *Characteristics of the species*

The properties of the codling moth are well suited for the conditions which

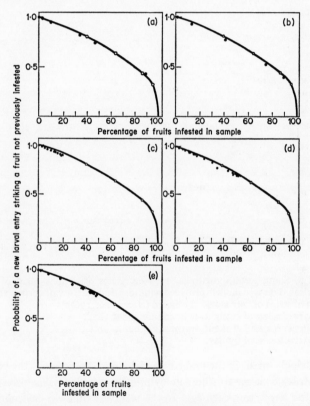

FIGURE 7. Canberra 1960–63. Observed distribution, between fruits, of larval entries (full dots) in relation to random distribution (line):
  a. 1960–61, 200 clusters totally infested by mid-January;
  b. 1960–61, 100 clusters totally infested by mid-March;
  c. 1962–63, 100 clusters, interrupted spray schedule;
  d. 1962–63, 1,000 clusters, exposed to attack throughout the growing season;
  e. 1962–63, 1,000 clusters exposed to attack by late generations only (after Geier 1964).

prevailed in its original habitats in the temperate forest zones of western Asia and Europe, where it probably infested sparsely-distributed thickets of rosaceous trees and shrubs.

Most adult moths do not range far from the place in which they pupated, although some individuals appear to be capable of substantially greater displacements of up to one mile or more. The species reproduces bi-sexually. A few days after emerging and mating, sometimes repeatedly, females begin to lay an average complement of about fifty eggs over a period ranging normally from one to two weeks. As a general rule, the eggs

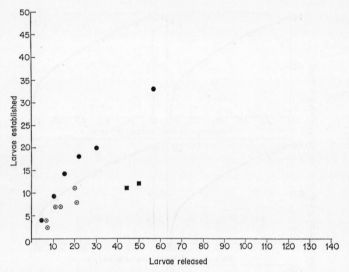

FIGURE 8. South-eastern Australia, 1961–62. Rates of establishment of mature larvae released on tree models provided with identical supplies of cocoon shelter in the form of strips of corrugated cardboard (after Geier 1963a).
● Larvae released at night, temperature about 16°C.
■ Larvae released at night, temperature below 16°C.
⊙ Larvae released by day.

are laid singly on, or in the immediate vicinity of, host fruits – the presence of which is necessary to stimulate oviposition – and females make a short flight after depositing each egg. In the relatively uniform environment of a commercial orchard, females tend to select fruits as oviposition sites unsystematically within and between trees, which results in an almost random distribution of larval infestations (figure 7).

The eggs hatch after one to two weeks, and newly-born larvae make for a suitable point of entry into the nearest fruit, which they penetrate to the full length of the body in a few hours. Larval development proceeds wholly within fruits, and normally lasts three to four weeks. Codling moth larvae are cannibalistic, and, when two or more larvae are present simultaneously in a fruit, there is a strong probability that only one will survive. The random distribution of eggs between fruits, and the cannibalistic behaviour, provide jointly the conditions for a form of intraspecific competition amongst immature larvae.

Upon reaching maturity, codling moth larvae may either pupate without delay, or enter a prolonged period of diapause which defers pupation until the following spring (or even longer). The mature larvae leave the fruits and seek sheltered places in which they can spin a cocoon (or hibernaculum). The search for cocooning sites proceeds apparently in an unsystematic manner – mainly on the trunks and limbs of infested trees, and in their immediate vicinity. The average time spent in searching decreases, and the percentage of larvae which succeed in establishing cocoons increases, with increasing supplies of suitable cocooning sites on the trees, i.e. sites that are sufficiently sheltered, readily accessible, and vacant. This was confirmed by a series of experiments (see figure 8) which strongly suggested that cocoon establishment can involve a form of intraspecific competition whereby some larvae are excluded from favourable sites, and thus exposed in a varying degree to hazards which threaten unprotected individuals.

Codling moth is well adapted to exploit fully the varying environmental resources provided throughout the range of its principal host plants. In areas where the growing seasons are short, 'overwintered' individuals reproduce in spring and early summer, and, without exception, their progeny enter diapause upon reaching larval maturity. In areas where the growing seasons are long, the progeny of overwintered individuals reproduce for the most part without hibernating. In the ensuing generation, the majority of larvae enter diapause, but some develop immediately and produce a third seasonal generation, some larvae of which mature and overwinter, whereas others perish as fruits decay and winter sets in. Diapause appears to be induced mainly in response to critical photoperiods (Dickson 1949, Geier 1963b), the lengths of which vary with latitude.

Besides the risks of death entailed in competition for fruit space and for cocooning sites, codling moth is exposed to a number of environmental hazards which may destroy individuals before they can reproduce. Under natural conditions, mortality due to hazards occurs most frequently in the mobile stages, i.e. amongst newly-hatched larvae before they have entered the fruits, and amongst mature larvae seeking a place to spin their cocoons. Such mortality results mainly from predation by other arthropods and, to a lesser degree, from adverse physical circumstances such as rain or extreme heat. Larvae in cocoons, particularly diapausing individuals, may be

F   67

attacked by a number of natural enemies and pathogens, and some are apparently unable to withstand the rigours of severe winters. Eggs may be destroyed by parasites and predators, and certain hymenopterous species are capable of parasitizing larvae shortly after they have entered fruits. Larvae are sometimes drowned while feeding, or compelled to withdraw from fruits, following a sudden increase in water uptake by the host trees after rain or irrigation. Adults can be caught in flight by birds and bats, and by spiders while mating or laying eggs.

Although conspicuous by the concentration of its activity on the fruits of its host plants in orchards, codling moth never occurs in great numbers at any one time, nor does its feeding in developing fruits influence the numbers of fruits set from year to year.

4.212 *The life system of codling moth in Nova Scotia*

Apple growing has always been one of the major industries of the Annapolis Valley of Nova Scotia. At the outbreak of World War II, this industry was so severely hit by export restrictions that energetic measures had to be taken to ensure its survival. In particular, a determined and sustained effort was made after 1942 to reduce the current cost of crop protection against noxious insects and mites. Extensive surveys were carried out in the course of this work to evaluate the injuriousness of the principal pests, and to determine their population trends over the years. For codling moth, Pickett (1959) cites the following figures, each based on a sample of about eighty *commercially-sprayed* orchards selected at random throughout the Annapolis Valley:

Years	1948	1949	1950	1951	1952	1953	1954	1955	1956	1957	1958
Injuries per 100 fruits	30·8	8·1	11·2	13·9	13·4	14·9	5·5	6·5	6·9	3·3	4·1

The marked decrease in the injuriousness of the pest after 1953 was concomitant with general adoption of a 'modified spray programme' designed to avoid the disturbances which the indiscriminate use of broad-spectrum insecticides can cause in the structure and dynamics of arthropod communities. It was therefore concluded that natural enemies were probably capable of 'containing' codling moth populations at very low levels of abundance in Nova Scotia. This assumption was supported by MacLellan's (1963) observation that: 'In *fully neglected* orchards on the fringe of the apple growing areas in the Annapolis Valley codling moth infestations in the past 12 years have varied between one and 12 injuries per 100 fruits.'

TABLE I. The life system of codling moth in Nova Scotia. Summary of observations recorded in 1960 in four study plots (after MacLellan 1962).

Numbers of	Plot				Total
	1	2	3	4	
Overwintering larvae (spring count) (per 12 vertical feet)	5	2	6	7	20
Adult moths (per two pans*)	24	24	59	37	144
Total eggs in samples (2586 clusters)	89	74	108	105	376
Eggs preyed upon in samples (2586 clusters)	12	7	19	16	54
Total eggs calculated by trees	1,188	642	349	529	2,708
Eggs preyed upon calculated by trees	169	67	69	84	389
Injuries on fruit	349	294	91	224	958
Deep entries (wormy fruit)	324	271	76	187	858
Fruit set (14 June)	21,063	11,870	3,911	9,404	46,248
Harvested fruit	6,029	2,844	1,112	2,791	12,776
Overwintering larvae (fall count) (per 12 vertical feet)	11	8	4	7	30

* Lure pans.

From the evidence published by MacLellan (1962), it is possible to infer
the probable schedule of mortality in codling moth populations if they
(and the associated orchard fauna) were not treated with broad-spectrum
pesticides. Assuming that females each lay approximately fifty eggs in
Nova Scotia, the twelve study trees referred to in table I should have produced about a hundred adults of both sexes in the spring and early summer
of 1960 to account for the total of 2,708 eggs estimated from observed
samples. Those eggs resulted in only 858 'deep entries' into fruits, which
amounts to a reduction of 70% in the young progeny. If each entry is
taken to represent 0·9 mature larva, as would be the case under comparable
conditions in Australia, 772 fully-fed individuals would have emerged from
the infested fruits of the twelve study trees to search for cocooning sites.
Of these, no more than 150, or about 20%, would probably have been
established if, as for the previous overwintering generation, the numbers of
cocooned individuals actually found on twelve vertical feet of trunk represent approximately one fifth of the total population of the twelve trees. In
the present instance, applying the same rate of winter mortality as that
observed in the previous generation, i.e. about 60%, sixty adult moths
could be expected to emerge from hibernation and to reproduce the following season. This inference is corroborated by MacLellan's (1963) actual

observations, particularly by his estimate of the total number of eggs laid on the same study trees in 1961, i.e. 1,312.

In 1960, population increase on MacLellan's trees was limited by heavy mortality at three well-defined stages: in the first few days of life, before the young larvae entered the fruits (70% of eggs and newly-hatched larvae destroyed); during the search for cocooning sites by mature larvae (80% of the estimated numbers of fully-fed larvae lost); and during hibernation (60% of overwintering population killed). The mortality in eggs and young larvae was attributed almost entirely to predation by a number of species, prominent amongst which were five mirids and one mite, *Anystis agilis*. Other predators, including a mirid, chrysopids, pentatomids, nabids, clerids, two species of thrips, and spiders are considered to have played a contributory role. No observations were made on the fate of the mature larvae which failed to establish cocoons, but it is very likely that most of them were also destroyed by predators (including perhaps ants and spiders) – in spite of the abundance of suitable shelter provided by the characteristically rough bark of the local trees. Most of the established larvae which failed to survive the winter were taken in their hibernacula by woodpeckers; a few were parasitized by the braconid *Ascogaster quadridentata*.

By considering MacLellan's findings in the light of the events which regularly follow the application of certain broad-spectrum pesticides, it is possible to generalize on the nature of the stabilizing mechanisms which contain codling moth numbers at low levels in Nova Scotia. When comparing the effects of DDT and lead arsenate with those of ryania, a selective insecticide which is practically harmless for most beneficial species, Pickett (1959) stated:

The following figures show the average injuries by the codling moth to apples in a 5-acre orchard after treatments with 3 insecticides during a 5-year period:

Year	Insecticide	Stings per 100 apples	Deep entries per 100 apples
1950	DDT	1·0	1·0
1951	None	5·0	38·0
1952	Lead arsenate	21·0	32·0
1953	Ryania	7·0	0·2
1954	None	0·4	1·4

The main point of interest in this table is the amount of damage by the codling moth when DDT was discontinued, in contrast with that in the year after ryania was used, and the ineffectiveness of lead arsenate in this orchard.

An explanation of the difference between ryania and DDT is suggested by the numbers of several beneficial groups taken by fumigating whole trees that had received three successive sprays of the respective insecticides:

Treatment	DDT	Ryania
Predaceous thrips	9	293
Miridae	3	151
Coccinellidae	0	9
Pentatomidae	1	14
Hymenoptera	41	252
Arachnida	15	98

Pickett's explanation is supported by the results of an experiment by MacLellan (1963). The outcome of this test is shown in table 2, about which MacLellan comments: 'The sharp decrease in the numbers of predators on the control trees one week after fumigated trees were treated was caused by the loss of *Diaphnocoris* sp. as they became adults . . .'. Furthermore, in the course of his detailed observations, MacLellan (1962, 1963) was able to establish a close relationship between the degree of predation on codling moth eggs and newly-hatched larvae – and the frequency distribution of a number of species of general predators, principally mirids.

TABLE 2. The life system of codling moth in Nova Scotia. Predation on codling moth eggs placed on fumigated and control trees on four occasions after treatment. Data on predators are expressed as average numbers of predators per 1,000 clusters (after MacLellan 1963).

Days from fumigation	Fumigated trees			Control trees		
	Eggs placed	Eggs preyed upon	Egg predators	Eggs placed	Eggs preyed upon	Egg predators
—1 to —2	—	—	13·7	—	—	14·6
+5 to +6	80	1	0·2	86	13	7·3
+11 to +12	31	0	0·7	27	3	8·5
+15 to +16	42	0	1·5	35	3	6·3
+18 to +19	119	2	2·8	127	16	8·2
Totals	272	3	—	275	35	—

However, it is clear from MacLellan's (1962) estimates that the absence of predation in the early developmental stages of codling moth, following applications of DDT, does not in itself suffice to explain the magnitude of the increase in crop damage apparent from 1950 to 1952 in Pickett's (1959) experiment with insecticides. Even allowing for large differences in crop size, this progression requires the additional postulate that a considerable increase occurred in the numbers of adults reproducing in 1951 and 1952, which could only result from a much higher survival rate in hibernating larvae after the use of DDT.

Because most of the newly-hatched larvae in 1950 would have been killed by DDT, the associated destruction of their predators would have had no noticeable effect before 1951. If it were considered that the individuals which survived the sprays and achieved deep penetrations into the fruits in 1950 had been exposed as mature and hibernating larvae to the mortality rates apparent in MacLellan's (1962) findings, the lack of predation on eggs and newly-hatched larvae in 1951 could not have resulted in more than a ten-fold increase in the relative frequency of deep entries from 1950 to 1951.

It is probable that the observed thirty-fold increase could not have occurred *unless the sprays had also suppressed the species which must be assumed to prey upon mature larvae during their search for cocooning sites.* Moreover, winter mortality amongst the survivors should have been exceptionally low. This is explainable only in part by lack of parasitization by *A. quadridentata*, due to the sprays. If woodpeckers were present, one would need to assume either that they do not search sprayed orchards as effectively as unsprayed plantations, or that, within their feeding zones, searching does not normally cover all the possible cocooning sites for codling moth larvae. In that case, the numbers of larvae escaping predation by woodpeckers would automatically increase as the numbers of hibernating codling moth larvae increased.

These considerations are strengthened by the fact that the frequency of codling moth damage to crops was significantly higher and more variable when broad-spectrum pesticides were widely used in the Annapolis Valley than after the general adoption of the 'modified spray programme' in 1954. When the adult moths are not very abundant, one or two sprays of DDT or parathion are quite as effective as natural enemies in keeping infestations by *univoltine* populations of the species down to commercially tolerable levels. However, the rates of mortality which insecticides inflict upon adults, eggs, and young larvae do not increase with the numbers of the pest. Thus, the higher infestations recorded under the regime of broad-spectrum pesticides resulted not so much from the absence of predation in the early developmental stages of the pest (for the sole loss of which insecticides could make up easily) as from an overwhelming increase in the numbers of reproducing adults – of whose progeny insecticides could only destroy an almost constant percentage. The increase could be induced by no other cause than a sharp decrease in the effectiveness of natural enemies affecting the later developmental stages of the pest, as was demonstrated beyond reasonable doubt by the events which followed the introduction of the spraying schedule designed to avoid the destruction of beneficial species.

It is practically certain, therefore, that the natural stabilizing mechanism of codling moth in Nova Scotia involves both the predatory action of a known array of species which feed on eggs and newly-hatched larvae, and of organisms, as yet unidentified, which are capable of destroying large percentages of fully-grown larvae, and are affected as adversely as the natural enemies of the young stages by the use of broad-spectrum pesticides.

This stabilizing mechanism contains codling moth populations at unusually low levels, so low in fact that they often do not exceed the limit which is commercially tolerable for fruit growers. Its operation is conditioned by a number of circumstances (amongst which the density of the subject population appears to play a subordinate role) i.e.: (*i*) the short growing season which restricts codling moth to producing only one generation each year; (*ii*) a high and relatively constant rate of predation by birds in winter, which appears to be largely independent of codling moth densities and which 'reduced the pest population in orchards to a level where other natural control agents were able to prevent the succeeding generation from damaging the fruit to an uneconomical degree' (MacLellan 1959); and (*iii*) a very large number of natural enemies whose densities are determined mainly by the abundance of other prey, but whose variety tends to ensure that some are usually sufficiently active to inflict effective, density-related mortality on eggs, newly-hatched larvae, and mature larvae of the subject species. The natural life system of codling moth in Nova Scotia can be said to involve a broad section of the animal species belonging to the ecosystem of local orchards, and may thus be representative of the great majority of insect species whose populations generally remain small.

4.213 *The life system of codling moth in the Australian Capital Territory*
Codling moth has probably existed for three centuries in Nova Scotia, but only for half as long in Australia. The natural environment of Nova Scotia is closely related in climate, flora, and fauna to that of the pest's original habitats in the old world, and self-sown apple trees are numerous in Nova Scotian forests. In Australia, codling moth is restricted to exotic host plants the fauna of which is largely native, and less closely integrated than the assemblages of animal species in the orchard ecosystems of the northern hemisphere. Apple trees in Australia are usually shaped differently to those of Nova Scotia, with lighter frames and considerably smoother

bark, thus providing much less primary shelter for codling moth cocoons. In the Capital Territory, where the main study of the life system was conducted, the long growing season enables the pest to produce three generation cycles annually, and favourable weather conditions throughout the season result in a somewhat higher number of eggs being laid per female than is usual in Nova Scotia.

In the absence of control measures, it is characteristic of codling moth infestations in the Capital Territory that (i) they usually affect a very high percentage of apples, and (ii) they show very little variation from season to season. The typical seasonal progression of attacks on fruit is illustrated in figure 9, resulting in a loss which exceeded 90% of the potential crop. Under natural conditions, infestations vary between a minimum of 85% and total destruction, with a mode of about 95%. Those differences are due essentially to differences in the size of successive crops, there being a strong tendency to biennial bearing in the orchards of the Territory. The overall stability of population numbers is revealed by the following figures based on annual counts of overwintering larvae made on a number of naturally-infested trees in a study orchard:

Year	Size of previous crop	Number of trees examined	Mean number of overwintering larvae per tree	Standard error
1959	large	12	17·75	4·787
1960	large	12	20·58	4·182
1961	very large	15	16·60	6·014
1963	medium	15	18·13	3·845

Experiments showed that differences in numbers of larvae overwintering on unsprayed trees between seasons, between orchards, and between single trees resulted primarily from differences in the supply of suitable cocoon shelter provided by the host trees for mature larvae.

The constancy of such yearly events as the percentage infestation of crops and the cumulative total of overwintering larvae contrasts sharply with the variability of the seasonal trends in population numbers, of which those regular events are the outcome. Depending upon the relation which exists each spring between the numbers of moths emerging from hibernation and the numbers of fruits set on the host trees, the densities of codling moth (as measured by numbers of young larvae penetrating into the fruits) may either increase, decrease, or remain almost the same from the first to the third seasonal generation. The greater the relative size of the spring brood of moths, the lower was the rate of increase between generations. This trend is illustrated in figure 10, using the ratio of diapausing to non-diapausing larvae in the course of a season as an index of population increase throughout that season.

On detailed investigation of the mortality schedule, it was established that it usually took about three eggs to produce one successful larval penetration, regardless of generations, crop size, and previous infestation. The survival of larvae which had gained entry into fruits depended essentially upon whether or not the fruits entered had been penetrated before. If they had been penetrated previously, the likelihood of a larva's survival

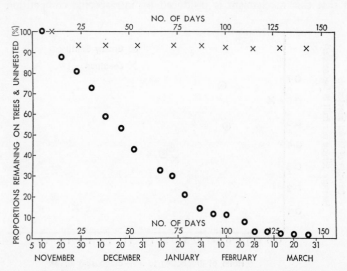

FIGURE 9. The life system of codling moth in the Australian Capital Territory. Proportions of initial fruit numbers remaining on trees and uninfested by codling moth throughout the growing season 1961–62. O: records of 200 apple clusters marked on unsprayed trees. ×: records of 200 apple clusters marked on sprayed trees, in which only one infested fruit was observed (after Geier 1963a).

was reduced abruptly for two reasons: (*i*) because of probable cannibalism in apples occupied *simultaneously* by more than one individual; (*ii*) in the case of subsequent occupation, because infested fruits are shed and/or decay prematurely. As for larvae which matured, their successful establishment was contingent upon the amount of readily-accessible cocooning shelter available to them. No mortality of any significance was noticed amongst established individuals. As for adults, there was no indication that they suffered any significant mortality before they reproduced.

Some predators and parasites contributed in a subordinate way to the mortality schedule as incidental, alternative, or substitutive destructive agents whose absence would not have affected population trends notice-ably. In particular, predators such as ants, spiders, and earwigs are probably the most frequent 'executioners' of the mature larvae which compete unsuccessfully for cocoon shelter and fail to become established.

The high degree to which larval food, i.e. fruit, is utilized; the constancy of yearly events; and the sharply reactive changes manifested in population trends within seasons all point to the existence of an extremely effective stabilizing mechanism in the local life system of the codling moth. The nature of the subtractive processes involved in the mortality schedule indicates that this mechanism is produced by intraspecific competition for

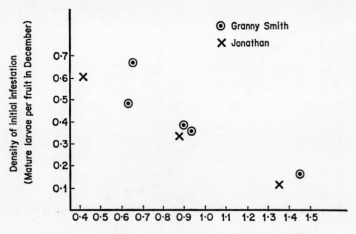

FIGURE 10. The life system of codling moth in the Australian Capital Territory. Densities of initial infestation and proportions of diapausing larvae produced per tree, 1957–58 (after Geier 1964).

limited supplies of suitable fruit-space and for cocoon shelter. This mechanism is conditioned by the general favourableness of the environment which maximizes the power of increase inherent in the species.

When fruits are normally abundant, and the spring brood of moths is not excessive, competition is not severe between individuals of the first generation (either for fruit-space or for cocoon shelter) with the result that the numbers of adult moths produced are higher than the numbers produced from overwintered individuals. Consequently, more entries into fruit are effected by young larvae of the second generation than were by those of the first. This causes the supply of uninfested fruits to decrease and mortality amongst feeding larvae to increase. The mature larvae must now compete for cocooning sites in which an increasing proportion will remain sheltered until the following spring. For these reasons, fewer moths are usually produced by the second generation, whose progeny are stressed increasingly as infestation continues to progress in fruits, and readily accessible cocooning sites are taken up by diapausing larvae. A sequence of this kind is shown for a large crop in figure 11. It followed a moderate initial infestation, and resulted in a winter population equal to that of the previous season.

When population numbers are extremely low in spring, their build-up is rapid, for it proceeds at a rate which is inversely proportional to the

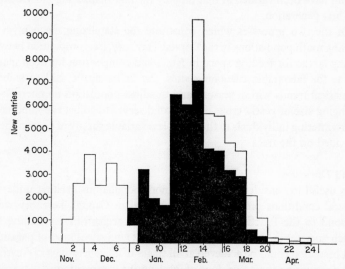

FIGURE 11. The life system of codling moth in the Australian Capital Territory. Estimated numbers of new larval entries in the observed crop, distributed between generations, on successive sampling occasions in a study orchard, 1962–63. Open columns: first and third generations; solid columns: second generation (after Geier 1964).

probability of multiple entries into fruits. If, despite such favourable circumstances, the crop is not heavily infested at the end of the season, competition for winter shelter is not likely to be severe. Mortality at that stage will be correspondingly light, resulting in a larger brood of spring moths than the previous year, and, consequently, in a higher initial infestation of the following season's crop. A population may thus be expected to increase in numbers until the resources of its habitat are fully exploited, i.e. until population numbers have become adjusted to the production of fruit and the supply of potential cocooning sites in the locality.

When population numbers are very high in spring, the risk exists that the crop may be destroyed by the larvae of the first summer generation, very few of which enter diapause. Consequently, the ensuing number of overwintering individuals might be so reduced as to threaten population persistence. That threat is minimized by the random distribution of larval entries amongst fruits, which makes it unlikely that all fruits will be infested at once, and highly probable that some will remain available for the later generations from which most diapausing larvae are produced. Those individuals could be expected to suffer little mortality from competition for cocoon shelter, because of their small numbers and because cocooning sites would have been vacated at that time by the non-diapausing individuals of the first generation.

Of the two processes which constitute the stabilizing mechanism for codling moth populations in the Capital Territory, i.e. competition between young larvae for feeding space in fruits and competition between mature larvae for favourable cocooning sites, the first may be said to stabilize numerical trends within seasons and to adjust population numbers to the changing size of yearly crops. The second serves to adjust the numbers of overwintering individuals to the much less variable supply of cocoon shelter provided on the trees.

4.214 *Discussion*

It is useful to consider how codling moth populations existing under the general conditions prevailing in the Australian Capital Territory would respond to the functioning of a stabilizing mechanism resembling that which operates in Nova Scotia, assuming that equivalent rates of parasitism and predation could be achieved at all stages of all generations in Australia, and discounting the occurrence of intraspecific competition.

A suitable basis for such a calculation may be found in the case examined by Geier (1964), in which an estimated population of 1,000 overwintered moths caused an estimated total of 55,611 deep entries in the course of the season (i.e. 13,576 in the first generation, 31,870 in the second, and 10,165 in the third, respectively). It was inferred from observed evidence that a little over thirty eggs were laid on an average per adult that season, which would have resulted in about 10,000 deep entries in the first generation if predators had destroyed a total 70% of eggs and young larvae as could be expected in Nova Scotia. As no predation by woodpeckers would occur on non-diapausing cocoons, the mature larvae resulting from those entries could have produced 1,800 adults, allowing for a loss of 80% before establishment and a further destruction of 10% of the cocoons caused by the parasite *Ascogaster quadridentata*. The progeny of those adults would have made 18,000 deep entries after predators and parasites had again taken 70%

of eggs and young larvae of the second generation. Of the 3,600 cocoons which surviving larvae could establish, one quarter, or 900, would develop that season, yielding 800 second generation adults from which a further 8,000 larval entries would be expected, while the other 2,700 established larvae hibernated. In total, 36,000 deep entries would have been recorded that season if the Australian population had been subjected to the rates of mortality which local predators and parasites can induce in the single codling moth generation produced each year in Nova Scotia.

Further, assuming that one half, or 4,000, of the larvae causing deep entries in the third generation reached maturity, and that 800 of them established hibernacula, the total winter population would be initially 3,500 individuals. Allowing a loss of 70% amongst them, as would be possible in Nova Scotia, the initial population of adults emerging the following spring would be 1,040 moths. This is close enough to the original figure of 1,000 individuals the previous year to indicate that a system which incorporated the additive processes characteristic of the Australian environment and the subtractive processes operating under Nova Scotian conditions could conceivably be possible – provided a suitably-adapted predacious fauna, capable of performing its containing function on codling moth as effectively as in Nova Scotia, could be assembled and established in Australia.

It must be noticed, however, that an achievement of that magnitude would probably fail to ensure in Australia the same degree of crop protection as it allows in Nova Scotia. Whereas eight deep entries may be normally expected to result from each individual which survives the winter in Nova Scotia, the number would be thirty-six (i.e. more than four times greater) if the same stabilizing mechanism were made to operate under the more favourable conditions for codling moth which prevail in the Australian Capital Territory. This is obvious, in view of the numbers of entries which three successive generations could accumulate in one crop before population numbers were finally reduced to their initial levels by winter mortality.

4.22 The life system of *Phaulacridium vittatum* (Acrididæ)

Phaulacridium vittatum, a small species of grasshopper, is widely distributed in eastern and southern Australia. Before the land was occupied and developed for grazing and farming by European settlers, the species could not have been very abundant. In the climax woodlands of the Southern Tablelands of New South Wales, it was probably restricted in distribution to the immediate vicinity of trees where the cover of perennial grasses such as *Themeda australis* and *Poa caespitosa* was relatively sparse. *P. vittatum* is now one of the most numerous pasture insects on the Southern Tablelands and Southwest Slopes. The abundance of the species was investigated in the Australian Capital Territory (A.C.T.) and adjoining areas on the Tablelands by D. Clark (1962, and *in prep.*).

4.221 *Characteristics of the species and its environment*

P. vittatum, a species with very limited powers of dispersal, has only one generation per year. The eggs are laid in the summer and autumn and enter a state of diapause in which they remain until the following winter (July). First instar nymphs appear in October, November, or December, the timing of the hatching period being influenced by weather conditions, e.g. temperature, and the density of the vegetative cover present. The adults occur in December, January, or February, and substantial percentages of both sexes survive until April.

There are two distinct types of adult. One form is macropterous with functional wings, and the other is brachypterous and incapable of flight. The brachypterous form is usually more numerous than the other in open areas, whereas amongst shrubs, in gardens, and along the margins of woodands and forests the macropterous form predominates. The determination of wing size is not understood. It does not seem to be affected by sex and population density.

The number of eggs laid by females depends upon the food supply. When seasonal conditions are favourable the females produce their first egg pods ten to fourteen days after moulting to the adult stage. Thereafter, until death, pods are deposited at varying intervals of time, the length of which depends mainly on the prevailing temperatures. Under laboratory conditions, females provided with ample food laid an average of nine pods, and the maximum number of eggs per pod was sixteen. The mean number of eggs per pod did not differ much over a wide range of food intake. Other experiments showed that females subjected to food shortage in the nymphal stage were smaller and laid fewer eggs than those reared on ample food.

Although they feed on a wide range of plant species, the nymphs and adults of *P. vittatum* exhibit marked food preferences. The plants most attractive to nymphs include such species as *Trifolium subterraneum*, *Plantago varia*, *Plantago lanceolata*, *Solegyne belloides*, and *Salvia verbenacea*. Other favourable but relatively unattractive species are *Hypochoeris radicata* and *Modiola caroliniana*. Laboratory tests showed that only a fraction of the plant species fed upon are favourable for growth and reproduction. Without exception, the favourable plants are dicotyledonous species – all but *P. varia* being exotic. With the exception of the grass *Hordeum leporinum*, all of the unfavourable species, which include grasses and some herbs, are indigenous to Australia. Inadvertently, man has augmented and improved the food supply of *P. vittatum*.

The pastures in the Capital Territory and surrounding areas usually achieve their maximum production of green herbage during the period of spring growth from September to November, and begin to 'dry off' in November with the death of annual species, e.g. *T. subterraneum*. In December and January, the rate of drying off is accelerated by increasing heat and evaporation. Many young perennial plants which germinated during the previous autumn die in the early summer whereas older plants survive but become dormant. Well-established, deep-rooted individuals of some plant species, e.g. the 'flatweeds' *H. radicata* and *P. lanceolata*, remain green, but do not produce new growth in the absence of concentrated rainfall exceeding one inch. Some growth occurs in thistles such as *Cirsium lanceolatum* and in grasses such as *Chloris truncata* and *Panicum effusum* which not only remain green but also produce new shoots after light falls of rain. In general, however, green foliage is scarce in the summer, and the pastures consist mainly of dry herbage interspersed with patches of bare ground.

At light to moderate rates of spring grazing by sheep, the plant cover present in October and November is heterogeneous both in height and density. In contrast, heavy grazing results in almost-uniform low cover. In summer, grazing and trampling by sheep tend to obliterate the structural patterns in plant cover produced by growth in the spring. However, the well-established perennials, e.g. *Plantago* spp. and *H. radicata*, and thistles, which provide favourable summer food for *P. vittatum*, remain largely inaccessible to stock.

4.222 *The abundance of* P. vittatum *in relation to weather, grazing, and pasture type*

General trends in the abundance of *P. vittatum* were followed systematically in the area around Canberra (A.C.T.) and Yass (N.S.W.) from 1954 to 1959, but only fragmentary information is available for previous years. After 1953, the abundance of *P. vittatum* was estimated annually in November in a number of study sites (twelve in 1954, up to thirty thereafter) by a rating method which employed three arbitrarily-selected levels of infestation: *low*, if the population density was one to five individuals per sq. yd; *moderate*, if the density was between five and ten individuals per sq. yd; and *high*, if the density exceeded ten per sq. yd.

For convenience, the pastures in the study sites were classified into four types:

(*i*) *native pastures* in which the perennial grasses *Themeda australis* and *Poa caespitosa* had persisted as the dominant species;

81

TABLE 3. The late spring infestation levels of *P. vittatum* in different pasture types from 1954 to 1959 inclusive.

	Native pasture			Natural pasture			Improved pasture			Sown pasture			Percent high infestations
	High	Moderate	Low	High	Moderate	Low	High	Moderate	Low	High	Moderate	Low	
1954	—	—	2	1	1	2	5	2	1	—	—	—	50%
1955	—	—	3	—	—	2	5	4	8	—	—	3	20%
1956	—	—	3	—	—	7	4	3	10	—	—	3	13%
1957	—	—	3	3	1	4	13	2	1	—	1	2	53%
1958	—	—	3	—	1	6	4	4	9	—	—	3	13%
1959	—	—	3	—	—	7	2	8	7	—	—	3	6%

(*ii*) *natural pastures* of varying botanical composition (depending upon grazing rates) in which the original dominants had been largely or entirely replaced by other indigenous grasses, e.g. *Stipa falcata* and *Danthonia* spp.;

(*iii*) *improved pastures* which had been developed from natural pastures, and from the volunteer growth which followed cropping, by broadcasting the seed of *T. subterraneum* and fertilizer; and

(*iv*) *sown pastures* in which *T. subterraneum* alone, or in combination with an exotic species of grass, had been sown after cultivation. Improved pastures were more numerous than the other types.

Table 3 summarizes the history of the infestation from 1954 to 1959. *P. vittatum* was very numerous both in 1954 and in 1957. The limited amount of earlier data suggests that the grasshopper also reached a high general level of abundance in 1936, 1944, and 1953. The population peaks of 1954 and 1957 were associated with the occurrence of abnormally dry weather from August to November in both years. Similar weather prevailed on the occasions of high general abundance recorded previously. This indicates that the amount of spring rainfall was the key ecological event affecting the survival of *P. vittatum* nymphs for the number of eggs laid was nearly always high. The proximate environmental agency involved was plant cover.

This agency and the available supply of food were the principal environmental influences affecting the abundance of *P. vittatum*. Although the grasshopper was sometimes attacked heavily by birds, e.g. the ibis *Threskiornis spinicollis*, the effects of such natural enemies on the numbers of *P. vittatum* were largely substitutive for other causes of mortality. A species of *Scelio* parasitized the eggs of *P. vittatum*, but the percentage destroyed varied independently of egg density and was never high. From time to time, considerable numbers of adult female grasshoppers were sterilized by the parasitic action of a mermithid nematode, but, in general, the parasite exerted only a minor influence on abundance. The other pasture-feeding insects which live in association with *P. vittatum*, including acridids, had little or no effect on the abundance of the grasshopper.

4.223 *The functioning of the life system*

(*i*) *Survival in the egg stage.* The females of *P. vittatum* lay their eggs in small patches of bare ground usually less than 0·5 sq. ft in area. Only in ungrazed sown or improved pastures, and during unusual summers favouring plant growth, is the total amount of bare ground small enough to limit oviposition. In grazed pastures, plant cover and bare ground are intermingled in a small-scale mosaic which persists throughout the summer. In such pastures, ample space for oviposition is always available, and the

TABLE 4. The survival of eggs of *P. vittatum* in the laboratory and in study sites in the field (A.C.T.).

Locality and Year	No. of pods incubated	Total no. eggs*	Percentage parasitism by Scelio sp.	Percentage non-viable other than parasitized	Percentage survival	No. of pods examined	Total no. eggs†	Percentage parasitism by Scelio sp.	Percentage non-viable other than parasitized	Percentage survival
Hall 1955	55	550	14·0	11·4	74·6	31	326	14·0	17·0	69·0
Gungahlin 1957	116	1340	20·9	2·4	76·7	16	180	18·2	7·0	74·8
Gungahlin 1958	96	1051	13·0	1·6	85·4	125	1313	10·4	12·7	76·9
Gungahlin 1959	70	721	11·3	11·1	77·6	33	390	11·3	7·6	81·1

* in laboratory
† from field

distribution and abundance of egg pods corresponds closely to the density-distribution of the adults which produced them. The females of *P. vittatum* lay their eggs wherever they happen to be and the distribution of egg pods resembles that of the seeds of many annual plants.

Studies on the percentage hatch of *P. vittatum* eggs show that the probability of survival during the egg stage is usually high (e.g. see table 4) in spite of wide variations in weather conditions from year to year, and parasitism by *Scelio* sp. which sometimes destroys up to 20% of the eggs in an area.

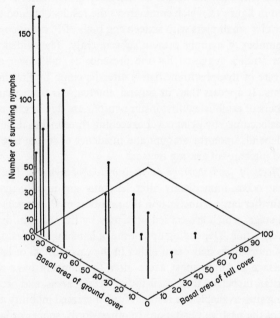

FIGURE 12. Relationship between the survival of first instar nymphs of *P. vittatum* and the basal areas of 'tall' and 'ground' cover (Majura, A.C.T., 1958).

(*ii*) *Effect of plant cover on the survival of young nymphs.* While in the first and second instars, *P. vittatum* feeds mainly on dicotyledonous plants. The young nymphs, which have very limited mobility, prefer to feed on prostrate and rosette-forming species, e.g. *T. subterraneum* and *P. varia*. They do not require tall plant cover as shelter, but seek protection from wind and low temperatures in mats of low-growing pasture vegetation, behind logs, and in small depressions in the ground surface. The food plants of the grasshopper usually do not contribute greatly to the total volume of plant cover in pastures, and, for practical purposes, food and plant cover can be regarded largely as separate environmental components. The spring pasture vegetation in the habitats of *P. vittatum* can be classified into two categories: (*a*) 'tall' cover which exceeds three inches in height and is provided mainly by grasses; and (*b*) 'ground' cover which is generally less than three inches high and is composed of dicotyledonous species including the favourable food plants of the grasshopper.

It was found that the percentage of newly-hatched nymphs which succeeded in establishing themselves in pastures was inversely related to the amount of 'tall' plant cover present (the area occupied by such cover being more important than its height in excess of three inches). The point is illustrated in figure 12 which summarizes the results obtained by 'seeding' each of twelve small plots with sixteen egg pods of *P. vittatum* and recording the number of nymphs present subsequently. The evidence from this and other studies suggests that the presence of 'tall' cover affected the survival rate of nymphs immediately after hatching by limiting access to food plants. It appears that, in general, fluctuations from year to year in the numbers of established first instar nymphs are due largely to variations in the area occupied by plant cover exceeding three inches in height, which in turn depends upon the amount and incidence of spring rainfall and the associated intensity of grazing by stock.

(*iii*) *Effects of food shortage on the survival of nymphs.* The population losses that occur immediately after hatching are usually insufficient to prevent further large reductions in the numbers of *P. vittatum* later in the nymphal stage, which are caused primarily by the seasonal drying out of pasture vegetation. Depending upon time of hatching and seasonal rainfall, etc., high mortalities may occur either in the early instars or later. Usually food shortage becomes most acute after the hoppers have reached the fourth instar, dispersed from their initial feeding areas, and occupied all of the feeding sites available as a result of their increased mobility and seasonal thinning of the pasture vegetation. In other words, sooner or later, hopper numbers usually become excessive for the amount of food that can be found and competition for that resource follows.

Figure 13 provides an illustration of numerical decrease in *P. vittatum* due to food shortage in the early instars. The data were obtained from five study plots in a sown pasture at Kambah (A.C.T.). Because of the insulating effect of a dense mat of *T. subterraneum*, egg development was slow and first instar hoppers were not seen until 14 December, by which time most of the annual vegetation present had dried out and the green foliage available as food consisted of a few rosettes of *H. radicata* and *Cymbonotus lawsonianus* and leaves and stems of the summer-growing thistle *Cirsium lanceolatum*. The nymphs which survived the hatching period concentrated their feeding mainly on the larger thistle plants and neglected the smaller ones. The larger plants could be eaten because the spacing of the spines on the leaves and stems permitted access to plant tissue. The nymphs fed mainly at the bases of the plants which began to dry out as a result of the damage caused.

By mid-January, the numbers of survivors per plot were related to the numbers of thistle plants present. Because the food supply was being

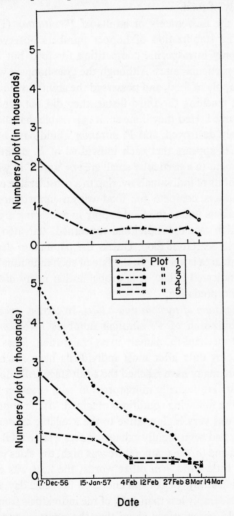

FIGURE 13. Trends in the abundance of nymphs of *P. vittatum* in five study plots in a sown pasture at Kambah (A.C.T.) in 1957–58.

depleted more rapidly than it was being replaced by the growth of smaller thistle plants, hopper numbers continued to fall in plots 1, 3, 4, and 5. The dependence of *P. vittatum* on the thistle plants was demonstrated by removing the foliage in plot 3 on 5 February. Numbers in this plot fell continuously whereas, in the other plots, they became stabilized by the time most hoppers had reached the final instar. Where the thistle plants were left to grow, a balance was achieved between the numbers of *P. vittatum* and the available supply of food.

Studies on the movements of adults of *P. vittatum* (D. Clark 1962) suggest that the stabilization of hopper numbers observed at Kambah involved not only intraspecific competition for food but also a form of attachment to particular sites. Although the grasshoppers were competing for a limited supply of food, and possessed the ability to move considerable distances after reaching the third instar, they did not concentrate where most food occurred. Had they done so, it is possible that the whole supply would have been destroyed, and *P. vittatum* would have been eliminated by starvation. It appears that each individual of *P. vittatum* develops a definite attachment to a particular small area or 'ambit' in which it forages, and that the ambits of individuals overlap to a considerable extent, with the result that hoppers compete for food within limited areas. This 'site attachment' persists unless the food supply in a foraging area is consumed entirely, in which case the individual concerned, activated by starvation, wanders away in search of food. Unless the population density of grasshoppers per unit area is very high, the fate of such individuals is difficult to ascertain. As indicated below, it is probable that many die of starvation, cannibalism, and predation.

(*iv*) *Mass migration of nymphs and adults.* In certain circumstances, the temporary stabilization of *P. vittatum* numbers involves an additional density-related mechanism, namely mass emigration. Mass movement by *P. vittatum* occurs only after most individuals have reached the fourth instar and before many have reached the adult stage. All adults involved in mass movements are sexually immature. On each occasion that swarming was observed, the following conditions obtained: (*a*) the population density of *P. vittatum* was very high relative to the available amount of food; (*b*) the food supply had been rapidly exhausted over a large total fraction of the area concerned; and (*c*) the temperature was high, the skies were cloudless, and there was little wind – in other words, the heat was extreme. Mass emigration which always began and ended on the same day, resulted in the removal of considerably less than 50% of the individuals from an area.

Repeated field observations show that the nymphs and adults which migrate invariably exhibit signs of physiological stress due to hunger or thirst. They bite objects indiscriminately and cannibalism and corpse eating occur frequently. In contrast, the individuals which do not migrate show no signs of stress and are presumably the more successful competitors for a rapidly dwindling food supply. The emigrants move off in streams which are orientated towards conspicuous objects, e.g. clumps of trees or other green vegetation in the form of shrubs and crop plants. Often several

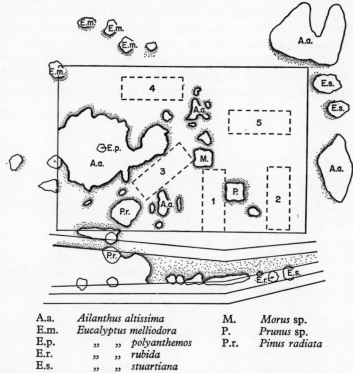

A.a.	*Ailanthus altissima*	M.	*Morus* sp.
E.m.	*Eucalyptus melliodora*	P.	*Prunus* sp.
E.p.	” ” *polyanthemos*	P.r.	*Pinus radiata*
E.r.	” ” *rubida*		
E.s.	” ” *stuartiana*		

FIGURE 14. The distribution of emigrant *P. vittatum* in relation to trees at Majura (A.C.T.) in December 1957. Grasshoppers indicated by stippling, study plots by broken lines.

streams of grasshoppers may be observed moving independently towards the same landmarks. On reaching trees, etc., the emigrants struggle to get at edible material.

Figure 14 shows the distribution of emigrants of *P. vittatum* in relation to trees at Majura (A.C.T.) in December 1957. After 11 December the numbers of surviving emigrants remained almost constant except along the lower margin of the area where numbers were reduced by the attack of birds which searched for their food along the woodland margin. At Majura, as in other areas, few of the emigrants reproduced, and only a small percentage of them returned to the study plots.

Depending upon the available supply of food, the numbers of *P. vittatum* may remain almost constant or fall to a lower level after the removal of individuals by mass emigration. If the food supply continues to decrease as a result of seasonal conditions and feeding by *P. vittatum*, its numbers fall before becoming stabilized.

(*v*) *Effects of food shortage on the adult stage.* The food shortage which is usually initiated before the adult stage is reached affects not only percentage survival but also the mean size and mean reproductive ability of the adults. Moreover, the amount of food available to adults influences their reproductive ability and the time required for sexual maturation. When favourable dicotyledonous food is available to adults, sexual maturation

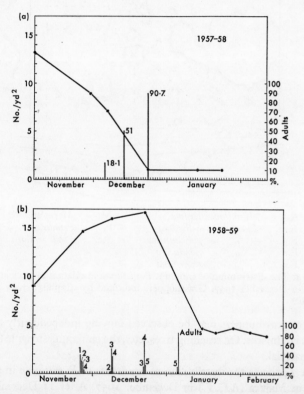

FIGURE 15. Numerical trends shown by *P. vittatum* at Hall (A.C.T.). Vertical lines in (*a*) indicate the percentage of individuals that had reached the adult stage. Vertical lines in (*b*) show the percentages of individuals in nymphal instars 1–5 and in the adult stage.

occurs within two weeks. If shortage occurs after reproduction has begun, premature mortality in females reduces their numbers to a level at which the survivors obtain enough food to mature eggs and oviposit at a rate determined by the prevailing temperature conditions. Stabilization occurs when the numbers of reproducing individuals are adjusted, *per medium* of intraspecific competition, to the food supply. Sometimes the food available initially to adults is sufficient for the survival of many individuals but inadequate qualitatively for reproduction. In such circumstances, population numbers tend to remain unchanged until favourable dicotyledonous food becomes available again and reproduction can begin.

Figure 15 shows how sexually immature adults persisted at almost constant densities until rain initiated the production of the food required for egg development. The data were obtained in 1957–58 and 1958–59 from a study area at Hall (A.C.T.). At the beginning of December 1957, much of the annual herbage in the study area had disappeared almost completely and green plants, e.g. *Alternanthera denticulata, H. radicata,* and the summer-growing grasses *Chloris truncata* and *Panicum effusum* were relatively scarce. By 23 December, the dicotyledonous species had been consumed completely, but most surviving individuals of *P. vittatum* had reached the adult stage.

The adults survived by feeding upon new shoots of *Chloris truncata* and *Panicum effusum,* but the onset of sexual maturation was delayed. The situation was essentially similar during the following season, although more dicotyledonous food was available for the development and survival of nymphs and consequently many more adults were produced. By the middle of January, most dicotyledonous plants had been defoliated completely and the adults were eating new grass shoots. Between 15 January and 6 February, the quantity of new foliage produced by *Chloris truncata* and *Panicum effusum* was less than that consumed, and density of both grasses decreased. However, as shown in figure 15, this decline had no effect on the number of adult grasshoppers.

Neither in 1957–58 nor in 1958–59 did intraspecific competition for food function as a stabilizing mechanism. The supply of dicotyledonous food was small for the numbers of late instar nymphs competing for it and there was no addition by plant growth. Consequently grasshopper numbers could not adjust to supply, and competition continued until the favourable food was consumed almost entirely. By then, the grasshoppers had reached the adult stage, and the population could persist. Clearly the ability of the adults of *P. vittatum* to survive on a diet unfavourable for reproduction is of great adaptive value to the species.

4.224 *Discussion*

The life system study of *P. vittatum* is of interest because:

(*i*) It describes more adequately than previous ecological investigations on grasshoppers (e.g. section 3.221) the processes involved in population persistence when the food supply diminishes – primarily as a result of seasonal conditions – and secondarily because of depletion by competing individuals. Competition for food within overlapping foraging areas provided a density-stabilizing mechanism only when the food supply was maintained by plant growth.

(*ii*) It shows evidence of a form of site attachment which influences the intensity and outcome of intraspecific competition for food, and it thereby draws attention to the importance of adaptive behaviour as a conditioning influence in the stabilization of numbers.

(*iii*) It provides an example of density-related emigration, conditioned by weather and food depletion (not by mutual stimulation as in locusts). The mass movement of individuals out of an area reduces the intensity of intraspecific competition for food and thereby increases the probability of population persistence during periods of acute food shortage.

4.23 The life system of *Perga affinis affinis* (Pergidæ)

This sawfly defoliates woodland eucalypts in south-eastern Australia where its distribution is centred on the twenty-two-inch isohyet of average annual rainfall and restricted largely to the region defined by the eighteen- and twenty-eight-inch isohyets. The ecology of the species was studied during the period 1958–66 by Carne (1962, 1965, and *in prep.*).

4.231 *Characteristics of the species and its environment*

*P.a. affinis*** was rarely found in other than open woodland and extensively thinned sclerophyll forest in which at least one of the following tree species was present: *Eucalyptus blakelyi*, *E. camaldulensis*, and *E. melliodora*. In general, other species of eucalypt were attacked only when sawfly numbers were very high. Within stands of the favoured species, young trees invariably suffered more severe attacks than old individuals of the same species. Oviposition by *P.a. affinis* on large trees of the principal host species, and on less favoured eucalypts, appeared to be an 'overflow' phenomenon which occurred after the majority of those leaves available for oviposition on young host trees had already received one or more egg batches.

P.a. affinis is able to reproduce parthenogenetically (Carne 1962) and, although about 20% of adults are males (with functional testes), mating was never observed. The adults emerge in the autumn from masses of

---

* *P. affinis affinis* is one of three geographical subspecies (see Riek 1961).

cocoons formed just below the soil surface near trees. The leaves selected for oviposition are of full size but still soft and succulent. Most females lay three separate batches, each of twenty to twenty-two eggs, in leaves of the same, or an adjacent shoot. After a period of twenty-nine to thirty-two days, the eggs hatch.

The larvae of the sawfly are strongly gregarious, and exhibit forms of sub-social behaviour, e.g. signalling between individuals in a colony, and group defence reactions. At first, the individuals from an egg batch congregate during the day on a leaf in a rosette-like cluster with their heads facing outwards, and move off together at night to feed, side by side, at the edges of the leaf. The colonies arising from individual egg batches coalesce when chance encounters occur, and, when population numbers are high, the final aggregations may include many thousands of larvae. During the day, the older larvae form compact, almost cylindrical clusters around the branches of trees, and move along the limbs at night to reach their feeding sites. By the time the larvae reach the sixth (final) instar, all of the original clusters on a host tree may have combined to form one large colony. Because of their colonial habits, the larvae of *P.a. affinis* live normally in a state of crowding. This form of behaviour plays an important part in the survival of the species.

The feeding period of the larvae ends in the early spring, and the colonies leave their host trees and burrow into the soil where they form masses of cocoons. Because the larvae begin to feed after the seasonal growth of their host trees has ceased, and leave them before new growth is produced in spring, their food supply cannot be replenished during the period of consumption. In this regard, and in having its feeding stages active during the coldest months of the year, *P.a. affinis* stands in marked contrast to the majority of phytophagous insects in *Eucalyptus* woodlands.

After constructing their cocoons, the larvae moult to the prepupal stage and enter a state of diapause. Frequently, morphogenesis is resumed in the late summer, and adults emerge in the autumn, thus completing an annual life cycle. However, some prepupae do not pupate in the first autumn, but remain in diapause for a further twelve, twenty-four or even thirty-six months. Under favourable conditions, prolonged diapause is entered mainly by the smaller prepupae – but, with exposure to temperatures exceeding 36°C, an increasing proportion of the larger individuals are similarly affected. Prolonged diapause is advantageous to the species in that it ensures the survival of some individuals during a sequence of adverse seasons. The percentage of individuals that survive prolonged diapause is usually low and, for practical purposes, such diapause can sometimes be regarded as a form of mortality in the generation under consideration.

93

Climatic stress is greatest for *P.a. affinis* during the period from October
to March which includes the times of soil entry by the larvae and emergence of the adults. Figure 16 shows the average temperature and rainfall
for this period for areas in which the sawfly is normally present in open
woodlands, and for areas in which it is absent from such communities. The
species is most abundant in areas with average temperatures ranging from

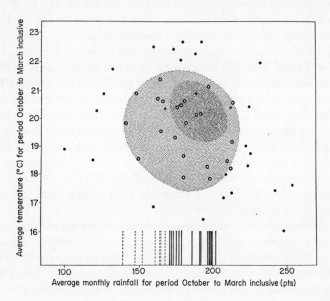

FIGURE 16. The distribution of *P.a. affinis* in relation to average temperature and
rainfall for the period October to March. The open circles represent the data for
localities where the sawfly was found in eucalypt woodland during the period
1958–64; the smaller solid circles, the data for localities from which it was absent.
The large stippled area represents the range of climatic conditions within which the
sawfly was found, and the smaller, more heavily stippled area the range within
which the insect most frequently occurred in high numbers. The vertical lines
represent the rainfall data for stations not recording temperature; those in bold face
are for stations situated in areas of high sawfly abundance. (Modified from Carne
1965.)

about 19 to 21°C and average monthly rainfalls ranging from 170 to 210
points (100 points = 1 inch); and absent from areas with average temperatures less than 17°C or more than 22°C and monthly rainfalls less than 140
or greater than 220 points. Favourable eucalypts are absent in the relatively
cold wet areas but present in the unfavourably hot dry areas (e.g. *E. melliodora*).

4.232 *Causes and extent of the mortality suffered by the sawfly*

(*i*) *Egg stage.* Egg mortality in *P.a. affinis* is caused by desiccation, fungal infection, and by erratic predation due to insectivorous birds. In samples of egg batches taken from sites throughout the study region in different years, the total mortality tended to be similar, and appeared to be un-influenced by the numbers of the sawfly in the season of sampling or that preceding it. For samples collected from twenty-eight sites in 1958, the range in mortality was 16–72%, including eighteen values lying between 31 and 50%. In 1960, the mortalities in eight out of ten site samples were also between 31 and 50%. Table 5 shows estimates of egg mortality made in five successive seasons for a study site near Tarcutta (New South Wales).

TABLE 5. Gross mortality of eggs of the sawfly *Perga affinis affinis* in samples taken from a site near Tarcutta, N.S.W., in successive years. During these years, the abundance of the sawfly varied considerably, but the egg mortality remained almost constant.

Year	Total egg batches examined	Mean no. eggs/batch	% egg mortality
1958	73	16·3	55·8
1959	59	19·2	47·7
1960	40	18·5	49·8
1961	72	17·1	49·1
1962	33	18·3	51·6

(*ii*) *Larval stages.* The larvae were found to be remarkably free from attack by general predators, e.g. birds. Although attacked by several para-sitic species of insect, none had any discernible effects until the sawfly larvae had constructed their cocoons. For example, a series of counts made of total larvae in a plantation of eighty small trees of *Eucalyptus maculosa*, situated in an area of *E. blakelyi – E. melliodora* woodland, gave the follow-ing results:

First instar larvae (*counted April* 1958)	Third instar larvae (*counted July* 1958)	Sixth instar larvae (*counted Sept.* 1958)
5,961	6,026	6,175

During the period concerned, there were no additions to the population. Any mortality that occurred was less than the errors involved in counting the larvae present.

The maintenance of almost constant numbers during the larval stage is typical of sawfly populations at intermediate density levels. However, at both low and high levels of abundance the mortality rate tended to be high.

The small colonies in low-density populations did not forage as actively as larger colonies. Under conditions of only slight stress (e.g. unusually warm spells of weather in the late autumn or early spring), some larvae were unable to maintain their water balance and succumbed. In laboratory experiments in which conditions were not optimal, it was unusual for any uncaged larvae to remain on the foliage supplied and to survive if the initial number of individuals in a colony was less than twenty to twenty-five. There is some reason to believe that only a minority of larvae are capable of initiating normal colonial behaviour, and that the unthriftiness of small groups may be due to shortage or absence of such individuals. High mortality in small colonies was also evident during the process of entry into the soil. The larvae of *P.a. affinis* have difficulty in penetrating hard dry soil. Except under the most favourable conditions (e.g. friable soil or soil softened by rain), the larvae in small colonies usually died before any succeeded in penetrating to a depth which protected them from desiccation. Large colonies were much more successful in their efforts to break the soil crust.

At high population densities, variable numbers of host trees were defoliated almost completely. The colonies on them descended to the ground and moved off in search of other trees. Under very favourable conditions, colonies were observed to move up to seventy yards to other trees, but their range of movement was often much less. The percentage mortality suffered by the species because of density-induced emigration – which exposed the larvae that left their original host trees to a severe hazard of desiccation – varied according to population numbers throughout an area, the distribution and density of host trees, the ground surface and plant cover between trees, and weather conditions.

TABLE 6. The fate of sawfly larvae on *E. blakelyi* saplings at Black Mt., A.C.T., during the winter of 1959, in relation to their initial density.

Class of tree	Density of larvae (no. of 1st instar larvae per square foot of crown surface)	
	Range	Mean ± S.E.
Those on which larvae declined in numbers until mortality was almost or quite complete	0·33–1·02	0·54±0·06
Those on which larvae reached maturity without appreciable losses	0·29–2·40	1·29±0·20
Those from which colonies emigrated with consequent losses after causing almost total defoliation	0·79–8·88	4·25±0·69

Table 6 provides an example of the differing mortality rates that occur at low, intermediate, and high population densities. The observations were made in a plantation of sapling *E. blakelyi*, most of which were in poor condition as a result of repeated infestation by a variety of phytophagous insects. The initial sawfly numbers on each tree were estimated by direct counts of first instar larvae, and population density was calculated as the number of such larvae per square foot of the crown surface of the tree. Before the larvae matured, almost complete defoliation occurred on most trees with an initial larval density greater than two individuals per square foot. At the time of dispersal from these trees, the prevailing conditions were such that about 70% of the larvae failed to find undefoliated trees and died. There was scarcely any mortality on trees with intermediate infestations, whereas larval numbers declined to a very low level on the majority of lightly-infested trees.

(*iii*) *Cocoon stage.* The mortality resulting from parasite attack on the larvae occurs after the cocoons are formed. The parasites bred out (all apparently host-specific) include the tachinids, *Froggattimyia wentworthi*, *F. hirta*, and *Froggattimyia* sp.; a trigonalid, *Taeniogonalos venatoria*; and an ichneumonid, (?) *Hypopheltes* sp. Like their sawfly host, *Froggattimyia* spp. and *T. venatoria* are all capable of remaining in diapause for long periods. When batches of cocoons were held in emergence cages, the tachinid adults commonly emerged both in the first autumn after parasitization and during the second autumn. As shown in the following tabulation, *T. venatoria* was able to remain in diapause for an additional season.

Cocoon masses collected in March, 1958

Site	Species	No. of emergences in autumns of:		
		1958	1959	1960
Benalla	*P.a. affinis*	86	5	0
	T. venatoria	104	8	3
Chiltern	*P.a. affinis*	4	2	0
	T. venatoria	20	28	2

In the eastern zone of the study region (i.e. that portion east of a line drawn approximately NNE through Albury, N.S.W.), *Froggattimyia hirta* and *Froggattimyia* sp. occurred in mixed populations. In the western zone, *F. wentworthi* was the dominant tachinid. Parasitism by these three species varied greatly (0–70%), and without apparent relationship with the current or previous abundance of the host. In contrast, *Hypopheltes* sp. was found only in a few localities where it rarely caused more than 5–10% mortality.

At one time or another, *T. venatoria* was found in most study sites, but only in the western zone did it occur in sufficient numbers to cause high mortalities. It is probable that this trigonalid is of major importance in the limitation of sawfly numbers in the western zone of the study region.* For example, in 1958 fairly high numbers of *P.a. affinis* occurred in the area between Benalla and Springhurst in Victoria, and around Gerogery in New South Wales. Both in 1958 and 1959 very heavy parasitism occurred in these areas and sawfly numbers decreased greatly. The percentage gross parasitism of samples of individuals which had established themselves in cocoons was as follows: Benalla, 81% (range 60–96%) in 1958, and 90% (range 83–98%) in 1959; Gerogery, 93% (range 89–97%) in 1959 (no record for 1958). In the Gerogery area, there was a brief upsurge of sawfly numbers in 1963 followed by decrease to a low level. The percentage gross parasitism by *T. venatoria* was 74% (range 17–93%). In the Henty area, to the north of Gerogery and near the inland limit of the sawfly's distribution, the parasite was present in low to very low numbers from 1959 to 1961. In the few cocoon masses recovered, no trigonalid individuals were recorded. In 1962, the sawfly became moderately abundant in this site, and parasitism by *T. venatoria* averaged 29% (range 12–48%). Numbers then declined to a very low level and no further cocoons were recovered in 1963 or 1964.

Other causes of mortality in the cocoon stage were excessive heat, desiccation, infection by the fungi *Metarrhizium anisopliae* and *Beauveria tenella*, and casual predation by the larvae of asilids and carabids.

4.233 *The functioning of the life system*

Each year, surveys were made throughout the study region to record the relative abundance of *P.a. affinis* at the time when the colonies had almost completed feeding and were beginning to leave their host trees (early October). Relative abundance was assessed by rating (into four categories) the amount of defoliation caused by the colonies. In some study sites, the host trees were divided into three age groups, and mean defoliation ratings were calculated for each.

In association with the observations on relative abundance, analyses were made of the meteorological data recorded at four stations, two in the western, and two in the eastern zone (Wangaratta, Wodonga, Wagga, and Canberra, respectively). It was found that, in terms of departures of mean daily temperature and monthly rainfall from average conditions, weather variations in all four places were distinctly correlated. This suggested that

---

* Owing to the difficulties involved in sampling the cocoon stage of the sawfly when its numbers were low, it was not possible to determine whether or not *T. venatoria* acted in a density-related manner.

the seasonal climatic stresses affecting *P.a. affinis* were comparable through-out the region.

However, in spite of the similarity of weather patterns, two broadly different patterns of fluctuation occurred in sawfly numbers – one in the western zone, and the other in the eastern zone. As indicated above, sawfly numbers in the western zone were moderately high in 1958, substantially

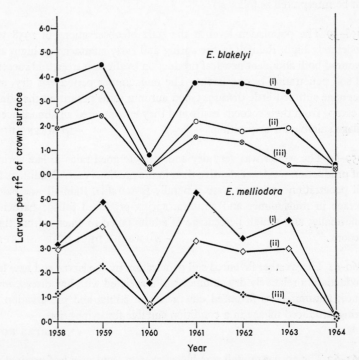

FIGURE 17. Seasonal trends of abundance of *P.a. affinis* on three age groups of two eucalypt species on a 7-mile traverse between Book Book and Ladysmith, N.S.W. Estimates of larval numbers were derived from mean defoliation ratings made during annual surveys in early October. The data show that young trees were always more severely infested than older trees. The changing levels of abundance in this area were similar to the fluctuations recorded in surveys made throughout the eastern portion of the study region.

(*i*) saplings and regrowth, (*ii*) poles, (*iii*) mature trees.

lower in 1959, and very low thereafter in most sites. In the Henty area in 1962, and in the Gerogery area in 1963, numbers increased considerably and then fell to a very low level. In a number of sites within the zone, heavy parasitism, mainly by *T. venatoria*, was associated with the observed decreases in relative abundance. Density-induced emigration and conse-

H

quent mortality occurred in only a few of the many sites under observation

In the eastern zone, where percentage parasitism was lower and varie
erratically, the pattern of fluctuation in sawfly numbers was very different
It is exemplified by the results of surveys made along a seven-mile travers
between Book Book and Ladysmith, N.S.W. (see figure 17). In terms of th
principal environmental influences involved, changes in sawfly number
can be interpreted as follows:

1958–59 The population level at the start of observations in 1958 wa
moderately high. Rainfall in the spring and early summer was high, an
favoured both abundant new leaf production by the host trees, and success
ful soil penetration by the larvae. The midsummer period was dry, an
prepupae suffered little disease. Good autumn rains permitted the adult
to escape from their cocoons easily and they encountered an abundance c
foilage suitable for oviposition.   – NUMBERS ROS

1959–60 The winter was very dry and, despite good rains in late spring
leaf production was less extensive than in the previous year. Conditions fo
soil penetration by larvae were generally favourable. Rainfall was belov
average in midsummer and autumn; spring-produced foliage hardene
abnormally; and a high percentage of adults failed to emerge from thei
cocoons.   – NUMBERS DECLINED SHARPL

1960–61 The weather favoured soil penetration by the larvae and new lea
production; a relatively dry summer was associated with low disease inci
dence; autumn rains favoured emergence of adults and preservation o
spring-produced foliage in a condition suitable for oviposition.
                                                              – NUMBERS ROS

1961–62 The spring rainfall was below average, and new leaf productio
partially inhibited. The summer was abnormally wet, and disease cause
serious mortality to prepupae. Those that survived to the adult stag
emerged with few losses.   – NUMBERS DECLINE

1962–63 Spring rainfall was satisfactory and favoured leaf production and
penetration of the soil by larvae; dry conditions in early summer favoured
prepupal survival. Rains in late summer and early autumn, although belov
average, permitted satisfactory adult emergence.
                                    – NUMBERS SHOWED NO CONSISTENT CHANG

1963–64 Warm dry spell in spring caused severe mortality of larvae, anc
inhibited new leaf production by most trees; many prepupae entered pro

longed diapause. Adults emerging in the autumn found a shortage of suitable leaves for oviposition. — NUMBERS DECLINED SHARPLY

In 1964–65, spring conditions favoured leaf production and penetration of soil by larvae. Prepupal disease mortality was low, but the hot and excessively dry summer and autumn caused severe mortality of adults attempting emergence; those that emerged found very little suitable foliage in which to oviposit, and numbers declined almost to zero.

In the winter of 1965, *P.a. affinis* was observed only in a few of the most favourable sites – in low numbers. Following the severe summer and autumn drought of 1965–66, numbers declined even further.

In this, and in other localities in the eastern zone, density-induced emigration and consequent mortality occurred widely in 1959, 1961, and 1963, less frequently in 1958 and 1962, rarely in 1960, and were not observed in 1964 and 1965.

4.234 *Discussion*
The life system of *P.a. affinis* is of interest for the following reasons:

(*i*) The sawfly has a form of diapause which tends to ensure population persistence in advance for periods of up to three years.

(*ii*) In the group activities of its larvae, the sawfly exhibits forms of sub-social behaviour which favour survival. Because of the interdependence of individuals, the survival rate of larvae was highest at intermediate population densities. At low levels of abundance, 'underpopulation' effects occurred and relatively few individuals survived. At high population densities, competition for food led to an 'overpopulation' effect – density-induced migration. Instead of all larvae succumbing to starvation after defoliating their host trees, a variable proportion survived by migrating successfully to other trees, the remainder dying rapidly from desiccation.

(*iii*) Over much of the region favourable for the persistence of *P.a. affinis*, density-induced emigration and the resulting mortality due to desiccation served as a stabilizing mechanism which opposed population increase to the level at which all of the food in stands of woodland would have been consumed. In the other part of the region, it appears that parasitism largely prevented the occurrence of defoliation.

(*iv*) In the zones in which percentage parasitism was relatively low, weather conditions played, directly or indirectly, a dominant role in the causation of numerical fluctuations.

Depending upon the results of further investigations, it may be decided to regard *P.a. affinis* as having two life systems: one in the eastern zone of the area colonized by the species, and one in the western zone.

4.24 The life system of *Brevicoryne brassicæ* (Aphididæ)

The cabbage aphid lives on annual and biennial crucifers, including brassica crops, in all temperate regions of the world. The features which adapt the species to the wide climatic range of its geographical distribution, and enable it to persist in large numbers despite the brief existence of its host plants, result in a remarkable life system which was described by Hughes (1962, 1963) from his studies in the Australian Capital Territory. The findings of other authors, e.g. Herrick and Hungate (1911), Bonnemaison (1951), Markkula (1953), George (1957), and Hafez (1961), tend to support Hughes' conclusions and to confirm the general validity of his model.

4.241 *Characteristics of the species*
B. brassicae displays great flexibility in its adaptation to climate, particularly to winter conditions, which maximizes its ability to exploit the resources supplied by widely differing environments. In the course of its seasonal development, the cabbage aphid can produce five different forms of individuals, each showing particular adaptive qualities. These are:

(*i*) *Females:*
 (*a*) the *fundatrices* – wingless, parthenogenetic females from winter eggs, which initiate the colonies of the species in spring;
 (*b*) the *apterae* – wingless, parthenogenetic females produced viviparously by either fundatrices or apterae;
 (*c*) the *alatae* – winged, parthenogenetic females produced viviparously by apterae;
 (*d*) the *oviparae* – wingless females produced viviparously by parthenogenetic forms which, after mating, produce diapausing winter eggs. The oviparae appear in the late autumn, in response to short days and low temperatures.

(*ii*) *Males:* winged individuals which mate with *oviparae*.

Winter survival can depend wholly upon the formation of eggs, as in Finland (Markkula 1953) and Holland (Van Hoof 1954). Under less severe conditions, as in southern England (Petherbridge and Wright 1938), small numbers of apterae can also survive the winter. The proportion of overwintering apterae increases in milder climates, as in France (Bonnemaison 1951), and winter eggs almost cease to be produced in Israel (Bodenheimer and Swirski 1957), and in the Australian Capital Territory.

Although wingless forms are capable of moving between adjacent plants, the colonization of new hosts results almost entirely from the aerial dispersal of alatae. After taking off, the alatae are practically powerless to direct their flight and are carried passively by airstreams in so-called 'planktonic dispersal'. They alight on host plants and other vegetation indiscriminately at the end of their flights. Although most of them take off again, there is a slight tendency for host plants to retain a higher proportion of alighting aphids, which increases an individual's chances of finally settling on a suitable host in the course of repeated flights.

The dispersal of alatae occurs throughout the growing season of plants, always with one or more mass flights which result in the colonization of the hosts on which the species overwinters, e.g. figure 18.

The tremendous wastage of individuals which this mode of dispersal and host location entails is compensated for: (*i*) by the correspondingly great numbers produced; and (*ii*) by the very high power of increase of the colonies generated by the successfully established alatae.

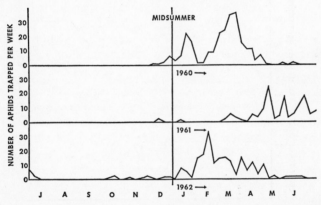

FIGURE 18. The numbers of cabbage aphid alatae collected each week from a Moericke water trap at Canberra. The trap operated from October 1959 until June 1962.

In the cabbage aphid, the production of alatae is induced by factors arising from the existence of dense colonies on short-lived host plants, i.e. the gradual deterioration of the food supply caused by concentrated feeding and/or ageing of the host; and the direct effect of continual contact amongst crowded apterae (Bonnemaison 1951). A close relationship exists between the densities of aphid infestations and the rates of production of alatae (see figure 19), whereby migrating forms appear at the onset of the critical conditions which ultimately lead to the destruction of a colony.

4.242 Observations in the Australian Capital Territory

The cabbage aphid has no native hosts in Australia and exists solely on crops and exotic weeds. Winter hosts support a succession of apterous

generations whose colonies are finally restricted to the flower head
which provide the only suitable feeding sites when plants mature in spring
As the winter hosts become more unfavourable, alatae are produced, which
in turn form temporary colonies on the flower heads of late
maturing spring hosts. Those new colonies usually persist for two genera
tions only, the first being the wingless progeny of the migrating individual
and the second consisting of alatae induced by the deterioration of the food
supply. The persistence of the species through spring and summer i
dependent upon the successive procurement by alatae of plants which ca
support colonies long enough for more alatae to be formed. This critic
period ends in late summer and autumn with the infestation of the youn

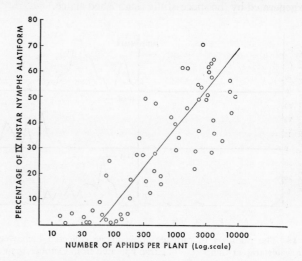

FIGURE 19. The relationship of the proportion of fourth instar nymphs which ar
alatiform to the number of aphids per plant.

biennial plants on which the aphids are to spend the following winter.

Numerical observations on the cabbage aphid were made in 1960, 1961
and 1963 on leaf samples taken two to three times per week from 150 plant
in a large field of kale (*Brassica oleracea* var.) at Canberra. All insects on
these leaves were identified and counted. Additional samples served to assess
parasitism by the wasp *Diaretus rapae*.

On all three occasions, the initial infestation appeared to result from a
sudden and massive influx of alatae. Numbers increased rapidly with the
first generation of apterae. Small dense colonies were formed, which became larger in the next generation. Alatae appeared in that generation,
causing the existing colonies to cease growing and, weather permitting, new

colonies to be formed on nearly every leaf. Those colonies could spread freely on the developing plants, which tended to prevent a rapid increase in the percentages of alatae produced in them. In two out of the three crops studied (1960, 1961), aphid numbers reached their peak in the autumn. Those infestations markedly damaged the plants, resulting in the death of many colonies and in the formation of high percentages of alatae in others. Thereafter, aphid numbers declined gradually in 1960, and abruptly in 1961 following the outbreak of a fungus disease which was prevalent only in that year. The infestations of 1960 and 1961 remained equally light in the winter, and did not increase significantly before the kale plants went to seed during the following spring. In 1963, unfavourable weather prevented the dispersal of alatae, and parasitism of the original colonies prevented the subsequent build-up of numbers in the autumn. This, however, simply deferred the peak infestation until the spring. In all three instances, large numbers of alatae were produced, which led ultimately to the occupation of most feeding sites available in the crop.

Aphid colonies on kale suffered mortality caused by a parasite, by predators, and by a pathogen. The parasite, *D. rapae*, was relatively abundant at two stages in the development of the infestation, i.e. shortly after the initial colonization of the crop, and again later when the aphid numbers rose to a peak and their rate of multiplication and dispersal decreased, following depletion of the crop (see figure 20). The apparent absence of a well-defined second peak in 1961 was due to the outbreak of fungus disease,

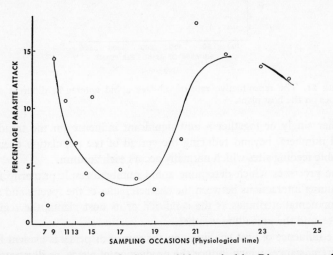

FIGURE 20. The percentage of cabbage aphids attacked by *Diaretus rapae* during the spring of 1963, showing the characteristic U-shaped trend.

105

which infected and killed parasitized aphids more frequently than the individuals which had not been attacked by *D. rapae*. The seasonal abundance of the predators was found to follow a similar pattern to that of the parasite.

Natural enemies were unable to curb the progressive development of infestations when other conditions allowed the aphids to multiply rapidly. Consequently, the parasite, the predators, and the pathogen did not exert

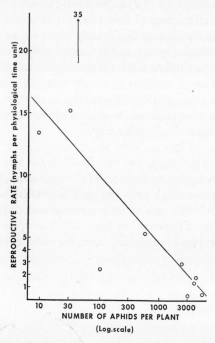

FIGURE 21. The reproductive rate of cabbage aphid apterae at different aphid densities on the host plant.

– either singly or together – any significant influence on the trends of aphid numbers, beyond reducing the spread of the population over the available feeding sites which normally occurs each autumn.

The processes which determine aphid numbers result primarily from continuing interactions between the characteristics of the species and such environmental attributes as the condition of its host plants, the regional climate, and the prevailing weather.

The influence of host condition on the rate of dispersal is evident from the circumstances which induce the production of alatae, as illustrated in figure 19. It was shown further that host condition can affect directly the reproductive rate of apterae, which tends to decrease with increasing density of infestation, i.e. with increasing depletion of the feeding sites on the host plants (see figure 21). This was confirmed in laboratory experiments which indicated that the chlorotic leaf tissue under dense colonies was lacking in substances necessary for reproduction, although still providing adequate food for nymphal development (Hughes 1963).

Besides setting the pattern of morphic development in winter and determining the rates of seasonal activity, climate and particularly temperature sequences exert a profound effect on the numbers of the species (*i*) by allowing the aphids to outpace rapidly their natural enemies in spring and summer, and (*ii*) by giving overwintering apterae a reproductive advantage in the spring. Regarding the latter effect, experiments showed that aphids reared in the laboratory at 13°C produced more young more rapidly *for three generations* when returned to 23°C than aphids held constantly at 23°C. Finally, wind regimes are a feature of climate which play an essential role in the life system of such insects as the cabbage aphid whose displacements are primarily dependent on planktonic dispersal.

The prevailing weather affects the rate of successful colonization by alatae. This, for example, is illustrated by the failure of aphid numbers to reach their peak in autumn 1963.

4.243 *Discussion*

Observations by authors other than Hughes indicate that the cabbage aphid is generally able to exploit its local supplies of food as fully as the condition of the host plants, the climate, and the weather permit. This suggests that the life system remains essentially uniform throughout the distribution range of the species.

In areas where the aphid overwinters as eggs, the gradual disappearance of active stages in autumn normally entails a corresponding increase in the relative abundance of natural enemies, particularly of parasites which hibernate as diapausing larvae in the bodies of mummified aphids. Although, as a consequence of this build-up, the rate of attack on fundatrices can be quite high in spring, the action of natural enemies can prevent neither the rapid development of initial infestations, nor the extensive spread of new colonies to suitable host plants, particularly crops, during the growing season.

The life system of *B. brassicae* is of particular interest for the following reasons:

(*i*) The planktonic dispersal characteristic of the species continues throughout the year except during the winter months when developmental processes are either slowed down greatly, or brought to a halt. The fact that, for much of the time, many individuals are drifting about in the air means that populations of the species do not have readily-definable limits.

(*ii*) *B. brassicae* depends for its existence upon phenological diversity in the short-lived plants which provide its food supply.

(*iii*) The species exploits to the maximum extent possible the food found largely by chance encounters. It is able to do so by adaptive polymorphism. The eventual settling of a migrant on a food plant is followed by the production of rapidly-multiplying apterous offspring, which continues until food shortage occurs – either as a result of increase in aphid numbers, or reduction in supply due to the translocation of food materials by a maturing host plant. Then winged forms are produced again, essentially in a density-related manner. In dense colonies, the production of alatae is associated with a density-induced decrease in the reproductive rate of apterae, which acts as a secondary means of minimizing the chance of untimely destruction of the source of food.

In the case of *B. brassicae*, the density-related processes associated with food shortage tend to maximize the production of individuals on the succession of host plants that are infested. In this way, they aid in population persistence, and so serve the same purpose as the stabilizing mechanisms of other life systems.

4.25 Artificial life systems for *Lucilia cuprina* (Calliphoridæ)

Some twenty years ago Nicholson (1950, 1954a, 1954b, 1957) began to investigate experimentally the determination of population numbers in laboratory populations of the sheep blowfly *Lucilia cuprina*. He was in-

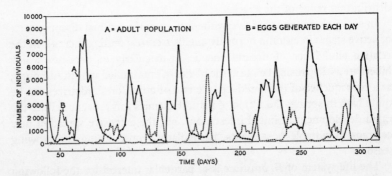

FIGURE 22. A population of *L. cuprina* governed by the daily supply of 0·5 gm of ground liver for the adults. A is the observed adult population; B is the number of eggs produced daily plotted at times two days before they were actually laid, this being the time taken for development after the intake of adequate food (after Nicholson 1954b).

terested especially in the role of intraspecific competition, both in the stabilization of numbers and in natural selection.

Nicholson introduced a small number of *L. cuprina* into cages supplied with food (water, sugar, and ground liver for adults and liver for larvae) and held in an artificially-illuminated culture room at a temperature of 25°C. During the experiments, conditions were held constant, including the rate at which food and water were supplied. Each population was left to its own devices except for the necessary observations and population counts, etc. Nicholson did not attempt to mimic natural conditions in the laboratory because his aim was to reduce a life system to essential components which could be investigated readily. In other words, he studied *L. cuprina* as an experimental animal, not as a 'sheep blowfly'.

4.251 *Stabilization of population numbers*

Figure 22 illustrates the population changes which occurred in a life system in which water and sugar for adult flies and also food for larvae (to which the adults were denied access) were provided in excess of requirements at all times (see Nicholson 1954b). The limiting resource selected 'was ground liver, which was available to the adults alone, and each day 0·5 g of this was placed in the breeding cage'. In common with the other experiment referred to later in graphs, the initial growth of the culture is not recorded in figure 22 because it is not relevant to the present discussion.

The outstanding characteristic of this culture was the maintenance of violent and fairly regular oscillation in the density of the adult population. The reason for this is simple. It will be observed that significant egg generation occurred only when the adult population was very low. At higher densities competition amongst the adults for ground liver was so severe that few or no individuals secured sufficient to enable them to develop eggs. Normal mortality, therefore, caused the population to dwindle until the consequent reduced severity of competition permitted some individuals to secure adequate liver and so to lay eggs. As it takes more than 2 weeks for the eggs so generated to give rise to new adults, the population continued to dwindle for this period, during which many more eggs were generated, for competition amongst the adults for ground liver continued to slacken. The eggs then generated in due time gave rise to new adults, which led to a rapid increase in the adult population, and the resultant overcrowding caused virtual cessation of egg production. A new cycle of oscillation then began. (Nicholson 1954b.)

If, as Nicholson (1954b) has said:

... increased acquisition of food were to cause fully mature adults to come into being immediately (instead of merely initiating the subsequent production of eggs and the still later development of adults) this prompt reaction would cause the system to be non-oscillatory. This is because reaction would cause the population first to approach, and then to maintain the *equilibrium density* of the species under the prevailing conditions, this being the density at which production of offspring precisely compensates for the loss of adults by death; for any departure from this level would immediately bring compensating reaction into play, and this would cease as soon as the equilibrium density was attained again. This, then, is the balancing mechanism which holds population density in general relation to the prevailing conditions; and the system of balance is often highly oscillatory, simply because animals commonly take a significant time to grow up, so causing a time lag between stimulus and reaction. During this lag period the stimulus continues to generate more and more reaction, and this continues to come into operation for a similar lag period after reaction has removed the stimulus.

Nicholson found that if he varied the supply of the limiting resource the average population density of the adult flies varied accordingly. In the life system discussed, 0·5 gm of liver was supplied per day and the average density of flies was 2,520. In another system, which differed only in that 0·1 gm of liver was supplied daily for the adult flies, the mean population density was 527. In other words, the average density was almost precisely proportional to the supply of the limiting resource.

4.252 Reaction of populations to externally imposed stress

In a series of concurrent experiments, constant percentages of *L. cuprina* at some stage of development were destroyed at regular intervals in order to observe the effects of mortality which operated independently of population density (see Nicholson 1954a, 1957). Table 7 gives some of the results obtained by destroying constant percentages (50, 75 and 90) of freshly-emerged adults. In these experiments, the supply of ground liver for adults was restricted to 0·5 gm per day, water and sugar for the adults and food for the larvae being provided in excess. The restriction of the supply of liver did not influence directly the mortality of adult flies, but it did affect natality. The greater the number of adults competing for the supply of liver, the smaller was the amount obtained, on an average, by individuals, and fewer of them obtained sufficient for the development of eggs.

The consequent inverse relation between population size and egg production is seen by comparison of columns *g* and *b* in Table 7 (for it is known that the mortality of larvae is negligible in cultures supplied with excess larval food, and so the number of pupae represents the number of viable eggs laid). The imposed destruction of emerging adults reduced the severity of competition amongst the adults for the limited supply of liver, and so increased their fertility, as shown in column *m*. If mortality were wholly due to the imposed destruction and the natural deaths of adults, the number of offspring an individual would be required to produce on the average in its lifetime as

TABLE 7. Effects produced in populations of *Lucilia cuprina* by the destruction of different constant percentages of emerging adults (after Nicholson 1954a). The populations were limited by the provision of only 0·5 gm of ground liver for the adults per day in each culture; water and sugar for the adults, and the food for the larvae (from which the adults were excluded) were supplied in excess of requirements at all times.

AVERAGES OF OBSERVED QUANTITIES

Situation	Imposed destruction of emerging adults a	Pupae produced per day b	Adults emerged per day c	Adults destroyed per day d	Accessions of adults per day e	Natural deaths of adults per day f	Mean adult population g
A	0	624	573	0	573	573	2520
B	50%	782	712	356	356	356	2335
C	75%	948	878	658	220	220	1588
D	90%	1361	1260	1134	126	125	878

DERIVED CHARACTERISTICS OF THE POPULATIONS

Situation	% of total mortality due to:			Mean adult life span (days) $k = g/e$	Mean birth-rate (per individual per day) $l = b/g$	Mean coefficient of fertility $m = b/e = kl$	Minimum coefficient of replacement $n = \dfrac{100}{100-a} = c/e$
	Pupal mortality $h = \dfrac{100(b-c)}{b}$	Imposed destruction $i = \dfrac{100d}{b}$	Natural deaths of adults $j = \dfrac{100f}{b}$				
A	8·2	0	91·8	4·4	0·25	1·1	1
B	8·9	45·5	45·5	6·6	0·33	2·2	2
C	7·3	69·4	23·2	7·2	0·60	4·3	4
D	7·4	83·3	9·2	7·0	1·55	10·8	10

replacements for those dying from these known causes is shown in column *n*. Actually the fertility (*m*) was greater than this, for there was a somewhat erratic pupal mortality (due to unknown causes) for which the population also compensated automatically by a further increase in fertility.

It will be observed that the increase of the coefficient of fertility (*m*) with increasing destruction was not wholly due to the increase in birth-rate (*l*) caused by the adults obtaining more adequate quantities of liver, but was in part due to an increase in the average life span (*k*) of the adults. This was due to a lessening of the adverse effect of adult crowding in the cages in which the populations were reduced by imposed destruction. So, although the percentage of individuals reaching maturity (*j*) varied approximately directly with the percentage (100–*a*) of flies not destroyed by the imposed factor, the mean adult population (*g*) varied to a lesser degree, for the surviving adults lived longer and produced more offspring, so in large measure countering the population-reducing influence of imposed destruction. (Nicholson 1954a.)

The ability of populations of *L. cuprina* to maintain themselves in spite of severe stress was also demonstrated by constructing life systems in which the supply of larval food was limiting, and in other ways.

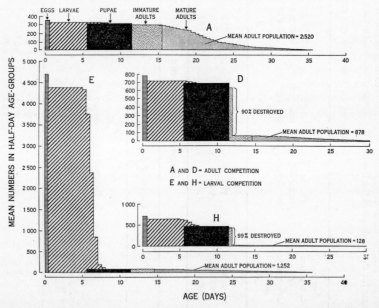

FIGURE 23. E: average age-stage structure of a culture of *L. cuprina* stabilized by competition between larvae for food, the adults having a separate and ample supply of ground liver; H: effects produced upon a similar culture by destroying 99% of the emerging adults; A: as for E except that the culture was stabilized by competition between adult flies for a daily supply of 0·5 gm of ground liver; D: effects produced upon a similar culture by destroying 90% of the emerging adults (after Nicholson 1957).

For example, the destruction of 50 per cent. of the total adult population every second day produced no significant change in the mean adult population compared with a similar culture in which there was no imposed destruction; and in another experiment the destruction of 50 per cent. of all eggs laid more than doubled the mean adult population, compared with a control culture. (Nicholson 1954a.)

The effects of imposed destruction on the age structure of *L. cuprina* populations are shown in figure 23 in terms of age-groups covering half-day periods (see Nicholson 1957).

The area included within the zones marked off for each developmental stage represents the number of individuals at that stage. The histograms show the numbers of each developmental stage which would be observed if it were possible to select a moment when all stages were represented in their mean numbers.

The age structure of the populations in which individuals were killed deliberately showed an increase in numbers for the stage preceding that subjected to imposed destruction. Histogram E for the control population which was stabilized by larval competition for food indicates the large 'emergency reserve' of fecundity in the blowfly. 'It is to this reserve that the great resilience of the species is due' (Nicholson 1957).

From such experimental systems Nicholson (1954a) concluded:

The recorded experiments all deal primarily with population limitation due to the reactive effects of depletion of food; but there can be little doubt similar compensatory reaction should result from the depletion of any other kind of requisite. Even in these experiments the reactive effects of adult crowding (that is, of competition for living space) upon mortality and fecundity are evident; and it is clear from the kind of reaction recorded that, in the absence of other reactive factors, this would itself compensate for adverse influences by changes in the limiting degree of crowding. Moreover, the observed compensation for destruction which is characterized by an increase in the density of the age-group immediately preceding the one subject to destruction, and by increases and decreases in the densities of other age-groups, is in conformity with conclusions reached elsewhere concerning the effects produced by subjecting a host population governed by the action of a parasite species to an additional destructive factor (Nicholson 1933 . . . ; Nicholson and Bailey 1935 . . .).

4.253 *Influence of fluctuating environmental conditions*
On theoretical grounds, Nicholson (1933) concluded that oscillations in population density resulting from such stabilizing processes as intraspecific competition should tend to conform to cyclic climatic fluctuations. With the facilities available for the manipulation of his *L. cuprina* systems.

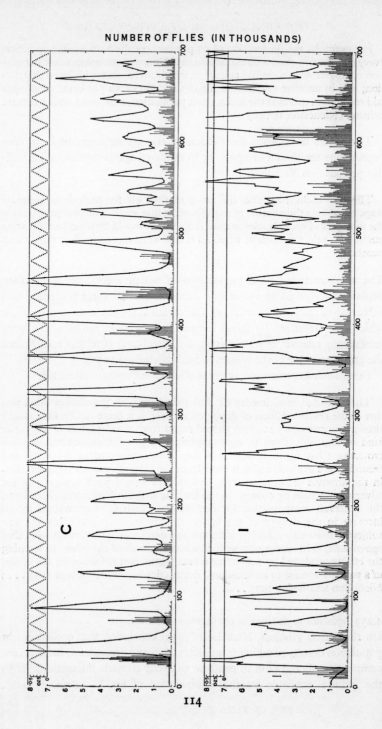

NUMBER OF FLIES (IN THOUSANDS)

114

I

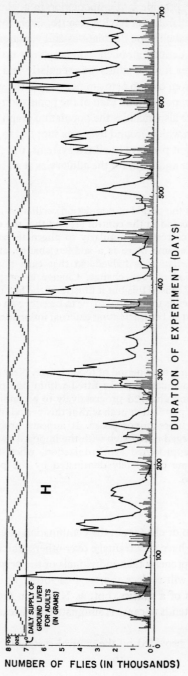

FIGURE 24. C and H: periodic fluctuation in the supply of ground liver for the adults is indicated at top of each graph; I: control culture with a constant supply of liver for adults at the rate of 0·4 gm per day. The larvae were always provided with plenty of food. Vertical lines show numbers of eggs laid daily (after Nicholson 1957).

115

Nicholson was unable to provide cyclic fluctuation in a 'climatic' agency. Instead he varied the availability of food, a resource likely to be influenced to some extent by seasonal climatic fluctuations and variations in weather.

To test his interesting deduction, Nicholson (1957) set up eight systems in which the ground liver for the adults was regularly and progressively varied from day to day from 0·05 to 0·50 gm per day, in the ways shown in the dotted graphs superimposed upon each of the population graphs C and H in figure 24. The figure also includes the population graph for one of the two control systems (I) in which ground liver was supplied to the adult flies at a constant rate of 0·4 gm per day. In all ten systems, the supply of food for the larvae and of water and sugar for the adults was at all times in excess of requirements.

It will be observed that the period of population oscillation in C is slightly longer than the natural period in the control (I) and that the oscillations up to about the 500th day correspond regularly to alternate periods of food fluctuation. At about this time there is a sudden change, after which the period of population oscillation is halved, so that each population peak corresponds to each period of food change. Change in properties due to natural selection probably caused this but it illustrates the fact that the period of population oscillation tends to be equal to, or to be either an exact multiple or a simple fraction of that of the fluctuating external influence.

System H:

was subjected to a much longer period of food change. Near the beginning of this experiment two population peaks fitted within one period of food change; but the population changed progressively to a condition in which there was only one major population peak within this period of food change, accompanied by one or more minor peaks. It appears probable that, by chance, this population began out of step with the imposed periodic fluctuation, but progressively approached synchronization, when the period of intrinsic oscillation became completely dominated by the period of food change. (Nicholson 1957.)

4.254 *Natural selection*

If, as a result of mutation or changes in the combination of genes, individuals are produced which have an advantage over others which causes them to leave more surviving progeny than individuals of the original form, the new kind of individual will replace the original form. This results in a change in the properties of a species, but, as Nicholson (1957) has said: '... the disturbance this tends to cause is automatically checked by density-governed reaction'.

An example of this is provided by the control system (I) of figure 24.

In this system, the minimal numbers recorded during oscillations tended to increase with time, and the form of the oscillations changed after the 400th day. This suggested that the properties of the flies were changing progressively. Eventually, flies from this system were compared with flies from the original culture maintained in the laboratory by giving equal numbers of individuals from each a very small quantity of protein food. Nicholson found that the flies from system I could lay large numbers of eggs whereas those from the original culture could not produce any eggs. He also tested flies from three other systems used in the same experiment and wild flies. The flies produced in the experimental systems laid numerous eggs, but the wild flies failed to oviposit.

Nicholson (1957) wrote:

It is evident that intense competition amongst adults for protein had led to selection of those flies which could produce eggs with a minimum intake of protein. There was evidence that there had been a similar change in properties in all ten of the cultures which were run in parallel, which strongly suggests that the change in properties was not due to mutation but rather to a new combination of the genes.

4.255 Conclusion
Like his earlier theoretical work on predator-prey interactions (Nicholson 1933, Nicholson and Bailey 1935), the studies of *L. cuprina* systems by Nicholson are a valuable and instructive attempt to demonstrate, in essence, the ways in which population processes and environmental agencies may operate under natural conditions.

4.26 Artificial life systems involving predator-prey interactions
A number of ecologists have endeavoured to investigate experimentally the functioning of life systems which involve predator-prey interactions, by setting up systems of increasing environmental complexity in the laboratory. This approach is well illustrated by the recent work of Flanders and Badgley (1963) and that of Huffaker, Shea and Herman (1963).

4.261 Life systems for Anagasta kuehniella (Pyralidae)
Flanders and Badgley studied simple life systems in which *A. kuehniella* was the subject species. The basic 'food chain' in the systems maintained by Flanders and his co-workers consisted of sterilized wheat flakes (processed grains); *A. kuehniella*; and bacteria which, under certain conditions, caused outbreaks of disease in moth populations. Added to this basic chain in most systems were the egg predator, *Blattisocius tarsalis*, a phoretic mite which disperses by clinging to adult moths, and/or the wasp *Exidechthis canescens*, an endoparasite of the moth larvae.

Populations of *A. kuehniella*, together with those of its natural enemies, were confined in glass-topped boxes, illuminated by indirect sunlight and held at a room temperature of approximately 27°C and relative humidities which averaged about 55%. The wheat supply of each system was introduced periodically in lots of 120 flakes (7·8 gm) in open containers. At all times, twenty-four lots of wheat were present in each system, replacements being introduced in sequence at intervals of either a week, a fortnight, or a month – the period required for the replacement of all twenty-four lots of wheat being set arbitrarily at either six months, twelve months, or twenty-four months, respectively. The numbers of moths and wasps produced per system were determined by counting the numbers of dead adults of each species daily. The relative abundance of mite populations was estimated by removing samples of adult moths, shaking the mites from them, and determining the mean numbers per moth. The moths and mites were then returned to the systems.

It was found that systems including both species of predator, or *E. canescens* alone, could not be maintained in operation unless *A. kuehniella* populations were protected from over-exploitation. For example, when *E. canescens* and *B. tarsalis* competed for unprotected *A. kuehniella*, *E. canescens* eliminated firstly the mite, then the moth, and died out. The devices used to prevent over-exploitation of *A. kuehniella* consisted of layers of vermiculite, containers providing different depths of wheat, and acaricides (Aramite and Kelthane).

Experiments showed that:

(*i*) *B. tarsalis* could function as a density-stabilizing agency for *A. kuehniella* if the wheat supplied was untreated and from 2 mm to 8 mm in depth;

(*ii*) *E. canescens* could also operate in this way if the wheat was untreated and 5–10 mm in depth;

(*iii*) the two predator species could act in combination as density-stabilizing agencies at wheat depths between 10 mm and 28 mm;

(*iv*) if vermiculite was used, neither predator could stabilize prey numbers; and

(*v*) if untreated wheat was less than 4·5 mm in depth, *E. canescens* eliminated the other species and died out.

In the absence of natural enemies, the moth larvae consumed, on an average, one lot of wheat in about nine weeks. When natural enemies were present, but unable to act as stabilizing agents because of a layer of vermiculite, the complete consumption of one lot of wheat took ten to eleven weeks. In both sets of conditions, moth numbers were adjusted by interactions between population density and the available supply of unconsumed wheat, which involved apparently two forms of intraspecific competition: (*i*) between newly-hatched larvae for space in which food was available; and (*ii*) between feeding larvae. When natural enemies were allowed to function as stabilizing agents, the average time required to consume one lot of wheat was increased. For example, when *E. canescens* acted as the only stabilizing agent, *A. kuehniella* did not consume one lot of wheat in two years. Increase in the average time taken by moth populations to consume one lot of wheat provided an index of the extent of the 'density-containment' achieved by the predators.

Figure 25 shows the numbers of *A. kuehniella* recorded for one of Flanders' systems (actually a sequence of three systems). During the period 1957–63 this 'system' was made (by the localized application of Aramite between July 1957 and July 1958, and by changing the depth of

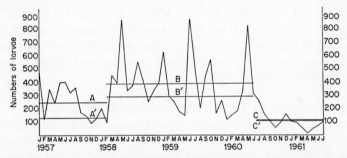

FIGURE 25. Graph based on adult mortality of *A. kuehniella* and *E. canescens* ascertained daily in System 1 depicting the population fluctuations of the fully-fed larvae of *A. kuehniella* during 55 consecutive months. The average abundance of this population of the moth as determined (*i*) largely by predation in conjunction with parasitism, (*ii*) by the wheat supply, and (*iii*) largely by parasitism are indicated by lines A, B, and C. The related parasitization is indicated by lines A', B', and C' (after Flanders and Badgley 1963).

the wheat lots from 14 mm to 5 mm between January 1960 and July 1960) to stabilize moth numbers in three different ways:

(*i*) density-containing action by the two predators together (intraspecific competition between newly-hatched moth larvae also contributing);

(*ii*) density-adjusting action resulting from intraspecific competition between moth larvae (*B. tarsalis* eliminated by the acaricide, and *E. canescens* acting as a non-reactive destructive agency); and

(*iii*) density-containing action by *E. canescens* (intraspecific competition between moth larvae contributing slightly).

During the first phase of population limitation (fourteen months), the moth population produced a total of 3,518 fully-fed larvae (parasitism –

52%): during the second phase (twenty-seven months), the moth population produced 10,516 fully-fed larvae (parasitism – 75%). For the first fourteen months of the third phase, *E. canescens* limited the moth population to a total of 1,636 fully-fed larvae (parasitism – 95%). Thereafter, between July 1960 and June 1963, parasitism held moth numbers at a mean density too low for significant intraspecific competition to occur between the larvae, and only 243 adult moths were produced.

In the *A. kuehniella* systems, the population numbers of each of the interacting species were stabilized at a mean density which varied according to the mechanisms operating and the extent to which non-stabilizing destruction was allowed to occur. The interactions between the prey and the predator populations were either reciprocally stabilizing, or stabilizing only for predator numbers. Like the systems devised for *L. cuprina* by Nicholson, those constructed for *A. kuehniella* by Flanders and his co-workers resemble automated factories with mean outputs set by input of raw materials and energy, and overall organization of processes – and stabilized by negative feed-back mechanisms. These mechanisms could be brought into operation as desired by employing the conditioning influence of simple structural and chemical devices.

4.262 *Life systems for* Typhlodromus occidentalis (*Phytoseiidae*)

For his laboratory investigations on the structure and functioning of life systems, Huffaker (1958a) chose the mite *Typhlodromus occidentalis* and its prey, another mite, *Eotetranychus sexmaculatus* which he fed on oranges, the surfaces of which were partly covered with paper or paraffin wax. He began the investigation by using very simple systems in which oranges were distributed in various ways among waxed, lint-coated rubber balls on open trays. The uncovered parts of the oranges were also coated with lint to increase their favourableness as living-space for *E. sexmaculatus*. The trays were kept in darkness at a room temperature of 28°C, and relative humidities over 55%. Because the food supply was progressively depleted, and because oranges deteriorated whether fed upon or not, a quarter of the oranges present were replaced every eleven days, i.e. all every forty-four days. The systems were started by infesting one or more oranges with *E. sexmaculatus* and later introducing *T. occidentalis* (except in the controls). Mite numbers were estimated by a method which involved counting the individuals present on sample areas marked on each orange.

In systems which included *T. occidentalis*, the general pattern of numerical change was similar for each species. The numbers of *E. sexmaculatus* rose to a peak and then 'crashed' as did those of the predator. In all systems, *T. occidentalis* starved to death after reducing its prey to

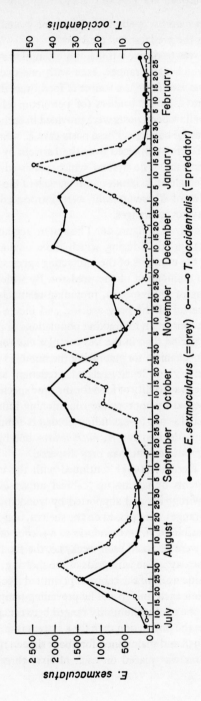

FIGURE 26. Three oscillations in population density of the predatory mite *T. occidentalis* and the orange-feeding mite *E. sexmaculatus* (using a 6-orange feeding area on a 120-orange dispersion) (after Huffaker 1958a).

low numbers. *E. sexmaculatus* was eliminated in some systems; in others, it multiplied again after the predator had died out.

Huffaker's next step was to devise a much more complex system (without rubber balls) in which 120 oranges, each with one-twentieth of its surface available to *E. sexmaculatus* as a source of food, were distributed in three communicating trays. Partial barriers (of petroleum jelly) restricted the spread of mites. Small wooden posts were provided in each of the major sections delimited by partial barriers. These posts gave *E. sexmaculatus* the best possible chance of being dispersed over the barriers by air currents (induced by an electric fan). The system which persisted longest was started by placing one female of *E. sexmaculatus* on each of the 120 oranges. Five days later, females of *T. occidentalis* were introduced, one being placed on each of twenty-seven oranges.

The results are summarized in figure 26. The system remained in being for approximately eight months, during which three obviously-coupled oscillations occurred in the numbers of the interacting species before over-exploitation resulted in elimination of the predator. By widely distributing the initial colonizers of both species, providing relatively favourable conditions for the dispersal of the prey species, and increasing its food supply, it was possible to maintain interacting populations of predator and prey for a much longer period than in the less complex environments used in the first systems. A mechanism for stabilizing the numbers of the interacting populations, involving density-related predation and density-induced variations in the availablility of food for the prey species, was made to operate for a long period by appropriate conditioning influences. The prey species was protected – not by excluding predators from part of the habitat as in the systems devised for *A. kuehniella* – but by restricting predator dispersal to a greater extent than prey dispersal.

Huffaker, Shea and Herman (1963) continued with the experimental construction of life systems by setting up 'cabinet universes' each with three shelves made of wire grids and supported by wooden dowel posts. In each 'universe' 252 oranges were placed on the shelves, one-twentieth of each orange being accessible to *E. sexmaculatus* as a source of food. One-seventh of the oranges were replaced each week, i.e. the food supply was renewed every forty-nine days. The wire grids of the shelving, the wooden dowel posts, and the inside walls of the cabinets permitted free but hazardous movement throughout each universe. The prevailing temperature was maintained at 27°C and the relative humidity ranged between 43 and 55%.

Figure 27 summarizes the population data for a system (no. II–3) which was started in August 1958 and maintained for about sixteen months. One female of *E. sexmaculatus* was placed on each of sixty-three randomly-

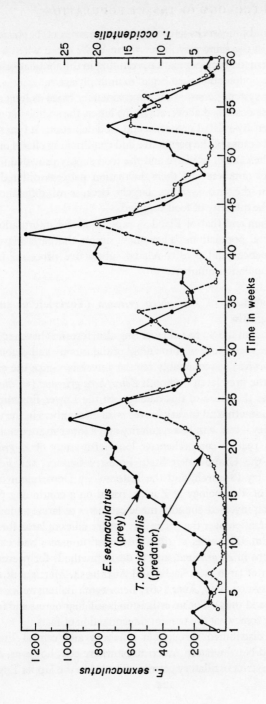

FIGURE 27. The predator-prey interaction with 1/20th orange exposed on a 252-orange dispersion (after Huffaker, Shea, and Herman 1963).

chosen oranges, and four weeks later twenty-one females of *T. occidentalis* were introduced in the same way. The system broke down when a virus disease developed in the prey population, resulting in the elimination of the predator. The prey population then began to multiply again.

This particular system persisted for approximately twice as long as the three-tray universe described above. As in the latter, the stabilizing mechanism involved density-related predation and food depletion. It functioned for a long period because of the permissive and conditioning effects of both the structure of the cabinet universe and the food supply provided for the prey species. Mite numbers and their fluctuation patterns differed considerably between the two systems, largely because of differences in structure and in the quantity of food supplied.

This investigation and that of Flanders provide useful information for the study of natural populations. They show simply the parts played by conditioning influences and density-related subtractive processes in the stabilization of population numbers.

4.27 The life system of *Zeiraphera griseana* (Tortricidæ) in the Upper Engadin

In the upper reaches of the Swiss valley of Engadin, foresters have recorded for many years the recurrence of 'browning' of the canopy and defoliation of larch (*Larix decidua*) at remarkably regular intervals. Since the end of the last century, the grey larch budmoth *Zeiraphera griseana* (= *diniana*) has been known as the cause of this damage. In the Lower Engadin, the numbers of the budmoth tend to vary in step with its numbers in the upper reaches of the valley – but with less regularity and a lower mean amplitude of fluctuation. In 1948, a comprehensive long-term study of *Z. griseana* was initiated by the Graubünden State Forestry Service, the Federal Institute of Forestry Research, and the Entomology Department of the Federal Institute of Technology at Zurich, based on a continuing population survey which involved soundly made estimates of larval abundance for each moth generation over the entire fifty square miles of larch forest in the Upper Engadin. The aims of the study were to assess and explain numerical variations in *Z. griseana*, and to devise methods for preventing serious defoliation of larch (see Kaelin and Auer 1954, Martignoni 1957, Bovey 1958, Maksymov 1959, Auer 1961, Benz 1962, Baltensweiler 1958, 1964a, b, and Bassand 1965). The investigation is still in progress and future findings may alter somewhat the present interpretation of facts.

Z. griseana is distributed throughout northern and central Europe, northern Asia, and Northwestern America. Nowhere else, however, do its numbers show the strict oscillatory pattern recorded in the Upper Engadin where maxima and minima are reached throughout the area at intervals of seven to ten years (see figure 28). In the fully-documented cycle which occurred between the population minima of 1949 and 1958/59 (see figure 29), the numbers of *Z. griseana* rose sharply from 1950 to 1953 (the 'progression phase' of four years), reached a peak in 1954 and declined in 1955 (the 'eruption phase' of two years), and continued to fall at a decreasing rate until 1958 or 1959 (the 'regression phase' of three to four years).

Baltensweiler's 1964b findings show that, in four of the eight oscillations of budmoth numbers recorded between 1890 and 1964, five-year periods of decrease were followed by four-year periods of increase. In three of the remaining oscillations, there were shorter periods of decrease followed by

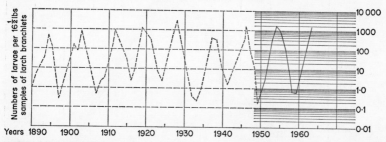

FIGURE 28. Changes in the numbers of the larch budmoth in the Upper Engadin. For the period 1890 to 1948, numbers were estimated according to records of damage; from 1949 onwards, they are census figures (redrawn from Baltensweiler 1964b).

correspondingly longer periods of increase. This compensatory trend in the duration of periods of increase resulted in more regular timing of population maxima than minima.

The damage caused by *Z. griseana* becomes noticeable during the latter part of the 'progression phase' and is widespread during the 'eruption phase'. However, a sudden change takes place in the injuriousness of the budmoth at the beginning of the 'regression phase'. Thereafter, no obvious damage occurs even though population numbers may be higher than those which cause readily-observed injury during the 'progression phase' (Auer 1961) . This suggests the possibility of a qualitative change in the individuals of successive budmoth generations.

4.271 *The characteristics of the species in the Upper Engadin*
Z. griseana exists as two distinct biological races or sibling species (Bovey and Maksymov 1959), one of which lives on larch and the other on pines. In the Swiss Alps, the two sorts of budmoth are isolated both sexually and ecologically, and only the larch form is considered here.

The larch form of *Z. griseana* is univoltine with an obligatory diapause in the egg stage. The diapause affects the early embryo in summer and is gradually eliminated during the following winter. In the Upper Engadin, the eggs hatch from late May until mid-June, and the larvae, which feed on the needles of the host plant, pass through five instars in about fifty days. When feeding is completed, the final instar larvae drop to the ground and pupate in the litter on the forest floor. The adults emerge about thirty days

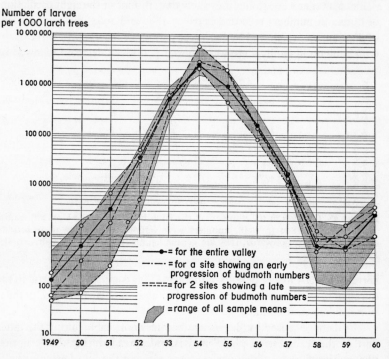

Number of larvae
per 1 000 larch trees

FIGURE 29. Changes in the numbers of the larch budmoth in the Upper Engadin during the cycle 1949–1958/59 (redrawn from Auer 1961).

later, i.e. in August and September. The adult moths, which have a 1 : 1 sex ratio, live for about thirty-five days. The females lay their eggs, usually in groups of two or three, on larch trees beneath the protective covering of lichens (Maksymov 1959). In their selection of oviposition sites, the females show a preference for trees with undamaged foliage. If only foliage damaged by budmoth larvae is available, oviposition occurs on the most lightly damaged parts of tree crowns.

It can be inferred from the findings of the authors that individuals of *Z. griseana* in the Upper Engadin tend to conform to one of two physiological types, a 'strong' and a 'weak' type (see Baltensweiler 1958), which appear to differ in:

(*i*) the winter mortality of eggs which can vary greatly, e.g. as between nil and 90% under the same conditions (Maksymov 1959);

(*ii*) the percentage establishment of newly-hatched larvae (Baltensweiler 1958);

(*iii*) larval behaviour, the 'strong' type showing greater food requirements, and hence injuriousness, and more ability to forage and to spin protective webbing;

(*iv*) the body weight of mature larvae and pupae (Gerig 1964b);

(*v*) percentage survival at pupation, which is greater in the 'strong' type (Maksymov 1959); and

(*vi*) the reproductive ability of adult females (Baltensweiler 1958).

In some circumstances, the larvae and pupae of the 'weak' type could be confused with 'stressed' individuals of the 'strong' type which occur at high levels of population density (see Maksymov 1959). However, respirometer tests carried out by Gerig (1964a) indicate that stressed individuals of the 'strong' type can be distinguished readily by their abnormal rates of metabolism.

4.272 *The environment in the Upper Engadin*

(*i*) *The host plant.* Larch is a deciduous conifer. It grows best at elevations favourable to *Z. griseana* which is by far its most important pest. Whole stands of larch may be defoliated completely when heavily infested by larvae of the 'strong' type. However, the host trees are rarely killed unless they are subjected to additional stress, e.g. drought or very severe frosts (Auer 1961). After early defoliation, larch trees replace their needles during the same season, but, during the following spring, the needles produced tend to be short and coarse. Such foliage appears to be relatively unfavourable as food for larvae and the reproductive ability of individuals is reduced (Baltensweiler 1964b). However, as Auer (1961) points out, the premature depletion of larval food and the production of unfavourable foliage are localized and have little overall effect on population numbers in the valley.

(*ii*) *Climate and weather.* In the Upper Engadin, temperatures suitable for diapause development in the eggs of *Z. griseana* prevail from November to late April, i.e. for 180–200 days, but diapause is actually eliminated after 120 days and morphogenesis proceeds slowly until rising temperatures in the spring accelerate it to completion and hatching. The eggs hatch in strict synchrony with the appearance of new foliage on the host plant, and the larvae thus have the best possible chance of establishment.

The most favourable temperature regime for overwintering in the egg stage and the establishment of larvae in the spring occurs at altitudes of 4,800 to 6,000 ft. Below 4,800 ft, earlier springs and warmer summers cause many eggs to hatch in the autumn instead of during the spring, and others die after an excessively long preconditioning phase at relatively high temperatures. The survival of the remaining individuals is jeopardized by poor synchrony between hatching in the spring and the production of new foliage by larch. Above 6,000 ft, the prevailing temperatures remain too low for too long to allow timely diapause development.

At altitudes of 4,800 to 6,000 ft, population trends in *Z. griseana* appear to be affected very little by variations in weather – even by extreme conditions (Auer 1961).

(*iii*) *Location*. Environmental conditions in the Upper Engadin vary according to altitude and aspect. This variability is reflected in the local departures from the overall trend of population numbers in figure 29. The locations colonized by *Z. griseana* can be divided roughly into two categories: (*a*) the more favourable sites characterized by a high proportion of pure stands of larch – southern, south-western and eastern aspects – and altitudes between 4,800 and 6,000 ft; and (*b*) the less favourable sites characterized by mixed stands of trees – northern, north-western and north-eastern aspects – and, in extreme cases, altitudes below 4,800 ft (see Auer 1961). The more favourable locations were termed 'sites of *early* progression' and the others 'sites of *late* progression'. In both types of site, budmoth numbers reach their peak in the same year although the form of the oscillation curve differs.

In the 'late' sites, the numbers of *Z. griseana* tend to be lower at the beginning of the progression phase than in the early sites and to increase at first more slowly and later more rapidly, reaching higher maxima. It appears that the synchronized occurrence of maximum budmoth numbers throughout the valley is due both to the extensive dispersal flights of the adults of *Z. griseana* and to an endogenous cyclic change in the budmoth population (see Auer 1961). The higher maxima recorded in late sites are probably due largely to immigration from the early sites where severe damage to larch occurs sooner than in the former.

(*iv*) *Disease*. The most destructive mortality agent in the Engadin is a granulosis virus which was discovered and described by Martignoni (1954, 1957). The virus occurs throughout the whole valley, but has never been found elsewhere. Outbreaks of virus disease occur only at high densities of *Z. griseana*, i.e. at the end of the progression phase, and cause the reversal of population trend during the eruption phase (Auer 1961).

Although the disease is operative during the first years of the regression phase, its virulence decreases sharply after the initial period of mortality, and no signs of it are detectable at the end of the regression phase. Martignoni (1957) found that the disease affected the budmoth for at least three years, 1953, 1954, and 1955, during the 1949–1958/59 oscillation of population numbers, and that the mean LD_{50} for field-collected larvae in 1955 was thirty-eight times higher than that in 1954.

Epizootics occur almost simultaneously throughout the Engadin, which supports the view that the virus is transmissible through the egg (Martignoni 1957), and persists in latent form within the budmoth population

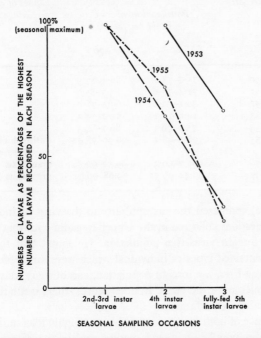

FIGURE 30. Successive reductions in the numbers of budmoth larvae during the first three years of the granulosis outbreak at Sils (redrawn from Martignoni 1957).

(Benz 1962). Pathogenic infection can occur by ingestion of virus particles, and the quantity of virus on foliage, etc., in the valley is believed to increase greatly after the disease begins to cause mortality. Figure 30 refers to a site in the Upper Engadin where the virus was first recorded in 1953 and indicates that, whereas mainly late-instar larvae were killed during the first year of the epizootic, the virus operated sooner and more drastically in the life cycle of the budmoth during 1954 and 1955.

The impact of the virus on *Z. griseana* is best shown by inference from estimates of total seasonal mortality calculated by Auer (1961) to account for the changes in budmoth abundance for successive generations. These estimates were made for two postulated levels of reproduction, i.e. forty and seventy eggs per female (see table 8).

TABLE 8. Estimates of actual total mortality in successive census intervals for all study sites in the Upper Engadin, budmoth cycle 1949–58/59 (after Auer 1961).

Census intervals	95% Fiducial limits of percentage mortality Postulated number of eggs laid per female		Causes of change in percentage mortality
	40	70	
1949–50	75·6–78·2	86·1–87·5	
1950–51	71·4–74·6	83·7–85·5	
1951–52	46·1–59·2	69·2–76·7	
1952–53	14·6–18·1	51·2–53·2	
1953–54	75·6–76·1	86·1–86·3	
1954–55	98·1–98·1	98·90–98·92	outbreak of granulosis disease
1955–56	99·2–99·2	99·52–99·52	granulosis
1956–57	99·44–99·51	99·68–99·72	granulosis +parasites

Benz (1962) compared the susceptibility to the virus of individuals of different generations collected in the Upper Engadin with that of individuals from a foreign virus-free population. He found that the Engadin population contained types of individual which were much more susceptible than those from the foreign population, and other types which were much more tolerant of the virus. In other words, there was a much wider range of variation in the Engadin.

The existence of both highly susceptible and highly tolerant individuals in the Engadin population would readily explain the change in LD_{50} observed by Martignoni, and the disappearance of the disease during the regression phase of an oscillation. One would expect that the susceptible individuals would be largely eliminated during the course of an epizootic, leaving a preponderance of the most tolerant forms. The virtual elimination of susceptible forms fits in with the idea of a qualitative change in the budmoth population mentioned above.

(v) Parasites. Of the array of natural enemies (including microsporidia) which live on Z. griseana in the Upper Engadin, only two types appear to be important, namely an ichneumonid Phytodietus sp.A and two related

TABLE 9. Observed and expected percentages of effective parasitism by sp.A on the assumption of random attacks and unrestricted access to all larvae of the host population, calculated from the data of Baltensweiler (1958).

Year	Observed effective parasitism	Relative frequency of supernumerary eggs	Potential parasitism	Expected effective parasitism	Departure from expectation
Sites of early progression of budmoth numbers					
1955	37·5	17·6	55·1	42	−4
1956	38·9	25·6	64·5	48	−9
1957	38·7	71·3	110·0	67	−28
Sites of late progression of budmoth numbers					
1955	34·7	17·0	51·7	41	−6
1956	15·7	2·4	18·1	16·5	0
1957	30·0	49·3	79·3	55	−25

K

eulophids (Baltensweiler 1958). The ichneumonid was observed in significant numbers only during the eruption and regression phases of the 1949–
1958/59 oscillation, and the eulophids during the regression phase.

The ichneumonid is bisexual and univoltine, and *Z. griseana* seems to be
its only host. The female parasites emerge about three weeks after the
budmoth eggs hatch. After mating, they continue to parasitize budmoth
larvae for about thirty days, laying their eggs on the thorax of fourth and
fifth instar individuals which are either fully exposed or only partly
covered by protective webbing, e.g. when the larvae are foraging. The
female parasite overcomes the active defence of a budmoth larva by stab-
bing it repeatedly with her ovipositor.

Baltensweiler (1958) observed that females of sp.A sometimes lay eggs
which fail to develop. This tendency was found to increase markedly as the
availability of unparasitized larvae decreased. Thus, the frequency of
undeveloped eggs can serve, as do rates of superparasitism, to assess the
abundance of the parasite in relation to that of the host species. Table 9
is compiled from Baltensweiler's (1958) counts of undeveloped eggs of
sp.A, instances of actual superparasitism, and single effective layings (with
and without co-parasitism by another species) expressed as percentages of
the total numbers of budmoth larvae per sample. Assuming that the total
number of eggs of sp.A had been randomly distributed within each
sample, the expected percentages of effective parasitism can be calculated
from the relation:

$$Y = 100 \left(1 - e^{-X/100}\right)$$

where Y is percentage effective parasitism, and X is the total number
of layings by sp.A expressed as a percentage of all budmoth larvae in a
sample.

In five out of six instances, the observed value is lower than the expected
value, and the departure from expectation shows the same trend in 'early'
and 'late' sites, i.e. a tendency to increase as budmoth numbers decreased
during the regression phase. The results strongly suggest that only a
fraction of the whole population of budmoth larvae was available to ovi-
positing females of sp.A.

This may have been due to a tendency on the part of budmoth larvae to
change their feeding sites less often and to be less frequently exposed as
their numbers decreased. However, a more likely explanation (which does
not exclude the other) is that sp.A could attack budmoth larvae of the
extreme 'weak' type (see section 4.273) more successfully than those of the
'strong' type, which are capable of defending themselves vigorously. This
explanation is consistent with the idea that extreme 'weak' types were most
numerous at the beginning of the regression phase and decreased subse-

quently in abundance, causing the numbers of sp.A to fall to negligible levels.

Of the two species of eulophid, one is bisexual and the other partheno-genetic. The females of these species begin to attack third to fifth instar budmoth larvae after mid-June. Unlike females of sp.A, they only attack individuals in closely-webbed tufts of larch needles. They paralyze bud-moth larvae and oviposit near them. After hatching, the parasite larvae find their hosts and feed externally upon them until pupation. About 50% of the parasite pupae produce adults in the late summer, whereas the others overwinter. Presumably the adults which emerge during the late summer attack an alternative host.

During the 1949–1958/59 oscillation, the eulophids were observed in low numbers in 1949 and 1951 and again in 1955. The following year, they attacked 29 and 34% of the budmoth larvae sampled in 'early' and 'late' sites, respectively, and 47 and 51% the following year – with a rate of superparasitism consistent with the assumption of randomly-distributed attacks throughout the entire budmoth population of third to fifth instar larvae. Thus, it appears that the eulophids did not suffer from a shortage of suitable hosts, despite the low numbers of *Z. griseana* during the regression phase.

Baltensweiler (1958) observed that individuals of the 'strong' type of budmoth larvae, which predominates during the progression phase, spend less time than individuals of the 'weak' type in their protected feeding sites; that they often leave their webbing when eulophids attempt to sting them; and that their defence reactions can be so violent that eulophids are dis-couraged from pressing their attacks. As in the case of sp.A, the abundance of the eulophids would be affected primarily by the numbers of 'weak' type larvae present, not by the overall abundance of budmoth larvae.

4.273 *The functioning of the life system*

From the results of their well-designed census work, and the associated studies on the characteristics of the larch budmoth and its environment, the Swiss workers reached the following general conclusions about the life system of the species.

Environmental conditions, particularly the food supply and climate, are so favourable in the Upper Engadin that budmoth numbers can usually increase from low levels to very high densities in four to five generations. As numbers rise, intraspecific competition intensifies sufficiently to compel larvae to forage widely, thus increasing their exposure to a variety of hazards. Food shortage reduces the reproductive ability of individuals, and the damage done to foliage may cause trees to produce relatively unfavourable needles the following year – which again restricts the reproductive ability of individuals. Food shortage and consequent intraspecific stress set the stage for epizootics of the granulosis disease which acts immediately to reverse the trend in population numbers. As the repressive influence of the virus fades out, the destructive action of parasites increases until further reduction in budmoth numbers causes parasite numbers to dwindle in turn. According to Baltensweiler (1964b), the parasites reduce budmoth numbers sufficiently to postpone the subsequent maxima for one or two generations.

This explanation does not seem to account adequately for the stability and consistency of the observed numerical oscillations, and does not consider the possible significance of physiological types among the budmoth larvae. Moreover, the stress induced by food shortage – invoked to explain both the fall in the rate of population increase and the virus epizootic – has not been demonstrated. The available evidence suggests that food depletion and deterioration sufficient to cause major stress are not general or frequent enough in occurrence to exert a key influence on population numbers (see section 4.272).

The published findings suggest a more comprehensive interpretation of the numerical oscillations, which calls firstly for an ecological evaluation of the two larval types whose existence must be inferred in the Engadin populations. These types are almost certainly genetic, and there is probably a gradient of forms between the extreme of each type. The extreme forms of the 'strong' and 'weak' types of larva both possess particular adaptive advantages and disabilities, and the 'modal' form of individual in the budmoth population probably varies according to the selective pressures experienced at different times and places. The 'weak' type appears to be present more consistently than the 'strong' type throughout an oscillation. This is thought to be due to lower requirements of food and living-space, and a much higher tolerance of the virus. The 'strong' type predominates for only a short time – during the progression phase of an oscillation – and appears to be more susceptible than the 'weak' type to intraspecific interference; and much more susceptible to the virus. Presumably, it carries the virus in a latent form – a possibility considered by Benz (1962).

If these assumptions are correct, it is probable that the 'strong' type of larva begins to appear in the first year of the progression phase, i.e. immediately after the season of minimal budmoth numbers when the virus disease has ceased to be epizootic and the 'weak' type of larva is still subjected to attack by parasites. The progression phase occurs because of the vigour and high reproductive ability of 'strong' individuals and freedom from disease and parasitism. Towards the end of the progression phase, the 'strong' larvae are stressed by mutual interference, e.g. frequent disturbance and consequent inability to utilize fully the available food (see Klomp and Gruys 1965).

Adults of the 'strong' type tend to leave the heavily-infested stands of the 'early' sites, and to oviposit in the still undamaged larch crowns of the 'late' sites. In the 'early' sites, the 'weak' type of individual becomes increasingly abundant. For this reason, plus stress in larvae of the 'strong' type, and emigration of adults of that type, the average number of eggs laid per female decreases and the rate of population increase is no longer sustained. This occurs somewhat later in the 'late' sites.

The virus disease is probably triggered by stress in larvae of the 'strong' type, and not only eliminates them but also destroys many intermediate forms of individual, shifting the modal form of budmoth towards the extreme 'weak' type within two years. However, population numbers continue to fall because of the density-related response of parasites to increase in the

TABLE 10. Inferred changes in the preponderance of physiological budmoth types, and the mean number of eggs laid per female – and the estimated percentages of actual total mortality between generations during the budmoth cycle commencing in 1949.

Year	Events	Eggs/female	Estimated percentages of actual total mortality between generations[*]
1949	Weak type preponderant, subtractive influences relaxing	40	77
1950	Strong type reappearing, weak type parasitized	intermediate	78
1951	Strong type preponderant, parasitism light	70	73
1952	Strong type preponderant, no parasitism	70	52
1953	Wide-spread damage to foliage – in some sites for 2nd year. Strong type stressed and dispersing. Weak type at selective advantage	40	76
1954	Strong type severely stressed – heavy mortality by virus. Weak type at great selective advantage	40	98
1955	Strong type eliminated by virus and stress. Weak type heavily parasitized	40	99
1956	Weak type very heavily parasitized	40	99·5

[*] See Auer (1961, table 16).

'weak' type of individual. As numerical decrease continues in the budmoth population, the rates of effective parasitism decline until they become negligible at the end of the regression phase of an oscillation. The destruction of the 'weak' type of individual by parasitism and the overall reduction of population numbers has the effect of shifting the modal form of the budmoth back towards the extreme 'strong' type of individual, and the progression phase begins again.

The operation of the life system of the larch budmoth, as inferred for the 1949–1958/59 oscillation, is summarized in table 10. Although some of the assumptions involved may require revision when more data are obtained, e.g. on the 'weak' and 'strong' types of individual and modal forms, the essential features of the highly-integrated system have probably been recognized.

4.274 Discussion

The life system of *Z. griseana* in the Upper Engadin is of particular interest because of the dominating influence exerted on numerical change by the mechanism which stabilizes the abundance of the species, and because of the complexity of that mechanism. In its dominating influence on numerical change, the mechanism resembles intraspecific competition for food in the basic type of laboratory system constructed by Nicholson for the sheep blowfly *Lucilia cuprina* (section 4.25). In complexity, the mechanism exceeds all of those described for other life systems, and suggests an unusually high degree of mutual adaptation and integration between a species and biotic agents in its environment.

The available evidence suggests that the mechanism responsible for numerical oscillation and stabilization in the life system of *Z. griseana* involves qualitative changes in the subject population, associated with increase in numbers (see section 3.24). The 'strong' type of individual, which is best adapted for existence at low population densities, is virtually eliminated by intraspecific interference and by density-related outbreaks of virus disease. This type is replaced to an increasing extent by a 'weak' type which is best adapted for the crowded conditions of existence at high levels of population density, and tolerant of the granulosis virus. Although resistant to the disease, the 'weak' type of *Z. griseana* is much more vulnerable than the 'strong' type to the attack of hymenopterous parasites which greatly reduce its numbers. Drastic reduction in the abundance of the 'weak' type is followed by production of the 'strong' type of individual in increasing numbers, and the cycle begins again.

4.28 A new life system for *Diprion hercyniæ* (Diprionidæ)

The European spruce sawfly probably reached Canada before 1900, but it was not discovered until 1930 after it had seriously damaged spruce trees (*Picea* spp., especially *P. glauca*) over an area of several thousand square miles (Balch 1960). As this sawfly is reluctant to eat new foliage, it took six or more years to kill trees. Birds and predacious insects other than parasites consumed considerable numbers of *D. hercyniae*, and small mammals and wireworms destroyed a substantial percentage of the cocoons in the soil. However, these natural enemies were unable to prevent increase in sawfly numbers to the limits set by the available supplies of food. By 1938 heavy infestations had developed west of the Gaspé Peninsula in Quebec, throughout New Brunswick and northern Maine, and in parts of New Hampshire and Vermont. Light to moderate infestations occurred between Nova Scotia and Ontario (Bird and Elgee 1957).

In 1934, Canadian entomologists decided to introduce parasites of *D. hercyniae* from Europe in the hope of providing a density-stabilizing mechanism which would hold sawfly numbers at tolerable levels of abundance. Of the many parasite species introduced between 1934 and 1939 only seven became established. Of these, two species – a cocoon parasite *Dahlbominus fuscipennis* and a larval parasite *Exenterus claripennis* – increased rapidly in abundance and began to destroy substantial numbers of *D. hercyniae* (Balch 1960).

In 1936, small percentages of the sawfly larvae reared in the laboratory began to die from a disease caused by a polyhedrosis virus which affects the midgut. The origin of the disease is unknown, but it seems likely that it was introduced inadvertently from Europe with imported parasites (Balch and Bird 1944). The mortality in laboratory-reared larvae increased until 1939 when it became impossible to rear them free of disease. In the spruce forests, few larvae that might have died from disease were observed before 1938. Late that year, however, diseased larvae became numerous in New Brunswick and were observed in New Hampshire and Vermont. From 1939 to 1942 the disease appeared to spread from south to north but caused no major reduction in central Gaspé until 1942. By that year, the disease was known to be distributed throughout most of the areas infested by the sawfly, and, except in the north, population numbers were reduced to very low levels. No reliable figures are available for the effects of the epizootic during the period 1939–42, 'but it is known that mortality exceeded 50% during this interval and was probably closer to 99% . . .' (Neilson and Morris 1964). The virus was undoubtedly of extreme virulence and could be transferred from adult sawflies to their progeny and by contacts between larvae. Techniques for the propagation and storage of the virus were developed and it was established successfully in Ontario and on the island of Newfoundland. By 1945 the outbreak of *D. hercyniae* in eastern Canada was over. After the epizootic ended the outbreak, the numbers of *D. hercyniae* remained below the level at which serious defoliation occurs.

In 1938 a study area (plot 1) was established in New Brunswick for systematic studies on the sawfly and its introduced enemies, and in 1943 a second study area (plot 2) was established five miles away. Neilson and Morris (1964) wrote:

> These studies are unique in forest entomology in that they cover the decline of an introduced forest insect pest over a period of seven years as well as its fluctuations about the endemic level during 18 subsequent years – a total of 25 years or 50 generations.

The analysis made by Neilson and Morris is useful both for the information obtained and for the methods used because it provides an example of the 'key-factor' approach advocated by Morris (1959, 1963). It is best described by quoting extensively from the description provided by the two workers (with the necessary changes in the numbering of their figures and table).

4.281 *Characteristics of the species*

Males of the European spruce sawfly are rare and the vast majority of females reproduce without mating. They lay their eggs singly and the larvae feed on the old foliage of white, red, or black spruce. After moulting to the final (sixth) instar, the larvae drop to the ground, burrow into plant litter or moss and spin cocoons. The eonymphs in the cocoons may either enter a state of diapause, or develop into adults within a fortnight.

In the study plots near Fredericton (N.B.) the sawfly usually has one complete generation and a partial second generation annually.

> The proportion of first-generation insects giving rise to a second generation in any one year is largely dependent upon the climatic conditions experienced in that year. Thus in a year of early spring emergence and rapid larval development the second generation may be complete, while in a year of later emergence and retarded larval development only a partial second generation is produced.

4.282 *Sampling methods*

The two study plots used by the Canadian entomologists were both situated in stands of black spruce *Picea mariana*. The relative abundance of *D. hercyniae* from generation to generation was determined when the majority of individuals were in the fifth larval instar by beating the branches of study

trees with poles and collecting the dislodged larvae. The samples of individuals collected were reared under sterile conditions in the laboratory.
In this way, it was possible to ascertain the percentages of diseased and
parasitized fifth instar larvae, and the parasite species involved, etc.

In plot 1, the sawfly population was also sampled when in the cocoon
stage. The cocoons collected were classified as 'sound, emerged, parasitized, preyed upon by wireworms, or preyed upon by small mammals'.
The sound cocoons were dissected to ascertain the numbers of live and
dead individuals. Between 1938 and 1943, and in 1961–62, wireworm
numbers were also estimated by sampling.

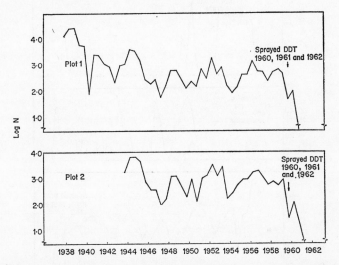

FIGURE 31. Number of fifth-instar larvae on plots 1 and 2 in each generation of the
European spruce sawfly. N = 1,000 (mean number of larvae per tree sample)
(after Neilson and Morris 1964).

4.283 *Results*
Figure 31 shows, on a logarithmic scale, the relative abundance of *D.
hercyniae* in the study plots. The data illustrate two points: '(1) that population fluctuations observed on one plot are not peculiar to one small area
but are generally widespread . . .; and (2), that surprisingly good results . . .
are obtained by the pole-beating method.'

Between 1945 and 1960, sawfly numbers fluctuated about a fairly low
mean level (0·5 larvae per tree sample) and it seemed likely that they would
continue to do so. However, in 1960–62, both plots were sprayed with DDT
to reduce the abundance of the spruce budworm, *Choristoneura fumiferana*

The three consecutive sprayings greatly reduced the numbers of the spruce sawfly.

In figure 32 the pooled counts of larvae for the two study plots are shown in relation to parasitism and disease. Of the various parasites attacking the sawfly population, *Drino bohemica* obviously had the greatest effect on numbers after the outbreak had ended. Neilson and Morris concluded that parasites 'seem to be more sensitive to minor fluctuations in host density during the endemic years than disease, their numbers increasing and decreasing with host density in a delayed density-dependent manner'.

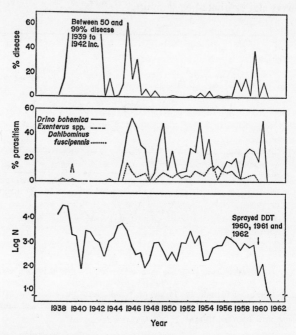

FIGURE 32. Disease, parasitism, and population density of fifth instar larvae for plots 1 and 2 combined (after Neilson and Morris 1964).

4.284 *Key-factor analysis*

Neilson and Morris wrote:

The type of data obtained on the epidemiology of the spruce sawfly during the past 25 years is ideally suited to an analysis by the key-factor approach of Morris (1963). Although Morris (1959) previously used some of the spruce sawfly data in illustrating a single-factor approach, he did not include any of the outbreak years in his illustration or proceed beyond the inclusion of parasites in his analysis.

Because of incomplete data some years have to be left out of the analysis.

In 1939, 1940, 1941 and 1942 mortality from disease exceeded 50% but because no actual measurements were made these years cannot be included. Two other years, 1945 and 1947, were also excluded because of a conflict to be described later in the part of the analysis involving weather.

To stabilize variance and provide linearity, sawfly densities were converted to common logarithms. All references to spruce sawfly density from hereon, unless otherwise specified, will actually refer to the logarithm of density. To avoid negative logarithms the mean number of larvae per tree-sample has been multiplied by 1,000 and the symbol 'N' will be used to represent the number of larvae per 1,000 trees.

The aim of key-factor analysis is to arrive at an equation that will permit prediction of population density in the next or subsequent generations from data already on hand. The proportion of the variance that can be explained in such models, and the ability to predict population changes with a reasonable degree of reliability, provide the only objective measures of how well the population dynamics of the insect are understood. In the spruce sawfly there are two generations a year but because results are better and the analysis can be carried to a more advanced stage between generation 1 and generation 2 of the same year than between generation 2 of one year and generation 1 of the following year, only steps in the first comparison will be illustrated graphically. The results of the second comparison will be presented in tabular form later.

It is obvious that the number of individuals in the generation immediately preceding the one to be predicted will be one of the most important factors in the predictive equation. The first step in key-factor analysis, therefore, is to find the relationship between these two densities. An r^2 of ·59 was obtained in this first regression (Fig. 33a), showing that 59% of the variance in the log of the number of larvae in generation $n+1$ is explained by the log of the number in generation n.

The second step is to learn whether predictability can be improved by including other factors. Since parasitism was sensitive to host density fluctuations throughout the period, it is logically the next factor to be taken into account. In Fig. 33b, the log of the number of larvae in generation $n+1$ is plotted over the log of the number of larvae in generation n that survived parasitism (log $N_n p$, where p is the proportion of larvae surviving parasitism). With the inclusion of parasitism predictability is improved considerably: r^2 has increased from ·59 to ·72 and the slope of the regression line has increased from ·82 to ·89. It should be apparent here that step 1 (Fig. 33a) was not carried out simply to demonstrate the obvious, that these two densities are related, but rather to avoid the pitfall of attributing the variation in the system explained by log N_n to a subsequently tested mortality factor.

The slope of these regressions has biological significance. If there were no density-dependent factors operating on an animal population, the rate of increase in density would not decrease with increasing density and the slope of the line relating log N_{n+1} to log N_n would be 1·0. Because of density-dependence (or delayed density-dependence), the slope of the line is less than 1·0 and the degree of density-dependence in the system is reflected by the extent of the deviation of the slope from unity. Only in the case where the numbers of hosts affected decreases with increasing host density could the

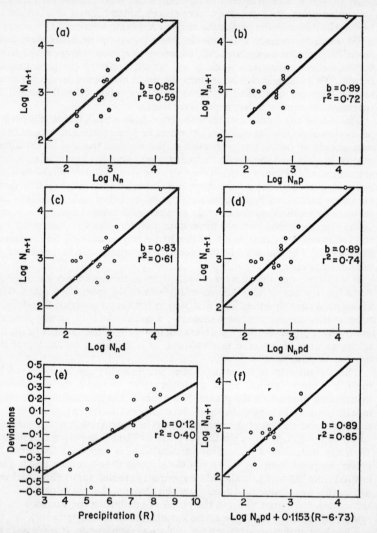

FIGURE 33. Scatter diagrams for the successive steps in the analysis of the European spruce sawfly data. N_n = number of larvae in generation 1 of any year; N_{n+1} = number of larvae in generation 2; p = proportion surviving parasitism; d = proportion surviving disease; R = May and June precipitation in inches (after Neilson and Morris 1964).

slope be greater than $1\cdot0$. As each density-dependent factor in the analysis is accounted for, therefore, the slope of the regression line should approximate more closely to unity.

The third step in this analysis is to test the effect of disease. In Fig. 33c, the log of larval density in generation $n+1$ is plotted over the log of the number of spruce sawfly larvae that survived disease in generation n (log $N_n d$). In this case neither the slope nor the explained variance changed appreciably; $b = \cdot83$; $r^2 = \cdot61$. This would be expected because, as pointed out earlier, disease did not appear as sensitive to changes in sawfly density as parasitism during the endemic period, and the years in which disease was effective in reducing outbreak densities – 1939 to 1942 – were omitted from the analysis because precise data on the proportion of larvae affected are lacking.

Although the contribution of disease to predictability was slight, it was included in the fourth step where the effects of disease and parasitism were tested together. In Fig. 33d, log N_{n+1} has been plotted over the logarithm of the number of sawfly larvae that survived both parasitism and disease (log $N_n p d$). The improvement gained by combining these two factors, as compared to the use of parasitism alone, is slight; $r^2 = \cdot74$ and $b = \cdot89$.

Neilson and Morris then attempted to explain some of the residual variation by considering the influence of rainfall which was known to affect the spring emergence period of adult sawflies. As indicated in figure 33e, they were able to obtain a relationship between the deviations from regression in figure 33d and the total rainfall in May and June. The final step in their key-factor analysis was to add the regression of figure 33e to that of figure 33d to ascertain how much the incorporation of weather would improve predictability. This was done by determining from the regression line of figure 33e the rainfall at which there was zero deviation – 6·73 inches. The regression of figure 33e 'is of the form: (The number of inches of rainfall in any year minus the rainfall at zero deviation) times (the slope of the regression line)'. As indicated in figure 33f, this expression may be added directly to the regression of figure 33d. By incorporating rainfall in the model, the amount of explained variance was increased from 74 to 85%. The slope of the regression line remained as in figure 33d because rainfall did not act 'in a density-dependent fashion'.

A summary of all steps in the key-factor analysis,

including the best predictive equations, is presented in Table II. In constructing the equations for predicting first-generation spruce sawfly density from the second generation of the preceding year, exactly the same steps have been used as outlined above. The 'explained variance' column shows that the predictive equations for each step in this period are not as reliable as those for predicting from one generation to the next in the same year. It is interesting to note, however, that in this between-years prediction

TABLE II. Correlation and regression statistics for key-factor analysis for (a) generation 1 to generation 2 of the same year and (b) generation 2 of one year to generation 1 of the following year (after Neilson and Morris 1964).

	Correlation (r)	Per cent variance explained $(100\ r^2)$	Intercept* (F)	Slope (b)
(a) generation 1 to 2 same year				
(1) $\log N_{n+1}$:$\log N_n$	0·77	59	0·75	0·82
(2) $\log N_{n+1}$:$\log N_np$	0·85	72	0·65	0·89
(3) $\log N_{n+1}$:$\log N_nd$	0·78	61	0·72	0·83
(4) $\log N_{n+1}$:$\log N_npd$	0·86	74	0·65	0·89
(5) Dev. from (4): May–June precip.	0·63	40	−0·78	0·12
(6) $\log N_{n+1}$:$\log N_npd + 0·12(R-6·73)$	0·92	58	0·65	0·89

Best predictive equation: $\log N_{n+1} = \log F + b_1 \log N_npd + b_2(R - \bar{R})$
$$= 0·65 + 0·89 \log N_npd + 0·12(R-6·73)$$

	Correlation (r)	Per cent variance explained $(100\ r^2)$	Intercept* (F)	Slope (b)
(b) generation 2 to generation 1 following year				
(1) $\log N_{n+1}$:$\log N_n$	0·60	36	1·10	0·57
(2) $\log N_{n+1}$:$\log N_np$	0·72	52	1·09	0·60
(3) $\log N_{n+1}$:$\log N_nd$	0·65	42	1·04	0·60
(4) $\log N_{n+1}$:$\log N_npd$	0·77	60	1·04	0·64

Best predictive equation: $\log N_{n+1} = \log F + b_1 \log N_npd$
$$= 1·04 + 0·64 \log N_npd$$

* Ordinate at $\log N_n = 0$.

disease contributed more to explained variance. We did not find a relationship between weather and the deviations from regression incorporating effects of disease and parasites, with the result that our best predictive equation here does not include weather.

After they had found that the effects of disease and parasitism 'did not remove all the density-dependence in either of the analyses', Neilson and Morris turned their attention to the influence of predation during the cocoon stage of the sawfly. Because of differences in the sampling procedures used for the larval and cocoon stages, the observed effects of predation on the latter could not be incorporated in the predictive equations. However, an analysis of the effects of cocoon predators suggested that they could account for 'some of the density-dependence left in the predictive equations'.

4.285 *Discussion*

Neilson and Morris concluded that both weather conditions and predation on the cocoon stage undoubtedly contributed towards the determination of sawfly numbers, but could not be considered responsible for the rapid decreases that occurred between 1938 and 1945. All available evidence indicated that parasitism and disease were the agencies responsible 'for both the collapse of the infestation and the subsequent regulation of numbers about a very low endemic level'. They found it difficult to assess the relative roles of parasitism and disease 'because both may be capable of regulating sawfly densities without the presence of the other'. After mentioning the evidence on this point, Neilson and Morris pointed out that, in combination, parasitism and disease formed 'an almost ideal regulating complex' as they were 'both complementary and compensatory' in their action on sawfly numbers.

The work of Canadian entomologists to reduce the abundance of *D. hercyniae*, which was rewarded both by the successful introduction of parasites and a bonus in the form of a highly-virulent polyhedrosis virus, is generally considered to be an outstanding example of the biological control of an introduced insect which became a pest. It has undoubtedly stimulated the study of viruses as potential agents in biological control. In ecological terms, the work provides an instructive example of the development of a new life system for an insect species – involving the direct intervention of man who, by empirical methods, was able to introduce appropriate stabilizing mechanisms into an existing system and thereby to manage the population according to his needs.

4.29 The life system of *Cardiaspina albitextura* (Psyllidæ)

Cardiaspina albitextura is one of a number of indigenous species of test-forming Psyllidae which live on the leaves of the redgum *Eucalyptus blakelyi* in the Australian Capital Territory (A.C.T.) and other areas on the Southern Tablelands and adjoining inland regions in eastern Australia. The abundance of this woodland psyllid was studied from 1952 to 1963 by Clark (1962, 1963a, b, c, d, 1964a, b, c).

4.291 *Characteristics and abundance of the species*

C. albitextura is a small insect with poor powers of dispersal. Field observations and experiments suggest that the vast majority of adults reproduce within a hundred yards of where they emerged and that long distance movements are limited to a relatively small number of individuals transported by wind. The mean number of eggs laid per female psyllid is frequently of the order of 50 ± 20, and varies between 1 and 300 according to population density and the variable influence of environmental agencies. The results of many experiments in which adult psyllids, collected in different areas and at different population densities, were caged on the same host trees for comparisons of reproductive ability suggest that the inherent vitality of the average individual does not vary much either in time or in space.

The number of generations completed per year by *C. albitextura* is influenced by temperature conditions. In the warmest parts of its known range, e.g. at Coolac on the South west Slopes of New South Wales, the psyllid normally completes three generations per year with scarcely any overlap – one ending in the spring, one ending in the summer, and one ending in the autumn. Usually most of the eggs laid in the autumn hatch by the end of April, i.e. well before winter. In the coolest parts of its range, e.g. the Capital Territory, *C. albitextura* completes two generations and a partial third in most years. If the average temperatures prevailing during the 'psyllid season' (the period from October to April inclusive) are well above normal, three generations are completed. Usually, however, in the late autumn and early winter, part of the generation resulting from oviposition in the late summer reaches the adult stage, reproduces, and dies (few eggs being laid by the relatively small numbers of adults which emerge during the winter). The other part of the generation overwinters as early instar nymphs which reach the adult stage during the following spring. The emergence period of the adult psyllids partly precedes and partly overlaps with that of the adults produced from eggs laid in the late autumn and winter.

During the period 1947–63, the numbers of *C. albitextura* (unlike those of the other psyllids which depend on *E. blakelyi* as host plant) rose from low to high levels in many places and, after fluctuating about a high mean level for up to thirteen years, returned to their original levels. In a few places numbers remained high. In other places, e.g. in parts of the Capital Territory, the numbers of the psyllid remained low although they fluctuated considerably (e.g. see figure 34). The available evidence suggests that, before the recent series of outbreaks, it was usual for *C. albitextura* to

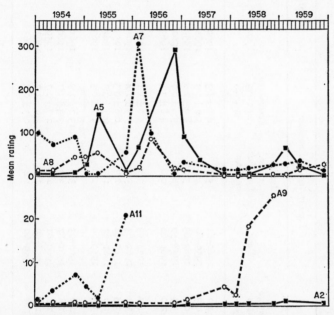

FIGURE 34. Mean ratings of the relative abundance of *C. albitextura* in three areas of persistent outbreak (A5, A7, A8), two areas in which outbreaks developed later, and one area in which numbers remained relatively very low (A11, A9, A2) (after Clark 1962).

remain at low levels of abundance for periods ranging from about five years to well over ten years and then to increase locally, often within three years, to population densities high enough to destroy most of the foliage of the host plant. Numbers then decreased greatly and either remained low for another fairly long interval, or multiplied again to 'saturation densities' and then declined to low levels. Since 1947 high numbers of *C. albitextura* have occurred concurrently over a much larger total area than during the preceding fifteen to twenty years and, especially on the Southern Tablelands, have persisted for much longer periods. In some areas up to 25%

TABLE 12. Survival of *C. albitextura* in study areas A1, A2 and A3 (A.C.T.) (after Clark 1964c).

Study area	Autumn–late spring			Late spring–late summer			Late summer–autumn		
	Year	Initial mean no. of psyllids per shoot	Percentage survival ± S.E.	Year	Initial mean no. of psyllids per shoot	Percentage survival ± S.E.	Year	Initial mean no. of psyllids per shoot	Percentage survival ± S.E.
A1	1962	10·0	14·0±2·2	1960–61	5·5	4·8±1·3	1960	7·8	62·7±4·9
	1958	8·3	5·2±0·7	1959–60	4·4	5·0±1·3	1961	2·5	40·7±4·6
	1960	6·8	3·4±0·9	1962–63	3·2	8·9±2·2	1959	2·0	33·1±4·2
	1959	5·8	7·8±1·4	1958–59	2·5	3·4±0·7	1962	0·4	38·5±4·8
	1961	1·5	7·4±2·0	1961–62	0·6	4·8±2·8	1963	4·1	—
A2	1958	5·2	6·2±1·7	1958–59	3·7	5·0±1·1	1960	3·0	32·0±3·8
	1960	2·6	9·8±3·2	1962–63	3·2	5·5±1·4	1961	2·8	25·3±4·0
	1962	1·6	15·3±3·5	1960–61	2·7	0·6±0·3	1959	1·3	20·4±3·3
	1959	1·2	2·9±1·0	1961–62	1·3	0·7±0·3	1962	0·4	32·3±47
	1961	1·1	17·2±3·3	1959–60	1·0	1·1±0·5	1963	3·0	—
A3	1962	5·1	7·6±2·0	1962–63	3·5	13·2±1·9	1961	5·4	38·4±4·4
	1958	2·0	7·3±1·8	1961–62	3·3	3·3±1·1	1960	2·5	43·7±5·1
	1961	1·9	10·9±2·2	1960–61	2·9	2·7±0·7	1959	1·7	27·9±3·6
	1959	1·7	4·2±1·0	1958–59	2·0	3·9±1·3	1962	1·6	23·7±5·6
	1960	1·7	13·9±2·6	1959–60	1·2	0·3±0·2	1963	8·1	—

of host trees have died as a result of the repeated damage caused by *C. albitextura*, and many others have suffered 'die back' to a variable extent.

4.292 *Survival and multiplication*

(*i*) *In areas of persistently-low psyllid abundance.* Table 12 shows data on the percentage survival of *C. albitextura* in three study areas near Canberra (A.C.T.) – A1, A2, and A3 – in which the numbers of the psyllid remained low from 1952 to 1963. In each of these areas, the mean numbers of *C. albitextura* per single leaf-bearing shoot (averaging five to eight leaves) were estimated by a method which involved searching the foliage of the same ten trees for shoots with eggs on them towards the end of psyllid oviposition periods, counting the eggs present, and recording the total numbers of shoots examined per tree in the search for eggs. With an appropriate correction for bias (see Clark 1964a), this procedure gave satisfactory estimates of the mean number of eggs for all shoots examined per tree and overall means for each area. The infested shoots were tagged and used thereafter for repeated counts and examinations to record and investigate mortality and survival.

The survival of *C. albitextura* was analyzed by dividing the twelve-month period from the autumn of one year to that of the next into the three intervals shown in the table. For the *autumn–late spring* interval, initial numbers were usually overwintering nymphs plus eggs produced by those individuals which reached the adult stage and reproduced before mid-winter. Final numbers for the interval, i.e. the number of individuals that survived to the adult stage, were estimated as the numbers of intact empty tests of fifth (final) instar nymphs plus the relatively few late instar nymphs which were present at the time of the final count made on the tagged shoots. For the following interval, *late spring–late summer*, the individuals present initially were eggs only, and final numbers were estimated as for the first interval. For the third interval, *late summer–autumn*, *C. albitextura* was present initially as eggs and finally as adults and overwintering nymphs, the numbers of adults being estimated as the numbers of intact empty tests of final instar nymphs.

Before describing the analysis of results, two points require mention. Firstly, for the *autumn–late spring* interval, fewer shoots were present per tree in each study area in 1958 than at other times and mean psyllid numbers per shoot for that year should be divided by a factor of 1·5 to make them more representative of relative abundance (see Clark 1964a, 1964b). Secondly the final densities used to estimate percentage survival for the *late spring–late summer* interval in 1959–60 and 1960–61 in A2 and in 1959–60 in A3 are probably underestimates and should therefore be omitted

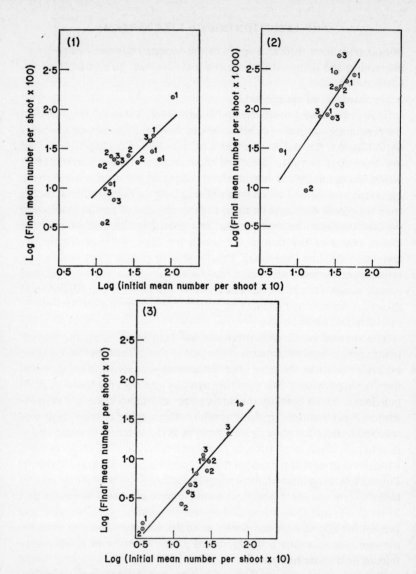

FIGURE 35. Relationship between final and initial population density in areas of low psyllid abundance (A1, A2, and A3, A.C.T.). The numbers beside the points indicate the data for each area. (1) Autumn–late spring; (2) late spring–late summer; (3) late summer–autumn (modified from Clark 1964c).

from consideration (when used to calculate the mean number of eggs laid per adult psyllid, those densities gave unrealistically high estimates – see Clark 1964b, table 3).

Inspection of table 12 shows that percentage survival at the end of each interval did not tend to decrease with increase in initial psyllid numbers. In other words, it seems likely that the survival of immature psyllids was not under the control of a stabilizing mechanism. This suggestion is supported by considering for each interval the regression of log final numbers on log initial numbers (the mean densities per shoot being multiplied by 10, 100 or 1,000 before transformation to avoid the inconvenience of negative logarithms). The regression lines are shown in figure 35 in which the adjustments and omissions mentioned above have been made. For each interval, the pooled data for the study areas are reasonably homogeneous, and the slopes of the overall regressions are 0·909, 1·461 and 1·133, respectively (significantly greater than zero at either $P < 0·01$ or $P < 0·001$) – from which it can be inferred that percentage survival to the adult stage was not under the stabilizing influence of a negative feed-back mechanism.

As Morris (1963) has pointed out, the value of the slope of a rectilinear regression obtained by plotting, as a scatter diagram, the common logarithm of N_{t+1} against that of N_t (where N_{t+1} and N_t are population numbers in a study area at times $t+1$ and t) provides 'an index of the degree of density dependence in the system', i.e. of the extent to which change in population numbers is under the influence of either positive or negative feed-back mechanisms. A slope of unity suggests that such mechanisms are not operating; a slope of greater than unity suggests the operation of positive feed-back; and a slope of less than unity suggests negative feedback. It must be mentioned, however, that when population numbers are estimated with sampling errors, a slope of less than unity does not necessarily indicate the operation of a negative feed-back mechanism. According to the errors involved, the slope calculated underestimates the regression coefficient of the underlying or functional relationship (Williams 1959 and *personal communications*). In the case of *C. albitextura*, the slopes of the functional relationships involved were all likely to have been greater than unity.

Although the percentage survival of immature psyllids tended, if anything, to increase with increase in initial numbers, the abundance of *C. albitextura* remained low in the study areas. It therefore appears that, either by chance or, more likely, by the operation of a negative feed-back mechanism, the mean number of offspring left per adult psyllid tended to decrease with increase in the density of psyllids which reached the adult stage. If, for the late spring and late summer reproductive periods, the same analytical procedure is used as above, and log mean number of eggs laid per shoot is plotted against log mean number of parent adult psyllids produced per shoot, the following regressions are obtained after adjusting the data:

Late spring			Late spring and late summer pooled		
Regression	Slope	Significance	Regression	Slope	Significance
A1	0·509	n.s.	A1	0·616	$P < 0.05$
A2	0·532	n.s.	A2	0·552	$P < 0.01$
A3	0·598	$P < 0.05$	A3	0·556	n.s.
Overall	0·474	$P < 0.01$	Overall	0·574	$P < 0.001$

The magnitude and consistency of these estimates of slope suggest that the mean number of offspring left per adult psyllid was under the influence of a stabilizing mechanism. The same suggestion is obtained if no modifications are made to the data, e.g. the overall regression for all data pooled has a slope of 0·268 (significantly less than unity at $P < 0.01$).

The observed decrease in the multiplication rate with increase in psyllid numbers was due almost certainly to predation. The adults of *C. albitextura* were attacked both at the time of emergence and during the reproductive period by birds, ants, and small spiders. Birds appeared to be the principal predators involved (see Clark 1964b). The adults of *C. albitextura* were attacked by at least ten species of bird.

In study areas A1, A2, and A3 predation was usually responsible for a very large fraction of the overall mortality suffered by the psyllid. None of the natural enemies concerned showed any evidence of a time lag in its response to change in prey numbers. The principal predators included:

(*a*) Birds. The late instar nymphs were attacked by *Pardalotus ornatus*, *Meliphaga penicillata*, and *Acanthiza chrysorrhoa*. These birds, which removed tests almost entirely, tended to destroy an increasing percentage of late instar nymphs with increase in psyllid numbers (Clark 1964b). This tendency, however, was frequently counteracted by variability in the influence of other natural enemies, and the total mortality caused by predators, including parasites, during the developmental period of *C. albitextura* was not correlated significantly with psyllid density.

The adult psyllids were attacked by the above species and by *Rhipidura fuliginosa*, *Rhipidura leucophrys*, *Pachycephala rufiventris*, *Acanthiza reguloides*, *Acanthorhynchus tenuirostris*, *Meliphaga gularis*, and *Lalage suerii*.

(*b*) Encyrtid parasites. The early instar nymphs of *C. albitextura* were parasitized by *Psyllaephagus gemitus* and late instar nymphs by *P. xenus* and *P. discretus* – all of which attack other psyllids. In areas of low psyllid abundance, the percentage destruction caused by *P. gemitus* and *P. xenus* was not related to psyllid density, but varied according to weather, host-parasite synchronism, hyperparasitism, and the time of year. The total apparent percentage parasitism due to these species tended to be moderately high in the spring and summer and high in the autumn when alternative hosts appeared to be scarce (Clark 1964a). *P. discretus* did not attack *C. albitextura* until the mean density of the psyllid reached approximately one late instar nymph per shoot. At psyllid densities above this threshold, the percentage destroyed varied independently of psyllid numbers and was usually low. On those occasions when *P. discretus* destroyed a substantial fraction of psyllid nymphs, it acted as a substitute for the other parasites which had been reduced to low numbers (see Clark 1964a).

At low psyllid densities, the primary parasites of *C. albitextura* were attacked by two species of hyperparasite *Psyllaephagus clarus* and *Psyllaephagus faustus*. On an average, these hyperparasites destroyed about 50% of primary parasites both at low and at high levels of psyllid abundance. When psyllid numbers increased to moderately high levels, a third hyperparasite *Echthroplexis psyllae* began to attack the primary parasites of the psyllid and continued to do so at the high psyllid densities that occurred during outbreaks (see section 4.293). It attacked the primary parasites over this range of psyllid density even when the fraction of nymphs parasitized by them was low. At moderate to high psyllid densities, the total percentage hyperparasitism due to the three hyperparasites averaged about 90% for *P. gemitus* and 66% for *P. xenus* and *P. discretus*, largely as a result of the addition of *E. psyllae* to the parasite complex (Clark 1962).

(c) Ants. All nymphal stages of *C. albitextura*, especially the third, fourth, and fifth instars, were attacked by ants, some small species of which probably also destroyed psyllid eggs. The percentage destruction caused by ants varied independently of psyllid density at low levels of abundance, and tended to be high in summer. The following species removed nymphs after tearing their tests or chewing holes in them: *Crematogaster scita*, *Monomorium leae*, *Iridomyrmex punctatissima*, *I. itinerans*, *I. rufoniger* and *Xiphomyrmex* sp. When attacking nymphs, the meat ant *I. detectus* removed tests almost completely (see Clark 1964b).

(d) Beetles. The malachiid beetle *Laius cinctus* fed on the eggs of *C. albitextura*, the percentage destroyed varying independently of psyllid density.

Minor natural enemies included the larvae of brown and green lacewings, coccinellid larvae, small spiders, and mites. In addition, at the maximal psyllid densities that occurred in areas of low abundance, a few late instar nymphs were occasionally destroyed by the larvae of an unidentified species of *Syrphus*. This syrphid attacked *C. albitextura* mainly in areas where the population density of the psyllid fluctuated about a high mean level (Clark 1963d).

Other causes of psyllid mortality which were sometimes responsible for substantial losses were: the shedding of old leaves bearing nymphs or eggs at times of foliage replacement by the host plant (see Clark 1962); other leaf-feeding organisms, e.g. scarab beetles of the genus *Anoplognathus*,

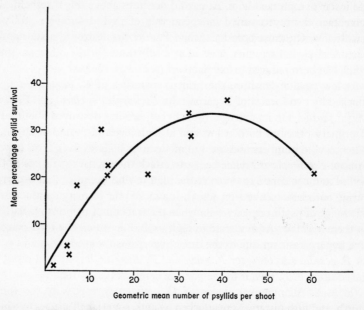

FIGURE 36. Estimated mean percentage psyllid survival in relation to mean psyllid numbers per shoot at Binalong, N.S.W. (after Clark 1963d).

which sometimes consumed much of the foliage on host trees and thereby destroyed psyllid nymphs or eggs; and frost as affecting newly-hatched nymphs and adults during the late autumn, winter, and early spring.

(*ii*) *In areas of high psyllid abundance.* In areas in which outbreaks were in progress, psyllid numbers, percentage survival, and the rate of multiplication were estimated either by collecting randomly the same number of shoots from the same trees after the emergence of the adult psyllids (at Binalong, N.S.W.), or by selecting shoots randomly, tagging them, and recording numerical changes from the egg to adult stages (in the Capital Territory).

Figure 36 shows estimates of percentage survival to the adult stage in relation to the mean numbers of psyllid nymphs that reached the third to fifth instars for the Binalong study area in which *C. albitextura* usually completed three generations per year. The regression of survival on numbers was curvilinear. The curve fitted to the points,

$$y = 1.763x - 0.0236x^2 + 0.382,$$

suggests that percentage survival increased with psyllid density at a decreasing rate and finally declined.

In this study area, the percentage destruction of psyllid nymphs due to syrphid larvae increased with increase in psyllid density, and was largely responsible for the decrease in survival at high densities. Although the syrphid larvae destroyed up to about 35% of the psyllid nymphs that reached the late instars, they were unable to reduce psyllid numbers to a low level because, as was usual in areas of *high* psyllid abundance (e.g. Clark 1962, table 18), the total percentage mortality due to such predators as birds, ants, and encyrtid parasites decreased with increase in psyllid numbers. Birds and ants were unable to respond numerically to increase in the population density of *C. albitextura* and, although they tended to destroy an increasing number of psyllids with increase in psyllid density, the percentage destroyed decreased (see also Clark 1964b). The reduction in the percentage destroyed by primary parasites is attributable largely to the restrictive influence of hyperparasitism.

From 1958 to 1962, the pattern of abundance shown by *C. albitextura* in this area (see Clark 1963d) was determined mainly by a great annual reduction in the psyllid's multiplication rate which occurred in the late spring. Each year, the host trees were forced to replace their foliage almost completely during the late spring–early summer growth period as a result of cumulative damage due mainly to the high abundance of *C. albitextura*. The effective multiplication rate of the psyllid was reduced because:

(*a*) most of the new leaves present at the time of psyllid reproduction were too young and soft to be attractive for oviposition (see Clark 1963a); and

(*b*) many of the eggs laid on the old leaves were lost by leaf shedding.

Table 13 summarizes the results of the observations made in A5, a study area in the Capital Territory. The numbers of *C. albitextura* rose from a low level in December 1957 and reached a peak twelve months later. They then fell to a relatively low level during the winter of 1959 and reached another peak in the late summer of 1960.

As in the areas of low psyllid abundance, a generation was completed in autumn 1958. The following autumn, only part of the generation resulting from reproduction in the late summer reached the adult stage and repro-

TABLE 13. Survival and multiplication in relation to the population density of *C. albitextura* in study area A5 (near Canberra) (after Clark 1964c).

Beginning of generation or partial generation	Initial mean no. of psyllids per shoot (eggs)	Final mean no. of psyllids per shoot		Percentage of psyllids which had reached adult stage at final count	Estimated mean number of eggs laid per female
		Nymphs	Adults		
Dec. 1957	17·4	0·1	0·4	2·3	117
Feb. 1958	23·4	1·0	3·7	15·8	71
Apr. 1958	131·8	15·8	15·1	11·5	37
Dec. 1958	281·8	69·6	47·9	17·0	8
Feb. 1959*	195·0	41·2	21·9	11·2	3
May 1959**	38·0	0·3	0·7	1·8	116
Dec. 1959	40·7	0·0	9·8	24·1	98
Mar. 1960	478·6	—	—	—	—

* Generation partially completed in April–May.
** Partial generation resulting from reproduction then.

duced. The eggs were laid on the leaves damaged least by a sequence of increasingly heavy infestations. The other part of the late summer generation, which was in the second and third nymphal instars at the end of autumn, failed to reach the adult stage because the supporting foliage died during the winter.

As at Binalong, percentage survival to the adult stage tended to be higher than in areas of low psyllid abundance, and the multiplication rate decreased with increase in the damage to foliage caused by the feeding activities of psyllid nymphs.

4.293 *The functioning of the life system*

A synthesis of the results of field studies in the Capital Territory, New South Wales, and Victoria suggests that the life system of *C. albitextura* determined the abundance of the psyllid in the ways outlined in figure 37.

(*i*) *Stabilization of numbers at low levels.* Observations made in areas in which the population density of *C. albitextura* remained low for five to ten years suggested that, in some stands of woodland, psyllid numbers increased during the intervals between outbreaks – at first gradually and later rapidly. In other stands, however, psyllid numbers showed signs of temporary stabilization, i.e. although they fluctuated considerably, they gave no indication of either progressive increase or decrease during the time taken to complete over ten generations.

It seems that the temporary stabilization, or near stabilization, of psyllid numbers at low levels of abundance depends partly on predation by birds on *adult* psyllids which tends to destroy an increasing percentage with increase in psyllid density per shoot. Predation by birds functions in a density-related manner to limit the probability of further increase as psyllid numbers rise. Variables other than psyllid density influence the intensity of predation by birds which therefore does not operate consistently according to changes in psyllid abundance, either in time or in space. Moreover, the ability of birds to prevent population growth is limited because their numbers do not increase together with psyllid numbers.

The available evidence suggests that the stabilization of psyllid numbers at low levels depends also on the percentage mortality caused by the whole complex of natural enemies (including birds) which attack the eggs and nymphs of *C. albitextura*. The total percentage destruction of eggs and nymphs due to predators does not increase with psyllid density. If, however, for a few successive psyllid generations, this destruction by predators is well below average, rapid increase to the outbreak level is likely to follow. For instance, in the areas used for intensive observations on parasitism, most psyllid outbreaks occurred where percentage parasitism had been

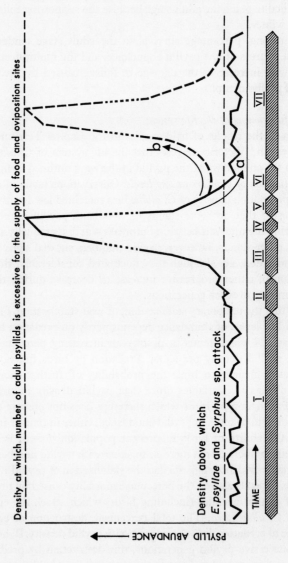

FIGURE 37. Summarized interpretation of the population dynamics of *C. albitextura* (after Clark 1964c).

I Psyllid numbers stabilized or almost stabilized because of the combined action of:

    (a) Predation by birds, ants, encyrtid parasites, etc., on the nymphal stage, the total percentage destroyed being independent of psyllid density;

    (b) The prevailing weather, especially temperature conditions;

    (c) Density-reactive predation by birds on adult psyllids;

II Stabilizing process fails, e.g. because unusually low temperatures reduce percentage parasitism. Psyllid numbers rise to a level at which the hyperparasite *E. psyllae* begins to destroy primary parasites. *Syrphus* sp. also attacks and destroys a few psyllid nymphs.

III Psyllid numbers increase rapidly because of:

    —(a) Decrease in percentage destruction by birds, ants, and encyrtid parasites;

    —(b) Failure of *Syrphus* sp. to compensate for waning influence of other predators.

IV Environmental opposition to population growth increases again because of increasing damage to foliage by psyllid nymphs.

V Damage to foliage very severe. Psyllid numbers decrease greatly because of:

    (a) Density-induced reduction in number of offspring per female;

    (b) Number of offspring being excessive for the number of favourable feeding sites available on foliage.

VI Psyllid numbers further reduced to an extent depending on:

    (a) Intensity of predation by birds, ants, encyrtid parasites, etc., which increases with decrease in psyllid numbers;

    (b) Foliage replacement and associated shedding of infested leaves by the host plant.

VII (a) If psyllid numbers are reduced below the level at which the hyperparasite *E. psyllae* operates, they are likely to remain low for some years.

    (b) If not reduced to this extent numbers tend to increase rapidly to the level at which the available amount of foliage again becomes limiting.

relatively low for a number of psyllid generations before the period of rapid increase (Clark 1964a).

There is little doubt that the recent high frequency and persistence of outbreaks was due ultimately to the prevailing weather (Clark 1962, 1964a). An analysis of outbreak occurrence in relation to weather suggested that rapid increase to the outbreak level was often triggered by the occurrence of unusually cool psyllid seasons (the periods from October to April inclusive). The principal effect of unusually low temperatures, and the above-average rainfall frequently associated with them, was probably to reduce parasite effectiveness by: (*a*) causing breakdowns in host-parasite synchronism; and (*b*) imposing restrictions on parasite searching (Clark 1962). It appears therefore that the stabilization of psyllid numbers at low levels depends to a large extent upon weather conditions.

(*ii*) *Increase to the outbreak level.* If, because of a temporary failure of parasites to maintain their usual destructive rate or of birds to react effectively to increase in the density of adult psyllids, the numbers of *C. albitextura* reach a mean density of approximately ten to fifteen late instar nymphs per shoot, rapid increase to the outbreak level is likely to occur.

At about this level of psyllid abundance, the hyperparasite *Echthroplexis psyllae* joins the complex of environmental agencies affecting psyllid numbers, and destroys a substantial fraction of the larvae and pupae of the primary parasites (Clark 1962). *Syrphus* sp. is also attracted into the complex, and its larvae attack late instar nymphs. However, syrphid larvae destroy few individuals at such psyllid densities and, unless an unusually heavy attack by birds intervenes or high mortality is caused by leaf shedding (which occurs independently of psyllid density at such levels), psyllid numbers tend to increase rapidly.

As numbers increase, the environmental opposition to population growth usually decreases because: (*a*) the percentage mortality caused by birds, parasites, and most other predators decreases; and (*b*) predation due to *Syrphus* sp., even when it operates in a density-related manner, is insufficient to compensate for the waning influence of other natural enemies (Clark 1963d).

(*iii*) *Reduction of numbers to low levels.* Before long, the environmental opposition to population growth increases again because the nymphs of *C. albitextura* become so numerous that their feeding activities (over one to three generations) greatly reduce the favourableness of the available foliage and finally cause most of it to die (Clark 1962, 1963a). As a result of density-related foliage damage and depletion, an increasing number of late instar nymphs die of starvation (Clark 1963b). However, the percentage of individuals which survive to the adult stage tends to be higher than at low psyllid densities.

The reduction of psyllid numbers that follows very extensive damage to foliage by nymphal feeding is due initially to limitation of the number of offspring left per female psyllid. The foliage damaged severely by nymphs is unfavourable to adult psyllids as a source of food and largely avoided for oviposition. The adult psyllids seek the small fraction of foliage that escaped severe damage. Because of its scattered distribution and the poor dispersal powers of adult psyllids, many individuals fail to find the favourable foliage and, consequently, produce scarcely any offspring (Clark 1963a, 1963b). The successful adults concentrate on the remaining undamaged foliage which has to provide both food and oviposition sites.

The numbers of successful adults are excessive for the available supply of favourable food, and the production of offspring is limited (Clark 1963b). There is some reason to believe that part of the remaining favourable foliage is utilized mainly for oviposition, and part mainly for feeding (Clark 1963a, 1963c). The presence of large numbers of eggs on individual leaves and shoots may limit feeding thereon by adult psyllids, particularly by females which have greater food requirements than males (Clark 1963b), and thereby conserve food for the psyllid progeny.

The numbers of eggs laid by the female psyllids on much of the favourable foliage that remains are excessive for the available number of feeding sites at which newly-hatched nymphs can establish themselves (Clark 1963c), and numbers are again reduced. While the psyllids of the new generation are still in the nymphal stage, the host trees frequently produce a large quantity of new foliage, and the associated shedding of old infested leaves causes a further decrease in psyllid numbers.

After psyllid numbers have been greatly reduced, the percentage mortality due to predation (including parasitism) increases; and, within a generation or two after the population 'crash', the prevailing circumstances determine if psyllid numbers will again increase rapidly to the outbreak level, or remain low for an extended period. The prerequisite for population increase is, of course, new foliage which is either available at the time of minimal psyllid numbers or soon after. Whether or not an immediate return to outbreak numbers occurs depends mainly on the intensity of attack by natural enemies.

If the percentage mortality due to natural enemies is sufficient to reduce psyllid numbers below the level at which the hyperparasite *E. psyllae* can exert much influence on primary parasitism, psyllid numbers are likely to remain low. If the percentage mortality is not sufficient to bring psyllid numbers below this level, a rapid return to outbreak abundance usually follows. Eventually, at a time of minimal abundance after a population 'crash', natural enemies prevent a rapid return to high population densities, and psyllid numbers are either stabilized temporarily again at low levels or begin to increase gradually.

(*iv*) *Stabilization of numbers at high levels.* In some of the areas in which prolonged outbreaks occurred, mortality and progressive 'die-back' were suffered by *E. blakelyi* as a result of repeated defoliation at intervals of three years or less. The increasing damage suffered by the host plant caused a progressive decrease in the amount of foliage available to *C. albitextura* and consequently, although psyllid numbers continued to fluctuate violently, they decreased progressively. In such areas, the density of *E. blakelyi* was high and *C. albitextura* was usually able to disperse readily from tree to tree.

In other areas of prolonged outbreak, in which the density of host trees and other eucalypts was either below-average naturally or had been reduced substantially by clearing, psyllid numbers frequently took longer than three years to build up sufficiently to defoliate the host trees which were able to recover almost completely between successive defoliations. Consequently, the amount of foliage present did not decrease progressively with time, and psyllid numbers continued to fluctuate between approximately the same upper and lower limits during the outbreak period. In such areas, the effective dispersal of *C. albitextura* was limited by the low density of host trees and by the insect's poor powers of flight. The direction taken by adult psyllids in flight is influenced by wind direction and, in open stands separated by cleared areas or in narrow tree belts left beside roads, etc., the prevailing winds cause many adult psyllids to lose contact with the host plant at times of moderate to high abundance, and to die of dehydration or starvation (see Clark 1962).

In other words, it seems that a relatively low density of the host plant is required for the stabilization of psyllid numbers at high mean levels. The intraspecific competition for food and associated processes, induced automatically in the interaction between psyllid population density and the available supply of food and oviposition sites, are unable to stabilize numbers unless the effective dispersal of the psyllid is limited by such factors as tree density and wind force.

4.294 *Discussion*

During the period of investigation, the psyllid population persisted in all areas kept under observation. In parts of the woodland colonized by the psyllid, its numbers showed evidence of temporary stabilization, i.e. of 'metastable states'. In some areas, stabilization occurred at low mean levels of psyllid abundance. In other areas, it occurred at high mean levels. Elsewhere, psyllid numbers changed progressively with time.

The study areas in which psyllid numbers were stabilized at low levels appeared to differ from those in which numbers increased progressively to the outbreak level mainly in the greater intensity of attack maintained either by natural enemies whose destructive effects varied independently of psyllid density (at low levels) e.g. parasites, or by those which reacted to increase in psyllid density by increasing the relative severity of their attacks, e.g. birds. The areas in which psyllid numbers were stabilized at high mean levels were characterized by a relatively low density of the host plant *E. blakelyi*.

On the basis of observed facts, numerical relationships, and reasonable hypotheses to explain observed phenomena, it is inferred that the temporary stabilization of psyllid numbers depended on:

(*i*) The extent of the mortality caused directly or indirectly by certain environmental agencies whose conditioning influence determined when and where stabilization was possible. Unless a sufficiently high number of psyllids died prematurely as a result of the influence of these agencies, stabilization could not occur. The agencies whose effects were decisive in this way differed according to psyllid abundance. At low densities, the principal conditioning agencies were probably the whole complex of species predacious upon psyllid nymphs and eggs, and weather – especially the prevailing temperatures. At high densities, the abundance and distribution of host trees, and wind, were decisive.

(*ii*) Negative feed-back mechanisms which were able to implement stabilization providing that sufficient mortality was caused by the conditioning agencies. The environmental agencies involved in the mechanisms also differed according to psyllid abundance. At low psyllid densities, birds predacious on adult psyllids appeared to be the operative or density-stabilizing agency. Because the intensity of their attacks depended partly on conditions other than the density of adult psyllids, the stabilizing mechanism involving predation by birds functioned in a probabilistic manner with respect to psyllid numbers. At high psyllid densities, food and space favourable for oviposition were the operative agencies. The limited availability of food and space brought into action a stabilizing mechanism which functioned automatically through forms of intraspecific competition.

Further investigations now in progress may well require modification of this interpretation of the ways in which particular environmental agencies contribute towards the stabilization of psyllid numbers. For example, it may be found that parasitism by *P. discretus* (see Clark 1964a), predation by birds on psyllid nymphs (see Clark 1964b), and predation by spiders on adult psyllids can all function sometimes as part of the stabilizing mechanism which operates at low levels of psyllid abundance – instead of acting as conditioning agencies. It may also be found (see Clark 1962) that rainfall and local differences in the quality of the psyllid's food supply sometimes play an important causal role in the increase in psyllid numbers above the levels at which the 'low-density' stabilizing mechanism can operate, i.e. in the causation of outbreaks.

Over a hundred years ago, the European settler became an environmental agency in the life system of *C. albitextura* and since then has exerted an increasing influence both directly and indirectly on the host plant and natural enemies of the psyllid. Increasingly intensive farming and grazing, town and city development, etc., have resulted in the removal of a very large proportion of the original trees and in greatly limited regeneration. Consequently, the composition and age-structure of the tree population has been modified, and *E. blakelyi* and associated eucalypts now occur in numbers approaching their original abundance only in relatively small areas.

Before the woodland was reduced by clearing and thinning, psyllid numbers must have been much more often low than high (Clark 1962), and the density-stabilizing action of natural enemies may well have been much less sensitive to weather conditions than now, e.g. because bird numbers were almost certainly higher in many places. The encyrtid *P. discretus*, which attacks *C. albitextura* when the population density of the psyllid rises above a low threshold level, was probably also more abundant. For population persistence, this encyrtid depends largely on other species of *Cardiaspina* which infest eucalypts growing in association with *E. blakelyi*, e.g. *Eucalyptus melliodora*. In many places, e.g. the Capital Territory, this eucalypt species has been reduced in numbers to a greater extent than *E. blakelyi*.

Because of the continuing modification of the life system of *C. albitextura*, it is likely that the average abundance of the psyllid will increase and that outbreaks will occur more frequently than during the first half of this century.

CHAPTER V

The study of natural insect populations

5.1 INTRODUCTION

The need for more research, and more adequate research, on natural populations of insects is frequently stressed by both economic entomologists and population theorists. The harmful side-effects of many insecticides and the development of resistant strains of insect have discouraged the search for a panacea that would solve all problems, irrespective of an understanding of individual species or of ecological principles. Instead, there is a growing emphasis on developing forms of population management to suit particular life systems (see chapter VI).

Although the need is widely accepted, the possibility of gaining an adequate understanding of natural populations is still sometimes questioned, largely because of the multiplicity of ecological events and processes in the life system of any subject species that could conceivably affect its population numbers. However, as pointed out in chapter IV, recent work tends to support the hypothesis (Morris 1959) that a few 'key' influences, operating usually in one or two critical age intervals, may very largely determine population trend. Many other elements in a life system may be known to influence natality or mortality, but with net effects that are either too small or not variable enough to influence population trend measurably from generation to generation. Although the study of natural populations requires more time and staff than the study of confined laboratory populations, especially when difficult sampling problems are involved, it is safe to conclude that the limited results achieved to date reflect only the lack of adequate effort and means, not the lack of possibility.

In this chapter, recognizing both the necessity and the possibility of securing an adequate understanding of natural populations, we shall outline the objectives and some of the approaches that appear to be promising for future work. Methodology will be discussed only in very general terms, both because it requires so much modification to suit individual problems, and because it has been discussed recently in detail by Southwood (1966). The treatment will be perspective rather than retrospective, with the emphasis on the life system as a whole instead of on particular processes, and particularly on the possibilities offered by mathematical modelling.

5.2 THE OBJECTIVES

The main objective in studying the life systems of natural populations is to learn enough about their functioning to devise efficient ways of manipulating them as desired. The successful management of insect populations calls for: (i) the effective integration of what is learned about species characteristics, environmental influences, and ecological processes, in particular life systems; and (ii) the integration of these individual syntheses into a body of useful ecological principles.

The syntheses made to describe the functioning of particular life systems are called models. Like other words that are used extensively, the term 'model' has acquired a wide meaning. Ziman (1965) wrote '. . . this is objectionable, because one does not like the sense of the word 'model' diluted until it becomes synonymous with theory. There ought at least to be a remnant, a reminder of the idea of a mechanically interacting system, and at least a suggestion that the system is amenable to mathematical analysis'. In this broad sense, models may be verbal, diagrammatical, or mathematical in form.

All of the syntheses given in chapter IV are formulated verbally and can therefore be described as 'verbal models'. Graphs and other forms of mathematical analysis were used extensively in the investigations concerned, but the various relationships demonstrated or inferred were not fitted together in an overall mathematical summarization. Verbal models, based on well-conceived observations and experiments, are very useful and much of our present knowledge of the characteristics of life systems is based on them. Sometimes they are all that is needed to solve a pest problem; in other cases, they are all that can be produced with the means and time available. However, verbal models do not provide the *quantitative* integration which is needed if we are to progress much further in our understanding of population dynamics and pest management. Such integration can be provided only by mathematical formulations.

A mathematical model is simply '. . . a mathematical formulation (preferably one that makes biological sense), which mimics numerical changes taking place in natural populations and by means of which quantitative predictions can be made.' (Lloyd 1962.) The equations referred to in chapter IV for *Diprion hercyniae* can be called mathematical models although they are crude, preliminary examples which apply only to two study areas (see section 5.33). The effects of additional independent variables, such as predation, were clearly recognized, but were expressed only indirectly through the slopes of regression lines. Further work, including experimentation, is necessary before the effects of other variables, particularly weather, can be modelled in a more informative way. However, the equations describe more efficiently what is understood about the insects concerned than could purely verbal integrations, and the amount of variance explained satisfactorily provides assurance that most, if not all, of the 'key' processes effecting numerical change during the period of study have been detected.

An *adequate* explanatory mathematical model for a natural insect population, e.g. the population of a pest species, would have the following uses, some of which have been described in more detail by Watt (1961, 1962):

(*i*) It would provide the only *quantitative* means of showing how much is understood about the life system of the subject species in terms of the influences and processes involved and the interactions between them. Such interactions have received little attention to date, but it can be shown that the actual impact of any variable on population trend is partly dependent upon the form and degree of its interaction with other variables, especially those operating contemporaneously (Morris 1965).

(*ii*) It could be used, together with experimentation, in the development of ecological principles. Computers could be operated to predict probable outcomes as parameters in the model are modified or removed, or new parameters added (e.g. Varley 1963). The accuracy of the predictions could be tested by field and laboratory experimentation. As physics has taught us, an exciting prospect for the theorist is that a possible consequence of model-building is the discovery of new principles.

(*iii*) It could be used by the economic entomologist in population management. The model could be used, with the aid of a computer, to optimize management procedures and tactics. Models complete enough for this purpose have yet to be devised, but Watt (1964a) has presented an example of a computer programme which illustrates the approach.

5.3 THE SUBJECT SPECIES, THE TIME, AND THE PLACE

5.31 The subject species

The insect to be studied is usually determined by economic considerations, and government agencies tend to support population work on pests rather than on innocuous species. This is reasonable because the sooner there are adequate models for important pests, the sooner can better management be implemented. It is suggested, however, that more attention should be given to innocuous species because, in confining so much of our work to pests, we are dealing mainly with atypical species and this introduces a bias in attempts to derive general population principles. Population studies on innocuous species assume additional value, both theoretical and practical, if man-made changes in the environment or accidental introductions to new environments raise such species to the status of pests. Models developed for *Operophtera brumata* in England (Varley 1963) were useful in planning the biological control of this species in eastern Canada, where its numbers reached tree-killing levels. Similarly, models for *Hyphantria cunea*, an innocuous defoliator in eastern Canada (Morris 1963), should be of use in central Europe and Japan, where it has become an introduced pest.

When a major pest is being studied it is often possible to count associated arthropod species on the same samples of foliage, etc., and to measure some of the independent variables that may affect them. Although the data are a 'by-product' obtained with little additional work, they can be very revealing. *Acleris variana* was one of several insects studied in this way during intensive studies on *Choristoneura fumiferana* and it is interesting to observe that the models for the former species, although crude and empirical, give a higher degree of predictability than the more detailed models for the latter. The life system of *A. variana* in the Green River area is more typical of Canadian forest insects and less difficult to model satisfactorily. This approach, when carried far enough, can also produce valuable data on community ecology. For example, it turned out that the two species of budworm were affected by some mutual parasites and predators and that the severe outbreak of *C. fumiferana* had repercussions on the population changes of *A. variana* (Miller 1966).

5.32 The time

With respect to time, our recommendation is for more time, better continuity, and a level of initial planning which recognizes the fact that useful descriptive models cannot be built by studying a natural population in one place for a few generations. Those who study confined laboratory populations, where most variables are held constant, are commendably reluctant to reach conclusions until the population has been studied through a considerable number of numerical oscillations. Yet those who study natural populations, where complex processes are acting and interacting, often discontinue the programme and publish analyses before the population has passed through even one oscillation or fluctuation.

For populations that oscillate in a more or less regular manner (e.g. see section 4.27), it is difficult to see how even a preliminary model can be developed without studying at least one complete cycle in numbers. Then the preliminary model should be tested through at least a second oscillation, for three reasons:

(*i*) to learn whether or not the course of events in the first oscillation appears typical of the population behaviour of the species;

(*ii*) to test the predictive powers of the model on fresh data not involved in its derivation, thereby losing no degrees of freedom; and

(*iii*) to refine the model with the aid of concomitant experimental work so that empirical parameters and functions can be changed to forms that are more satisfying biologically.

For populations that fluctuate irregularly, the preliminary model should similarly be based on a sequence of numerical increases and decreases long enough to define the pattern of fluctuations in time and space, then tested and refined on an additional sequence.

Once sampling techniques have been worked out and one or two oscillations or sequences have been followed, there is a considerable investment in a project and the decision to discontinue should not be made lightly. If the original investigators find themselves growing stale by following one population too long, it is often helpful if the project is turned over to new investigators who may bring fresh ideas and enthusiasm to it. *Diprion hercyniae* was studied during an outbreak in central New Brunswick and through subsequent fluctuations, involving some fifty generations (section 4.28). The work was about to be discontinued when a new and unexpected variable, namely the insecticide DDT, was added temporarily to the system. This is providing an exciting opportunity to test the model and to learn whether population numbers will return to the previous mean level of abundance after the severe disturbance caused by the insecticide.

5.33 The place

The corresponding suggestion with respect to place is for more places and for a more careful selection of places than has been usual in the past. One reason for studying a population simultaneously in different places (study areas) is simply to get replication so that adequate data are available for multi-variate analyses within a reasonable period of time. This is especially necessary for species that have only one generation a year. A more important object, however, is to replicate in very different places so that a model can be developed which includes not just the attributes of time that determine insect numbers but also the attributes of place, such as forest composition and age; meteorological differences associated with region, topography, or vegetation type; type of resource management being practised; differences in the complex of natural enemies or in their efficiency; and so on. As it is mainly the environmental influences associated with place that can be modified by man, it is not feasible to develop a model that will be generally useful for population management by studying a pest species in one place, however long the study is continued. Similarly, the only comprehensive theories of population dynamics (e.g. Nicholson

1933, 1958) are those which attempt to explain not only fluctuations in one place but differences in mean density from place to place; so that a model developed for one place will not be adequate for developing and testing population principles.

The criteria to be used in the selection of places are extremely important and will depend, of course, upon the hypotheses that have been formulated about the population behaviour of the subject species. This will be discussed later. For statistical reasons (see Mott 1963), the places selected should include not only modal values of the variables in question but also rather extreme values.

Some investigators seem to prefer natural 'unspoiled' environments for the conduct of population work, but Geier and Clark (1961) have pointed out:

The higher man's economic development of the environment the greater are the possibilities for protective management. Where land use is primitive and agriculture extensive, protective management is necessarily reduced to its simplest form by lack of financial resources and limitations of technique. . . . As the level of economic development rises, so do the potentialities of protective management. The more man has altered the environment, the greater are the chances that some new or old environmental factor could be modified critically to the disadvantage of a pest without adversely affecting crop production.

As one example, the development of more intensive forest management in Canada will afford better opportunities to create conditions unfavourable to outbreaks of *Choristoneura fumiferana*, providing that the pertinent variables associated with place have been correctly modelled (Morris, ed. 1963).

5.4 PRELIMINARY STUDIES AND HYPOTHESES

It is assumed that there is now a clearly defined objective, a subject species to work on, and a decision to follow the population through a sufficient number of generations and in sufficiently different places to produce and test models that will satisfy the objective. At this stage there is a natural urge to initiate measurements of population numbers and of all recognizable variables that may conceivably affect them. However, even if the resources should be available for such a programme, the history of science shows that rapid progress is seldom made by such a diffuse approach. Therefore the next step is to form some preliminary working hypotheses about the life system of the subject species. In the case of certain well-known pests, sufficiently good ecological information may already be available for this purpose; in other cases it may be necessary to carry out preliminary studies of various kinds.

It is difficult to discuss hypotheses separately from methods because the forming, discarding, modifying, and strengthening of hypotheses is a continuous process in population studies. However, the subject is sufficiently important to merit individual attention and the present section is concerned largely with preliminary working hypotheses – on the understanding that they will be subject to frequent revision as more detailed data accrue.

In the experimental sciences, a problem is chosen or a question asked and a working hypothesis to explain it is propounded and tested. Or better still, as proposed by Chamberlin (1965), alternative hypotheses are set up and experiments are devised which lead to the exclusion of incorrect explanations through an accumulative method of inductive inference (cf. 'strong inference', Platt 1964). The selection of multiple hypotheses avoids the sterility that often develops through mental fixation on one solution (Scheerer 1963), and is especially useful in experimental biology where there is sometimes more than one explanation of a phenomenon.

In the study of populations, good use can be made of experimentation, but generally we have to rely more on the direct analysis of observations made on events which occur naturally within life systems. By definition, all variables in the life system of a subject species have some effect on its population numbers. However, from recent studies on numerical change in natural populations, it appears that the effects of most variables will be inconsequential (section 5.1). The object, then, is to formulate hypotheses as to the key influences and processes determining the rate of population change and mean numbers, both in time and in space, and to test them by finding how much each suspected key influence contributes to the degree of population predictability. Two sorts of working hypotheses are necessary and will be discussed separately:

(*i*) What are the probable key influences determining the temporal population changes in one place and differences in abundance from place to place? Working hypotheses are selected by reviewing critically everything that is known about the species. In the case of important pests, there is often much relevant information in the literature. Historical data on the pattern of outbreaks in time and space, information on the type of area that consistently favours increase to high population numbers, data on natural enemies, and many other types of information are helpful in narrowing the choice of hypotheses. Examples are provided by Varley (1949) and Watt (1963b) for German forest pests, and by Miyashita (1963) for insect pests in Japan.

Equally useful information may be available for other species in countries which have annual surveys of insect abundance and natural control, based on the collecting and rearing of many species. For example, the distribution, relative abundance in different environments, pattern of oscillation, and parasitism of *Hyphantria cunea* over the past thirty years, as revealed by annual records of the Forest Insect and Disease Survey of Canada, were used along with other historical data in formulating working hypotheses about the key influences involved (Morris 1964).

If information of neither sort is available, it is necessary to conduct some broad-scale, necessarily superficial, studies on the abundance of the species, its ecological characteristics, and the environmental influences involved. The object is to learn at least enough to permit the selection of appropriate places for more intensive studies.

(*ii*) What is the probable mode of action of the suspected key influences? Is their intensity of action influenced by population density? What processes are likely to serve as stabilizing mechanisms? Hypotheses about mode of action and function are important if we are to measure the right attributes of the influences in question, measure them in the best way, and gain useful concepts about possible interactions and the form of the model which we hope to produce. Hypotheses of this sort should be based on a thorough knowledge of population theory (chapters III and IV), and on the form of models constructed to date for ecological processes (e.g. see Solomon 1964).

In the formulation of hypotheses about key influences and the ways in which they operate, we cannot assume that the average quality of the individuals of a subject species will remain constant (or almost so) during the course of numerical changes in a population. For example, Wellington (1965) has shown that the quality and quantity of food in the maternal generation of *Malacosoma pluviale* affect the amount of egg yolk and the quality and survival rate of the progeny. This is an influence on population quality that is transmissible, but not heritable in the usual genetic sense. There are also heritable changes in quality from generation to generation, associated with the fact that the natural selection pressures operating at high densities may be very different from those operating when numbers are low. Recent work by Ford (1964) and others demonstrates that changes in the nature of selection, operating often through polygenes, can vary population quality considerably during the course of numerical fluctuations. Consequently, in order to construct models that will explain variance arising from this source, it is necessary to be familiar with these possibilities when hypotheses are being formulated, and to remain alert throughout an investigation for possible changes in the reactions of individuals to environmental conditions.

5.5 MEASUREMENT OF VARIABLES

In the places selected for detailed studies, the first requirement is the development of a sampling technique to record population numbers. Population density, or its rate of change, will be the only dependent variable in the model that we hope to construct, and the lower the sampling error, the greater the chance to obtain good predictability of density through the independent variables. There are many points to be considered in developing sound techniques, selecting appropriate confidence limits, and reaching logical decisions as to the optimum allocation of sampling means. They have been reviewed elsewhere (Morris 1955, 1960) and need not be discussed here.

A study of the distribution of individuals in space is an integral part of the development of sampling methods. The frequency distributions for most insect populations tend to be 'over-dispersed'. They often approximate the negative binomial and variance can be stabilized to some extent, but not perfectly, by logarithmic transformations. The negative binomial distribution, however, can be approximated by a number of different explanatory models, some with two parameters and some with more than two. As Waters (1962) has pointed out, it is affected both by statistical elements, such as the size of the sample unit, and by biological elements, such as the oviposition and dispersal habits of the species and population density. More basic research on insect distribution than has been done to date, aimed at the development of explanatory models, might well contribute useful biological information on the species and might lead to new and more efficient sampling designs. Shiyomi and Nakamura (1964) describe an interesting approach in which individuals are stocked on plants in a known distribution pattern and changes in the form of the distribution are measured as the insects multiply and disperse.

The dispersal and migration habits of the subject species should also be examined at this stage of an investigation. Dispersal influences the distribution pattern and hence the size and location of sample units and of the selected study plots. Also, if displacement is found to be a primary event of considerable importance (e.g. as in *Phaulacridium vittatum*, see section 4.22), early recognition of this fact can lead to appropriate developments in the design of the study. The movements of insects can be studied in various ways (Southwood 1966), e.g. by capturing, marking, and releasing individuals, and then recapturing some of them. Mathematical models based on the assumption of random displacement can be used in the analysis of movements (e.g. Skellam 1951; Gilmour, Waterhouse and McIntyre 1946); they can be elaborated with the aid of computers by imposing restrictions on the initial postulates of randomness (Saila and Shappy 1963).

Finally, a very practical aspect of the investigation of population density in which early exploratory work may pay large dividends later is the development of mechanical or chemical techniques for separating insects from foliage or other substrates. The factor that most often limits the amount of sampling that can be done by existing methods is the number of man-hours of tedious and often error-prone labour involved in 'hand-picking' the samples.

We have stressed the need for adequate measurement of the dependent variable, population density, but measurement of the independent variables that affect density is no less important. For example, after very intensive studies on *Choristoneura fumiferana*, it surprised all of the investigators (Morris, ed. 1963) to learn that the principal factor limiting the value of predictive models was failure to measure all the pertinent independent variables, or to measure them in the best way. The measurement of independent variables is too specific to the individual species and to the hypotheses that have been formed about the functioning of its life system to be discussed here in general terms. It should, however, be recognized at the beginning of an investigation that there are two different ways of handling independent variables and that this will influence the form of the models that are developed. One way is to measure the independent variable itself, say temperature, to learn by regression analysis whether it appears to influence population trend, and to find by process studies (section 5.8) the causal pathways through which it affects survival or reproduction. The other way is to measure the *effect* of the variable on the population, for example the percentage of individuals parasitized or the extent of mortality. Mathematically, it is better to measure the variable itself (Watt 1961), but in practice it is sometimes easier to measure mortality. For example, it is easier to measure the degree of parasitism than to measure the population of adult parasites available to attack the host population, although this tells us less about the functional response of the adult parasites to host density. Both methods, or combinations of them, are commonly used, and the direct measurement of total mortality during one age interval is often used to estimate the population density at the beginning of the following age interval.

The development of field techniques for measuring both the dependent and independent variables, and the frequency with which the measurements are taken, are influenced by the type of mathematical model which is going to be produced. In general terms, the three possibilities are:

(*i*) models based on life-table studies, in which it is desired to model the change in population density for each developmental stage or age interval of the insect as a function of the independent variables operating during each age interval;

(*ii*) models in which the change in population from generation to generation, measured at one specific point in the life cycle, is modelled as a function of the key variables determining numerical change, irrespective of the particular stage or stages affected by them; and

(*iii*) models in which the main objective is to describe ecological processes, that is, the modes of operation of particular independent variables.

There are recent examples of all three types in the literature and, in the following three sections, it is proposed only to mention their relative advantages and disadvantages. Although the models are different, at least in mathematical form, it should be recognized that the three approaches are complementary as far as the field methods of study are concerned, with no sharp dividing lines between them. Where a choice is available, i.e. where the form of the model is not dictated by the difficulties inherent in studying a particular population, age-specific studies should generally precede or accompany the development of models based on one specific point in the life cycle, and in either case concomitant process studies are required. This will become clear in the following sections.

5.6 'LIFE-TABLE' STUDIES

Age-specific studies leading to the construction of life tables require the measurement of population density at a number of points in the life cycle during each generation of the insect. This permits the calculation of age-specific mortality or survival rates for each developmental stage or age interval. If only population densities are listed, as in the demographic life tables, an adequate series of tables will reveal, through regression methods (Morris, ed. 1963, section 7) or even graphical methods (Varley and Gradwell 1960), how much each age interval contributes to variation in total generation survival, and hence to changes in population trend.

In developing life tables for insect populations, however, the studies generally include data on the independent variables operating in each age interval, the mortality that they contribute, and additional data on both primary and secondary ecological events (Morris and Miller 1954). Thus life-table data permit the construction of sub-models for each age interval showing how population change is determined during each age interval, and these sub-models may be combined, sequentially, into a complete model for the whole generation (Watt 1961, Morris, ed. 1963).

The main advantage in developing life tables of one form or another is that the 'comprehensive' approach involved provides more complete data

THE ECOLOGY OF INSECT POPULATIONS

on population dynamics than do other approaches and affords greater scope for detailed modelling. Life tables are highly desirable for important economic pests, where resources are available to permit the construction of an adequate series of them. The age-specific data accrued in this way include the effects of both the key variables and other variables, and are ideal for use in population management. The models produced would permit us to test the consequences of manipulating variables that operate in different age intervals, and to attempt to reduce environmental favou-ableness at different points in the life cycle.

Where sustained resources are not available for long-term studies of this sort, or where comprehensive age-specific studies are either unnecessary or difficult to carry out with existing techniques, it is still desirable to collect as much age-specific data as possible for a few generations at least. In this case, the purpose is mainly to tabulate and analyze ecological events in the life system of the species, and to detect critical age intervals and key influences that deserve detailed study. In fact, if the historical data on the species or the preliminary survey studies (section 5.4) have not led to the formulation of satisfactory hypotheses, preliminary age-specific data of this sort are essential. In this situation, as contrasted to that described above, the age-specific methods are used on a short-term basis as a step towards the use of more abbreviated methods, rather than for the construction of detailed age-specific models.

A major difficulty in the 'comprehensive' approach that yields life tables is the sampling problem. It sometimes takes several years just to develop satisfactory techniques, especially where it is desired to sample all develop-mental stages on a comparable basis, and where different stages of the same insect occur in different sampling universes such as the foliage of trees and in the ground (e.g. Embree 1965). It is no easy task to develop comprehensive sampling techniques even for species which occur in high population numbers. Their development is much more difficult (and often out of the question with the means available) in the case of species which remain at low levels of abundance for much or all of the time. Ives (1964) has reviewed work on the development of life tables for a number of forest, orchard, and agricultural pests and drawn attention to the problems that are most frequently encountered.

Where it is desired to sample in many different places, precise pheno-logical timing also presents a problem. The survivorship curve for one generation of an insect slopes downwards, but more steeply in some parts than in others. When our aim is to produce life tables, we arbitrarily divide the survivorship curve into a number of sections and try to get population 'fixes' for sections that are relatively flat. Small errors in timing which result in sampling during periods of rapid numerical decrease can be disastrous.

It is not surprising that the most successful application of life table studies to date has been in latitudes where most insect species have only one generation per year, with relatively little overlapping of developmental stages. Widely overlapping stages and generations, giving rise to the simultaneous occurrence of recruitment, death, and dispersal in the subject species make the problem more difficult. However, considerable progress has been made in devising mathematical procedures for analyzing numerical trends in such species (e.g. Richards *et al.* 1960, Dempster 1961, Hughes 1963).

5.7 'KEY-FACTOR' STUDIES

'Key-factor' methods require a measurement of population density at only one point in the life cycle, the same point being used in successive generations. The resulting models are designed to predict population density from generation to generation by means of the key influences which largely determine population trend. This approach was proposed (Morris 1959, 1963) because it was found to provide good predictability in the analysis of certain long-term population data in which there was only one density measurement per generation, and because the analysis of life-table data revealed the existence of key intervals and key influences, so that the study of all age intervals seemed unnecessary for some species.

The advantages are that less sampling is required than for the preparation of life tables, and the sampling needed can be confined to a stable section of the survivorship curve where rapid methods are suitable and where exact phenological timing is not crucial. The analysis is much simpler than that of life-table data, but it permits separation of the effects of density-independent and density-related processes, and provides a method for modelling differences in mean density from place to place (Morris 1963). However, unless preliminary life-table work or adequate historical data have provided strong hypotheses as to the key influences in a life system, this approach is something of a gamble.

Except for the reduced sampling, the actual field methods do not differ very much from those of life-table studies which represent the other extreme in terms of scope. There are many examples of studies in which the approach is intermediate in scope between the two. Both approaches, or approaches intermediate between them, require work on ecological processes. Without such work, we cannot hope to understand the functioning of life systems.

5.8 THE STUDY OF ECOLOGICAL PROCESSES

Under this heading are included all studies directed towards the elucidation of particular processes, such as intraspecific competition or predation, as well as studies on the mode of action or effect of abiotic influences such as temperature or rainfall. Ideally, process studies should yield mathematical formulations in the form of sub-models which should fit into and refine an overall mathematical model describing the functioning of a life system. The results obtained in the study of particular processes must be integrated in some way, preferably mathematically, because ascertaining the existence and mode of action of a process in the laboratory, or even in a natural population, does not demonstrate its role in the fluctuation and stabilization of population numbers. For this an overall model is required, showing how all key influences contribute to the variance. When discussing the effects of social and endocrine factors on the regulation of mammalian populations, Christian and Davis (1964) wrote:

> Thus, proof or disproof of the hypothesis reduces to the problem of finding how frequently and under what circumstances the behavioral mechanism does operate. . . . The problem, then, is not that of proving the existence of a behavioral-physiological mechanism but that of proving the importance of such a mechanism in the regulation of populations.

To give a few examples of process studies: the work of Nicholson on intraspecific competition (section 4.25) and that of Park (1955 *et seq.*) on interspecific competition are well known; as also are various investigations leading to the development of models in population genetics. Holling's general studies (1959, 1966) on predation have produced both simple models that can easily be used with field data, and complex explanatory models with many parameters. The latter models, when programmed for a computer, can be used to calculate the properties of an 'ideal' predator, and are therefore very instructive. There are many laboratory studies of host-parasite interactions, designed to learn whether numerical oscillations are inherent in a system and what conditions are required to stabilize numbers (e.g. section 4.26). Unfortunately, the results have not been modelled mathematically and field workers (e.g. Varley 1947 and Miller 1960, respectively) are still using either the purely deductive model of Nicholson and Bailey (1935) or the deductive-inductive model of Watt (1959).

Process work on abiotic influences and on the quality of such resources as food has lagged far behind and no useful models are available. A promising approach is the development of life tables under laboratory conditions where such influences as temperature, humidity, and food quality are controlled over a wide range of favourable and unfavourable values. In this work, the continuation of rearing through a second or third generation is necessary because the effects of these influences are not necessarily immediate, but may manifest themselves during subsequent developmental stages of the insect or even during subsequent generations (section 5.4). It is desirable to study physical influences and food quality together because of the high degree of interaction between them. The attempt to construct detailed population models from field data on *Choristoneura fumiferana* would have benefited greatly if laboratory models had been available to show the effects of food quality, temperature, etc., on survival.

Process studies have been undertaken not only in the laboratory but also under semi-natural and natural conditions. For example, Burnett (1956) carried process studies to a semi-natural environment in his study of host-parasite interactions in large cages on a lawn. Wellington (1960) carried them to the field in his study of changes in population quality in relation to natural population changes. Clark (section 4.29) studied in the field the mode of action of many processes affecting the numbers of *Cardiaspina albitextura*, with particular attention to density relationships.

When many influences are being studied, a great deal of judgment is required in deciding how far to go with the analysis of processes. The investigator may find himself with an interesting host-parasite interaction that calls for experimental work, a need for laboratory models covering physical factors and food, and an interesting sequence of events in the field which appear to be due to genetic variability and require inbreeding and crossbreeding experiments for elucidation. Under these conditions, process studies can only be carried to the point where predictability is satisfactory, and cause and effect are demonstrated.

The advantage of process studies is that they can demonstrate the biological pathways through which influences affect population density. Spurious relationships can be obtained in the multi-variate analysis of field data, especially in the case of meteorological variables where the investigator has so many choices (McFadden 1963). Experimental work on the ecological processes involved not only discloses spurious relationships, but shows also how valid relationships can be modelled efficiently. It reveals the pertinent attributes of the independent variables, and the way in which they should be measured to provide maximum predictability.

There is a great advantage in having life-table or key-influence studies and process work develop together, because each gives direction to the other. This is, in fact, the soundest way to proceed in population studies. The observational field work reveals key influences, probably including some new ones not covered by preliminary hypotheses, and provides the final test of relationships and functions derived from field and laboratory experimentation; the research on ecological processes reveals causal pathways, discloses spurious relationships, and suggests forms of modelling observational data that are biologically satisfying. If the hypotheses suggested by historical data and/or extensive surveys are supported by a large percentage of explained variance in a mathematical model and a high degree of population predictability, and if this again is supported by process studies on cause and effect, we are getting about as close as we can to proof in population dynamics.

5.9 MODELLING

Although modelling is listed here as the final step, it should not be left until all of the field and laboratory work is completed. As suggested earlier, it is advantageous to construct preliminary models as soon as a reasonable amount of information has accumulated. In fact, the possible form of the model should receive attention during the period when preliminary hypotheses are formulated and field techniques are selected or developed.

The construction of mathematical models for insect life systems is in its infancy. Therefore, although the possibilities offered by modelling are obvious, it would be premature at this time to attempt a critical assessment of the value of the models which have been used. The few models published to date, although preliminary and crude, have demonstrated that a high degree of population predictability is possible. Various weaknesses which they contain, both mathematically and otherwise, have been pointed out both by their originators and by others, and numerous suggestions have been made which should lead to vast improvements in the future. For example, the team of investigators who developed age-specific models for outbreaking populations of *Choristoneura fumiferana* devoted much time to critical assessment of their efforts and to suggestions for improving both the design of their work and future attempts at modelling (Morris, ed. 1963, sections 16, 17, 18, 40). And subsequently Watt (1964b) pointed out a source of mathematical bias in one phase of the analyses. Similarly, key-influence methods have been critically reviewed by Varley and Gradwell (1963, 1965) and Solomon (1964). Careful examination both of the models published to date and of the assessments which have been made of them should be helpful to beginners and other workers who decide to attempt mathematical synthesis.

Approaches to modelling have been covered in a series of papers by Watt (e.g. see Bibliography) which will also provide valuable leads to the literature on this subject. The techniques developed for modelling and computer programming, both in entomology and in other fields of science, are far in advance of the quality and quantity of entomological data available. Therefore, until more field projects are completed and the results are modelled, we will not know what formulations are the most appropriate for describing life systems.

How complex and detailed should models become? In the order of complexity we can go from empirical predictive equations (which can sometimes be very simple if predictability rather than interpretation is the main object), to descriptive models incorporating major causal pathways, and finally to comprehensive models of great complexity. It is difficult to draw dividing lines between these different stages of what is really a continuum. Initial field models will be empirical and simple; they can be refined progressively to whatever extent is necessary.

The criterion for deciding how far to go is usefulness in describing, interpreting, and applying the results of a study. Although mathematical models can only approximate to reality, they yield more useful summarizations of quantitative studies than any other form of synthesis.

CHAPTER VI

The ecology of pest control

In chapter IV, we described the determination of insect abundance as the functioning of life systems in which containing or adjusting mechanisms, conditioned in their effects, implement the stabilization of population numbers. In science, the usefulness of a concept is measured ultimately by its contribution towards solving actual problems. The most pressing problem in entomology is that of pest control. Despite notable successes, man's performance in this field has not been nearly as impressive as his achievements in other fields of applied science. One reason for the slow progress of pest control is that the issues involved do not appear to have been grasped fully. A discussion of the subject based on the concept of life system may help to clarify ideas, while putting the usefulness of our approach to a practical test.

6.1 THE NATURE AND ORIGIN OF PEST STATUS IN INSECTS

Pests are species whose existence conflicts with people's profit, convenience, or welfare. The injuriousness of pests varies according to the nature of their damage, to the degree of man's sensitiveness to their depredations, and to the numbers in which they occur. Because of man's characteristics as a species, the diversity of his requirements, and the extent of his enterprises, he competes necessarily with a great array of life forms for the resources which he draws from nature. Most of the organisms which are capable of interfering adversely with man are not serious pests. The damage caused by them remains 'negligible', meaning that it would be uneconomic under the prevailing conditions to prevent or reduce that damage. Such species are 'potential' pests. Our main concern, however, is with the fewer, more serious, or 'actual' pests, i.e. with the species whose injuriousness is established and whose control is either a social or an economic necessity.

In the literature, it has been almost customary to consider that pest problems originate in the way envisaged by Uvarov (1964):

In most cases, [development] results in a drastic disturbance of the environment of the local insect fauna and in consequent changes in its composition. The essential practical feature of these changes is a radical reconstruction of the injurious fauna of useful plants. . . . The results of neglecting entomological aspects of development are clear in the older countries, where permanent problems of defensive pest control have been created and perennially require an expenditure on a vast and ever-increasing scale.

Clearly such statements imply, firstly, that pest problems are most often man-made, and result from artificially-induced upsets in 'natural balances' (see also Elton 1958, p. 145 ss.); secondly, that the disadvantageous effects of man's activities on insect populations could be recognized in advance if enough attention were paid to 'entomological aspects of development'; and thirdly, that pest problems could be avoided by devising suitable preventive measures.

These inferences need to be examined carefully for their relevance to pest control. If they are both correct and relevant, the most effective approach to pest control should be not only to avoid the creation of new pest situations, but also to try to remedy those situations from which present-day pest problems have arisen. However, consideration shows that, although they contain factual elements, the premises of Uvarov and Elton are too limited to serve as a basis for discussion in the present context.

Actually, pest status appears to originate in four ways: by the entry of species into previously uncolonized regions; by changes in the characteristics of species that did not previously compete or otherwise interact directly with man; by changes in man's activities or habits, which make him sensitive to the existence of species to which he was previously indifferent; and by increases in the abundance of species whose interactions with man were previously negligible because of the low numbers in which they occurred. Such increases happen for one of three reasons, i.e. a lasting increase in the supply of a limiting resource, a lasting decrease in the frequency or severity of repressive interactions that previously prevented the species from exploiting fully the resources of their environments, and the simultaneous occurrence of both of these changes.

Typical examples can be cited in each case – e.g., for the first, the European spruce sawfly which became a pest in Canada by 1930 (section 4.28). The second way is well illustrated by the sudden appearance in Japan of an unknown species of cynipid wasp which formed conspicuous galls on chestnut trees, and was eventually described as *Dryocosmus kuriphilus* by Yasumatsu. According to Nakamura *et al.* (1964), this parthenogenetic species was first noticed in 1941 in the Okayama Prefecture of southwestern Honshu, whence it has spread over the whole south-western half of Japan, causing severe damage in 1950–55 (Miyashita *et al.* 1965). The wasp is regarded as a recently-evolved species restricted so far to Japan.

In the third case, species can become pests without undergoing any change in their characteristics and usual abundance. Increased injuriousness follows man's need for greater returns or for new resources. New problems arise constantly in this way because higher demands are placed on the quality of natural products, because technological progress creates new possibilities of conflict with previously negligible species, or because changing social and economic outlooks make even relatively harmless insects increasingly objectionable. For example, some municipal authorities find it necessary to undertake the spraying of shade trees to avoid the soiling of cars by the excreta of aphids and other honeydew-producing insects.

The fourth way pertains to species gaining pest status after great and lasting increases in abundance due to favourable environmental changes. Thus, the recent development of continuous intensive crop production on the lower reaches of the Ord River of north-western Australia in the early 1960's entailed very severe attacks on cotton by *Prodenia litura*, because populations of the cutworm were able to increase, without seasonal checks, on the greatly increased supplies of food available at all times in and around the irrigated areas. Similar situations result from the disappearance or diminution of environmental influences that normally contain potential pests at commercially tolerable levels of abundance. For instance, Collyer (1953a, b) has shown that the rise of phytophagous mites to the status of major pests of orchards in Britain during the 1940's and early 1950's was caused primarily by the decrease in predator numbers which followed the extensive use of certain broad-spectrum insecticides. Finally, the Australian leafroller *Epiphyas postvittana* provides an example of an insect acquiring pest status under the combined influence of an increased food supply and of a decrease in the effectiveness of its natural enemies. The increase in food supply occurred with the introduction of various deciduous plants, notably fruit trees, into the environment of the moth. These provide an abundance of young, favourable foliage in summer, i.e. at a time when populations formerly reached minimum numbers on the ageing foliage of their native hosts. Now, heavy infestations of the leafroller tend to build up on fruit trees throughout the summer months. Although commercial damage to crops sometimes ensues, severe injury is usually prevented by an effective array of natural enemies. When predators and parasites are destroyed by insecticides which fail to suppress the moth, *E. postvittana* can cause losses so severe as to be one of the most harmful pests of apple orchards in south-eastern Australia (Geier 1965).

The examples cited were chosen for their simplicity and most of them probably represent exceptional instances rather than norms. Many pest situations eventuate under more complex conditions, involving influences of many kinds, e.g. as shown by the events surrounding the appearance and development of the pathological condition which causes the early degeneration and death of cacao trees in West Africa. The facts of this case are well-documented, thanks mainly to the outstanding work of scientists associated with the West African Cocoa Research Institute.

The cacao plant, *Theobroma cacao* (Sterculaceae), is an under-storey tree of the American rainforest, which is grown for bean crops in areas with a mean rainfall exceeding forty-five inches, and mean annual temperatures of 70–75°F (21–24°C) or higher. Until about 1920, all cacao was produced under conditions closely resembling those of natural forest. Later attempts at more intensive cropping remained largely unsuccessful until the 1950's when means became available to overcome the consequences of pest attacks

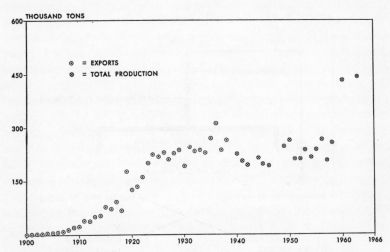

FIGURE 38. Yearly output of cacao in Ghana. (Data for 1900–38 from Hill (1956), data for 1940–46 from F.A.O. *Yearbook of Food and Agricultural Statistics*, Vol. 1, data for 1949–64 from *ibid*. Vols. V–XI and from F.A.O. *Production Yearbook*, Vols. 12–18.)

resulting from the removal of natural shade. Although yields could be increased substantially in open plantations, this was found to impose conditions of management which, as a rule, could not be met on peasant farms. Agronomic experimentation has served to demonstrate the delicate balance between the performance of the cacao plant and environmental variables such as soil type and plant association, which ultimately governs the productivity of extensive plantations (see e.g. Cunningham 1959).

Cacao was introduced to the West African mainland in 1879 and, in the short period of thirty-five years, production there caught up with that of Trinidad, one of the principal exporting areas at the time (Cunningham 1959). This development, which is illustrated in figure 38 for Ghana, was attended by an increasing incidence of pests and diseases which became critical in the 1930's and strongly depressed production during the following decades. Two agents were held primarily responsible for the crisis: a virus causing the disease known as 'swollen shoot' (SSVD); and mirid bugs (capsids) causing defoliation and loss of tree condition, often aggravated by fungus infection. Although both agents could act independently, it was found that their effects usually combined to produce compound and far-reaching sequels, and, therefore, that they were best

AETIOLOGY, PROGRESS AND SEQUELS OF CACAO DEGENERATION (TINSLEY 1964)

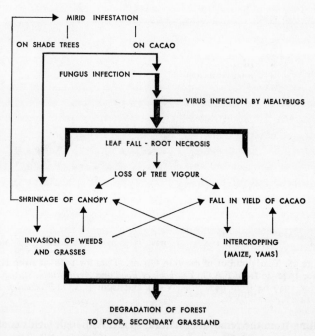

FIGURE 39. Development of cacao degeneration, Nigeria.

regarded as co-acting elements in a single complex process which determined the premature degeneration of cacao plants (e.g. Kay *et al.* 1961). The initiation, progress, and outcome of unchecked degeneration at Nigerian cacao farms are shown diagrammatically in figure 39 (see Tinsley 1964). In 1936–37, 81,000 trees were destroyed deliberately in Ghana in an attempt to stamp out the disease. This method was revived in 1945, resulting in the destruction of sixty-three million cacao plants during the next ten years (Hammond 1957).

The degenerative situation is believed to have evolved in three successive, overlapping stages:

(*i*) A *preliminary stage* from the time of introduction of cacao through to the 1930's, characterized by a growing sensitiveness of the industry to loss of yield and an increasing susceptibility of the trees due to the extension and ageing of cacao plantings, a cryptic spread of SSVD, and a progressive incidence of attacks by mirids.

(*ii*) A *primary crisis*, extending from the 1930's into the 1940's in Ghana, which was precipitated by an acute incidence of SSVD, aggravated by further consequences of prolonged extensive farming. This phase was marked by rapid and widespread destruction attributed to the unchecked dissemination of virulent strains of SSV. From 1939 to 1944, 74% of trees planted between 1904 and 1914, and 43% of trees planted between 1915 and 1922, were destroyed by virus in Eastern Province (Posnette 1945).

(*iii*) An *endemic stage*, originating in the late 1940's and continuing in the 1960's, which was characterized by a trend towards stabilization of the degenerative situation following: the abandonment of devastated plantations, and ensuing changes in vegetation; a reduced incidence of virulent strains of SSV due to a variety of causes; and finally increasingly effective measures of sanitation and control. Under those conditions, mirids emerged as a disturbing agent of primary importance, whose action could upset the precarious balance established between cacao and SSVD (see e.g. Longworth 1963).

The viruses affecting cacao fall into three distinct groups, each comprising a number of related strains (Thresh and Tinsley 1959). All appear to have existed in West African plants before the introduction of cacao. Of them, the SSV complex is by far the most damaging. This virus complex has produced numerous isolates of varying intrinsic virulence, whose effects on cacao can vary according to the age, vigour, etc., of infected trees. On the whole, infections of SSVD are most serious in old trees because those are least capable of regeneration. Infected cacao is the most efficient source of virus in the cacao-forest association.

Several mealybugs can transmit SSV, the most important being *Planacoccoides njalensis*, a polyphagous native species whose preponderant effectiveness as a vector is determined by its feeding habits and its abundance on cacao. *P. njalensis* is attended by ants and, according to Strickland's (1951) findings, its abundance is dependent mainly upon that of the attendant ants. Populations of *P. njalensis* tend to be stabilized at densities which maximize disease transmission (see Entwistle 1958). The rate at which SSV can spread is limited by the ability of its vectors to transfer to new plants in the short time that they remain viruliferent. Experience has shown that SSV spreads slowly under natural conditions, and can readily be made to spread even more slowly if the dissemination of infective material by people is controlled (Thresh 1958).

African mirids were recognized as potential pests of cacao at the turn of the century, and their incidence caused increasing concern during the development of the degenerative situation (Taylor 1954). The most injurious species are *Sahlbergella singularis* and *Distantiella theobroma* whose attacks were limited originally to mature trees and to young seedlings, respectively (Cotterel 1926). According to Taylor (*loc. cit.*), a change occurred in their feeding habits during the 1940's, resulting in the indiscriminate infestation of cacao of all ages by both species. The mirids feed on the vegetative parts of exposed, or inadequately shaded cacao trees which they can damage in two ways. Their primary effect results from feeding punctures and, more importantly, from the injection of histolytic saliva into injured tissue (Goodchild 1952). Whereas this is often enough to kill green shoots, hardened stems usually recover unless the wounds are invaded by the fungus *Calonectria rigidiusculus*. On unthrifty cacao, the fungus can spread from the site of invasion and destroy branches. Thus, the consequences of mirid attacks on cacao can vary from a 'slight temporary setback to death of the trees affected' (Taylor *loc. cit.*).

Each year, mirid numbers increase to a seasonal peak, following the growth pattern of the host plants. The processes which stabilize population numbers are insufficiently known, but the indications are that mirid densities might be limited both by competition for food and, more importantly, by competition for preferred oviposition sites in cacao pods and in the bark of sucker shoots (Williams 1953, Taylor *loc. cit.*).

Considering the West African cacao problem in its broadest terms, one observes that it becomes serious when and where the impact of degenerative agents exceeds the capacity of cacao for natural regeneration. The degenerative situation has its origin in the temporal and spatial coincidence of six independent elements: man's use of cacao; polyphagous mirids; a ubiquitous fungus; polyphagous mealybugs; plant viruses capable of infecting cacao; and the susceptibility of cacao under cropping conditions.

The degenerative situation was made conspicuous by its sociological repercussions (Voelker 1945). Because man is dependent for existence on a complex system of goods production, such repercussions can be so far-reaching as to be ultimately imponderable. They must therefore be considered in their more immediate aspects, such as changes induced in the economy of cacao farming or, more simply, in terms of crop yields. Using the latter criterion, the *seriousness* of the degenerative situation was found

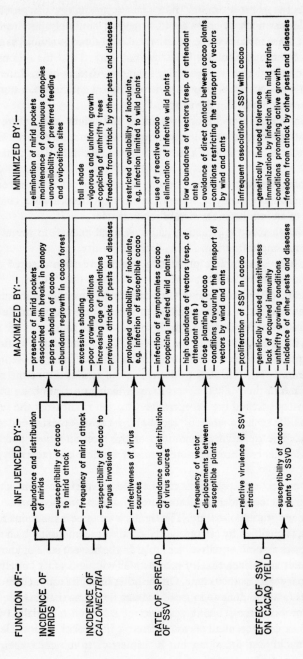

FIGURE 40. Operational analysis of cacao degeneration in West Africa.

to vary between broad limits. In certain circumstances, the problem was negligible inasmuch as crops could be grown profitably despite its existence. In other instances, the situation could become so serious as to cause the loss of entire plantations. Investigations showed that the seriousness of the economic repercussions resulting from the existence of the degenerative situation was dependent upon a series of topical conditions, a number of which are enumerated in figure 40.

Certain general conclusions regarding the origin and nature of the degenerative situation can be drawn from these facts. Firstly, the situation is seen to be the outcome of a network of natural events which man could not:

anticipate, because what might appear in hindsight to be a consistent causal chain is actually no more than the highly improbable, cumulative result of an infinite succession of random steps;

recognize, before the situation had developed enough to reveal its full economic implications and biological complexity; or

avoid, because complete prevention could have been ensured only by keeping cacao out of West Africa.

Secondly, of the conditions that contribute towards establishing the degenerative situation as an economic problem, some pertain to the specific characteristics of the six life forms involved. Those conditions are absolute and provide the 'constants' of the problem. Their economic significance as such is qualified, however, by conditions of another kind, whose nature is circumstantial. The latter act to determine the seriousness of the problem in space and in time. Their effects in maximizing or minimizing the economic consequences of the degenerative situation result from the functioning of the life systems whereby cacao and its pests co-exist under man's influence. The qualifying conditions of this pest situation, and of pest problems in general, are therefore naturally variable and recurrent in their effects.

To sum up, pest problems can be said to originate from situations created by the coincidence of absolute conditions entailed in the general evolutionary process of nature. The significance of pest situations for man, however, is qualified by circumstantial conditions, amongst which ecological processes assume a predominant role. In the present state of knowledge, man cannot steer evolutionary processes at will, and must largely accept evolutionary facts as they come. On the other hand, he can modify ecological events (and has done so in an ad hoc way for a long time).

It follows that the scope of pest control is limited essentially by man's ability to exploit potentially favourable ecological relationships. He cannot hope to avoid pest situations, but he can strive to minimize their repercussions on his economy by manipulating the life systems of the species concerned. For purposes of control, pest situations are therefore best conceived as problems whose solutions should, ideally, stabilize the numbers of the life forms involved – at levels entailing the least possible disadvantages under the prevailing economic conditions. This approach to pest control was termed 'protective management'* by Geier and Clark (1961).

6.2 THE APPRECIATION OF PEST SITUATIONS

Action to control pests is, of course, motivated by the will to improve an unsatisfactory situation. This motivation implies that, firstly, a situation is found to compare unfavourably with an ideal or factual standard; secondly, the elements which contribute towards making a situation unsatisfactory are known; thirdly, the changes needed for improvement are defined; and, finally, means are available to effect those changes.

The appreciation of a pest situation can be regarded as a dynamic process operating in a recurrent sequence of three phases within which information is acquired, integrated, utilized, and fed back:

(1) Recognition of a pest situation; identification of participating organisms; definition of the relevant characteristics and attributes of the species involved.

(2) Practical assessment and functional analysis of the pest situation.

(3) Definition of aims; choice of control strategy.

Phase 1 – As a rule, problems involving insect pests cannot be recognized

---

* Some authors have come to attach a somewhat similar meaning to the expression 'integrated, or harmonious, control' (e.g. De Fluiter 1962). In our opinion, this usage is confusing inasmuch as the term 'integrated control' was originally adopted to designate practical attempts either at reducing the destructive effects of current 'chemical control' on an existing fauna of beneficial species (e.g. Pickett 1961), or at combining the action of conventional insecticides with that of introduced inimical organisms for the control of a given pest, or group of pests (e.g. De Bach and Landi 1961). Consequently, 'integrated control' cannot be taken to define a conceptual approach to pest problems, but only to describe an empirical method whereby techniques are sought in specific instances to maximize the restrictive influences which synthetic and natural agencies can exert together on the actual injuriousness of pests (e.g. Bartlett 1964). In most published accounts of successful instances (e.g. Stern *et al.* 1959), 'integrated control' has resulted in a situation typical of procedure 2 discussed below (see section 6.3 and figure 43).

The popularity of the term 'integrated control' with the European authors who have been instrumental in expanding its meaning is probably due to the easy rendering of the word 'integrated' in the other Western languages. 'Protective pest management' cannot be translated as literally and, for instance, would need to be expressed by phrases like 'prévention de la nuisibilité des espèces parasitaires' or 'prévention antiparasitaire' in French, and 'vorbeugender Wehrbetrieb gegen Insektenschäden' in German.

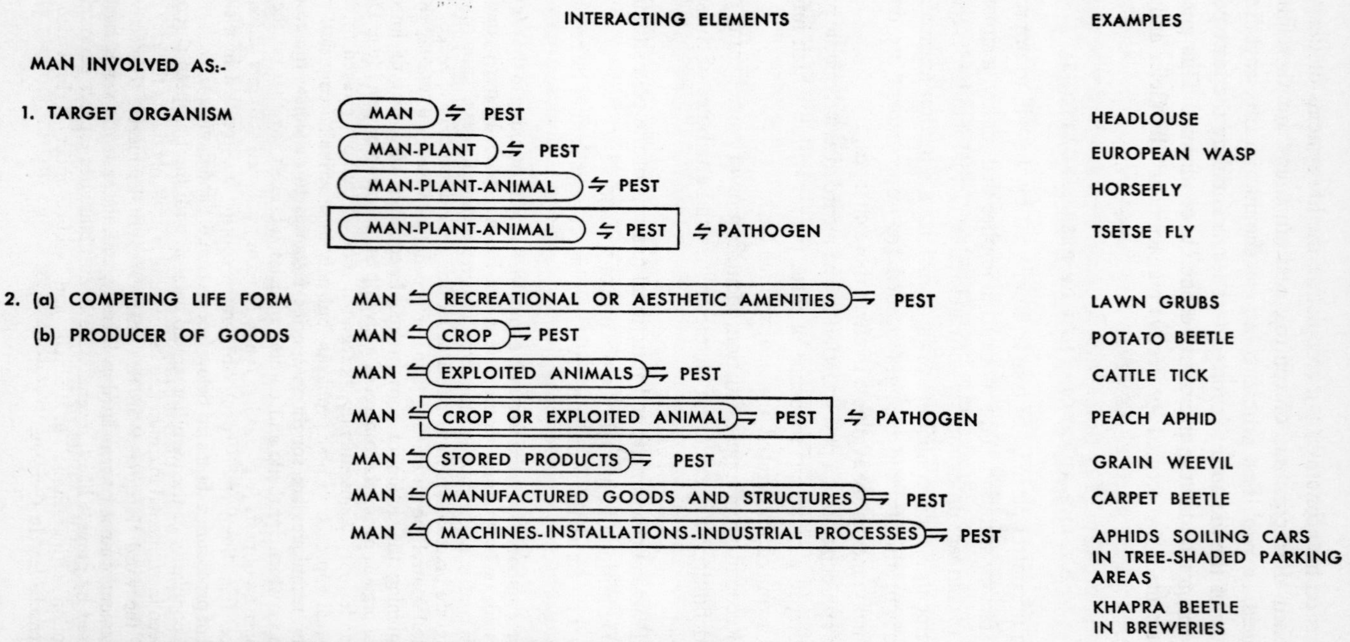

INTERACTING ELEMENTS   EXAMPLES

MAN INVOLVED AS:-

1. TARGET ORGANISM

   MAN ⇆ PEST   HEADLOUSE

   MAN-PLANT ⇆ PEST   EUROPEAN WASP

   MAN-PLANT-ANIMAL ⇆ PEST   HORSEFLY

   MAN-PLANT-ANIMAL ⇆ PEST ⇆ PATHOGEN   TSETSE FLY

2. (a) COMPETING LIFE FORM

   MAN ⇆ RECREATIONAL OR AESTHETIC AMENITIES ⇆ PEST   LAWN GRUBS

   (b) PRODUCER OF GOODS

   MAN ⇆ CROP ⇆ PEST   POTATO BEETLE

   MAN ⇆ EXPLOITED ANIMALS ⇆ PEST   CATTLE TICK

   MAN ⇆ CROP OR EXPLOITED ANIMAL ⇆ PEST ⇆ PATHOGEN   PEACH APHID

   MAN ⇆ STORED PRODUCTS ⇆ PEST   GRAIN WEEVIL

   MAN ⇆ MANUFACTURED GOODS AND STRUCTURES ⇆ PEST   CARPET BEETLE

   MAN ⇆ MACHINES-INSTALLATIONS-INDUSTRIAL PROCESSES ⇆ PEST   APHIDS SOILING CARS
                                                             IN TREE-SHADED PARKING
                                                             AREAS

                                                        KHAPRA BEETLE
                                                        IN BREWERIES

FIGURE 4I. Synopsis of inimical interactions between man and insects.

unless their manifestations are conspicuous to the layman. They represent essentially an interaction between man and other organisms – at least one of which is a pest. Pest problems can involve man in two ways, i.e. as a target organism exposed to direct attack, or, less directly, as a competitor for space, food, shelter, and other resources, as shown diagrammatically in figure 41.

Phase 1 is concerned with the facts determined by evolution that underlie a pest problem. The first aim is to relate recorded injury to causative organism(s), as illustrated by Kho and Braak's (1956) work in which serious reduction in the yield and viability of carrot seed in the Netherlands was traced back to early infestation by relatively low numbers of *Lygus* bugs. The second aim is to ascertain the range of effects which an identified pest can exert on the target organism or product. A fine example of such investigations is Liesering's (1960) study of feeding by the mite *Tetranychus urticae* on plant tissues.

Ideally, phase 1 is intended to produce a comprehensive picture of the injurious organisms participating in the pest situation and of their interactions. Although the defining of complex situations may require much time and effort, difficulties do not usually arise in pest control for lack of the information which phase 1 should provide.

Phase 2 – The object of the second phase is twofold. It consists firstly of appraising a pest situation with a view to deciding how much effort the problem warrants. The second purpose is to distinguish between those features of the problem that pertain to the evolutionary development of the pest situation, i.e. its 'constants' (section 6.1), and ecological events which pertain to the functioning of the life systems involved. The latter determine, in the immediate sense, the actual seriousness of the situation, and entail relationships more readily amenable to manipulation by man. In order to decide on appropriate control action, it is necessary to understand the ecological processes which keep pests operative, and to evaluate the respective functions of those processes according to their influence on injuriousness.

It is extremely difficult to make accurate estimates of the damage caused by insect pests (see Strickland 1956), the major problem in assessment work being that of method (Parker 1942). Ideally, investigations should proceed at two levels. The first concerns the overall injury which man's interests are actually suffering, or are liable to suffer, under the prevailing conditions. The second consists of evaluating the contribution of single pest species to the overall injury. The two levels of study are complementary. Without the results of the first, interpretations of specific findings remain arbitrary, whereas overall measurements provide no guidance for remedial action (Strickland 1952). The difficulties encountered in damage assessment are typical of ecological studies embracing functional communities of species, as distinct from studies which deal with the life systems of single species.

Of necessity, workers so far have reduced the 'community-centered' problem of pest appreciation to the conceptual level of single-species populations. A good example of this is seen in the studies by American authors of the injury which an array of pests could cause singly to cotton, e.g. spider mites (Canerday and Arrant 1964), *Heliothis* bollworm (Adkisson *et al.* 1964), and pink bollworm (Brazzel and Gaines 1957). The value of such unrelated assessments appears to be strongly qualified by the following statement made in the 'Report on Cotton Insects' compiled in 1965 by a panel of the U.S. President's Science Advisory Committee: 'Damage from the bollworm, spider mites and aphids would be relatively insignificant in boll-weevil-infested areas [which produce more than one third of the cotton crop in U.S.A.] except for the current procedures used to control boll-weevil.'

For the present, the difficulty created by the need to appraise the injuriousness of pests within the context of co-acting groups of species cannot be resolved, but only reduced. The difficulty is least in situations where one species predominates. It is partly overcome in other, more complex instances by the assumptions which experienced workers can make as to the dominant or 'key' species in a complex of pests, e.g. cotton boll-weevil.

The most comprehensive attempts made so far at evaluating the injuriousness of pests were carried out during the 1940's and 1950's in parts of the United Kingdom (Strickland 1952), and were conceived as an experiment to test the following three hypotheses: that relevant information which was lacking on the relation of pest numbers to injury, and on the conditions which determined changes in pest numbers, could, if available, be used with great profit; that the required information could accrue from the judicious interpretation of results obtained in simply-designed surveys, supported by detailed complementary studies under controlled conditions; and that certain common pest situations would provide particularly suitable objects for such tests, e.g. the cabbage aphid on brussel sprouts (Strickland 1957).

The results of this pioneer work reflect the *ad hoc* nature of the enterprise, and have not fulfilled the authors' expectations. The factual information produced is technical and economic rather than ecological. One cannot emphasize too strongly that this information contains many valuable findings too seldom produced by economic entomologists. The criticism is rather that the project did not yield the ecological information which it was meant to supply. In particular, the work has suggested no explanation of changes in pest numbers and, consequently, has provided no information of predictive value which could lead to significant improvements in control.

The large-scale experiment attempted by Strickland and his associates demonstrates the need for a more effective approach to the appreciation of pest problems than is allowed by the views on population ecology that inspired Strickland's work (essentially those of Andrewartha-Birch, see section 3.22). The generalized conception presented in chapter IV is considered to provide a more discriminating method for the analysis of pest situations than any of the previous theoretical formulations.

Predicting the future injuriousness of pests is customarily discussed together with the assessment of damage (e.g. Thomas 1948). Forecasts can be required for a variety of purposes, such as: *evaluating* the variability of a pest's injuriousness in time; *preparing* for possible increases in the injuriousness of a pest; and *timing* the application of recurrent control measures. So far, forecasting has been successful only in particular instances involving, for example:

(*i*) species with long life cycles, like the *Melolontha* cockchafers in Europe (Régnier *et al.* 1953), or slowly displacing infestations, like those of locusts;

(*ii*) pests whose seasonal power of increase is narrowly limited, and whose abundance in one year is therefore closely associated with numbers previously achieved, or with conditions prevailing at the outset of the season, like the cornborer in the American Mid-West (Bigger and Petty 1953);

(*iii*) species whose numbers and activity can be readily surveyed at a stage of development preceding that which causes damage, like codling moth; and

(*iv*) pests whose injurious outbreaks may be predicted on the basis of reliable (if unexplained) correlation with conspicuous precursory events, e.g. the spruce budworm (Wellington *et al.* 1950), and *Melanoplus* grasshoppers in Canada (Edwards 1964).

This forecasting serves and relies on *ad hoc* methods implicit in the empirical approach to pest control. It represents a temporary expedient rather than an object worthy of lasting ecological attention. As progress is made in analyzing pest problems ecologically, the role that prediction plays as an aid to empirical control will gradually be replaced by the more fundamental purpose of testing the goodness-of-fit of life system models in the process of elaboration. In the form of verifiable hypotheses, prediction and the search for predictability constitute an integral part of any ecological study (chapter V).

In phase 2, the relationship between pest and target species or product must be considered with a view to allowing an adequate evaluation of two critical variables, i.e. the levels of pest density which must be attained before the target is affected significantly, and the minimum amount of injury to which the target must be exposed in order to make control measures worthwhile. Tammes (1961) has discussed the principles and difficulties of such studies, pointing out that the relation between injuriousness and pest density is in the nature of a logistic function characterized by a 'threshold' of pest abundance (or 'compensation level') below which the target species can nullify the effects of infestation, and a level of maximum injury beyond which further increases in the density of the pest can have no more effect on the target (see also McKinlay and Geering 1957, Coaker 1957). Information of the kind required is primarily 'target-based', and is not available unless the ecology of target organisms is studied as carefully as that of pests, a point that has often been overlooked.

To conclude, phase 2 is by far the weakest link in the appreciation of pest situations. Frequently, it is either ignored in the elaboration of control measures, or else dealt with by assumptions extrapolated from phase 1 findings. The information which phase 2 must provide is the key to pest management. It cannot be gained for a pest situation unless some kind of a model has been produced of the life systems of the species involved.

Phase 3 – The appreciation of a pest situation is completed by reviewing the information available from phases 1 and 2 to decide upon a course of action. This implies determining in turn: the maximum injuriousness of the pest, or group of pests, which can be tolerated; the consequent efficacy required of control measures; the conditions influencing injuriousness which could usefully be modified or changed in order to achieve the degree of control needed; and the strategy, i.e. the approach and scheme of operation, most likely to be effective.

The extent to which man is prepared to tolerate the existence of a pest has never been evaluated in a strictly objective way. As a rule, the tendency is to exaggerate the danger of unfamiliar pests and, consequently, to set unrealistically low levels of tolerance for them. This is particularly obvious in the case of noxious species recently discovered in a new area, e.g. the San José scale in western Europe during the late 1940's and 1950's. As information and experience accumulate, a more balanced view can be taken both of a pest's true status and of man's ability to cope with the problem. On the other hand, practical workers would often regard as acceptable the damage which they cannot avoid by current procedures, and lift their standards only in consequence of progress in their competence to deal with pests in routine fashion. The definition of working levels at which the injuriousness of pests should be contained is bound to require some compromise between the desirable and the possible.

From the kind of operational analysis outlined in figure 40, those determinants of injuriousness which are amenable to change by man can be inferred. Which of them require changing in order to accomplish a stated intention, and the extent of change needed, are questions that have to be answered by trial and error until the variance of injuriousness can be apportioned adequately amongst the causative influences and their inter-actions. A predictive identification of the required changes would accrue only from a comprehensive mathematical model of the pest situation – of the type discussed in chapter V for single-species populations. This applies generally for pest situations, but, as yet, there is no realistic pro-cedure for selecting deductively the optimum pathways to efficient pest control.

The pathways leading to reduction in the injuriousness of insect pests can be defined as 'strategies'. Most of the examples given below to illustrate and support the views discussed are cases in which successful control was accomplished either intuitively or by good fortune. As a rule, such strokes of luck have resulted in uncritical attempts to emulate them – without regard to the prevailing circumstances, and without sufficient understanding of the principles involved. Successes of this sort can be made to serve a more useful purpose by helping to outline the pattern into which actions and reactions can be related predictably in a general theory of pest control.

Four basic strategies can be recognized in pest control. They are:

(1) To *evade* the consequences of pest activity by withdrawing the target organism or product from the range of attack by a pest, or by changing the use made of the target in such a way as to nullify the effects of the pests. For instance, seed potatoes are produced systematically today in districts specially selected for low incidences of virus-transmitting aphids, and characterized by geographic isolation and favourable wind regimes. During the mid-1960's in some fruit-growing areas, e.g. in Nova Scotia (MacLellan, *personal communication*), increasing proportions of the local crop are being processed in factories – with the effect of lowering the economic value of much of the injury caused by pests.

(2) To *eliminate* those characteristics and attributes of the target that make it susceptible to attack. For example, the practice developed during the last century of grafting susceptible grapevines on rootstocks unsuitable to the subterranean forms of the *Phylloxera* aphid has made vineyards practically immune to serious injury by the pest. Similarly, the Mules'

operation has served in Australia to reduce the susceptibility of sheep to blowfly strikes.

(3) To *suppress* those characteristics and attributes of a pest that make it injurious to the target. For example, the infectiveness of insect vectors of diseases can be suppressed either by reducing the number of infective sources, or by minimizing their intrinsic infectivity.

(4) To *reduce* the numbers of a pest to levels at which the species ceases to be injurious. Examples of this strategy are the most common.

Although the possibilities of strategies 1, 2, and 3 deserve more systematic attention than they have received from economic entomologists, there are relatively few instances in which one of them has provided the complete answer to a pest problem. Quite generally, there seems to be little justification at present to hope for panaceas in pest control, or even for simple solutions. Instead, effective solutions appear more likely to accrue from flexible approaches with a shifting emphasis on particular strategies as needs and convenience dictate. This applies as much to strategy 4 as to the others. However, because it is the most widely-adopted and successful of the four, and because it lends itself most to the application of ecological principles, this strategy will be our main concern in the next part of this discussion.

6.3 REDUCING PEST NUMBERS

Pest control is commonly envisaged as an operation, or series of operations, whereby one restraining agent is opposed to the normal multiplication of a noxious population. This is most often accomplished by means of an insecticide. In essence, control by insecticides is usually a kind of containment in which numbers are reduced whenever they reach critical levels of population density. Experience shows that populations treated in this manner tend to respond in one of three ways to the restraint imposed upon them:

(*i*) they die out immediately if the mortality suffered exceeds a critical limit;

(*ii*) their numbers begin to fluctuate in phase with the treatments, more or less violently according to treatment frequency, the extent of the mortality inflicted, the power of increase of the subject species, and the side-effects exerted on associated organisms; or

(*iii*) they reveal under pressure unsuspected qualities, e.g. the development of resistance to toxicants, which enable them to overcome the imposed restraint.

The second of the three responses is the most frequent. It typifies situations in which the stabilization of population density is no longer imple-

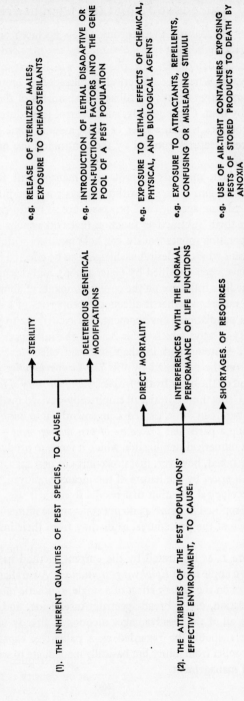

FIGURE 42. Synopsis of means available to influence restrictively the co-determinants of abundance in the life systems of pests.

mented by the natural mechanisms which operated originally. In such instances, the stabilizing role is assumed by the imposed restraining agent whose action determines the phase in which pest numbers fluctuate henceforward. Whenever numerical stabilization is brought about in this way, the operative negative feedback mechanisms of the system must be supplied by man. Consequently, such control procedures tend to become onerous routines which, sooner or later, assume some or all of the disadvantageous features entailed by the continuing use of insecticides (see Geier 1966).

Clearly then, methods of protective management for reducing pest numbers must aim to create, within life systems, conditions under which naturally-existing agencies and processes are so reinforced and/or supplemented in their 'subtractive' function that endogenous stabilizing mechanisms, operating spontaneously, can hold numbers within tolerable limits.

The means whereby desirable changes can be effected in the life systems of pests have been classified by Geier (1966), and discussed according to their immediate influence on the co-determinants of abundance (see figure 42). Each means, whether it affects the properties of a subject species or modifies a population's environment, can contribute to pest management in a variety of ways which differ both in the influences which they exert within life systems and in their intrinsic effectiveness. The latter is measured on the one hand by the *long-term reliability* of the protection offered, and on the other by the *frequency and intensity of human intervention* required. Using these criteria, all empirically-devised methods for reducing pest numbers can be classified conveniently into nine categories, each representing a particular *procedure of pest management* – characterized by the sort of numerical stabilization which it tends to produce (see figure 43). It must be noted, however, that procedures of pest management cannot be identified *a priori* by the nature of the means employed, but solely by the ultimate ecological situation that results from their use. Further, the distinctions proposed in figure 43 do not concern the immediate efficiency and convenience of the procedures, as distinct from their intrinsic, long-term value.

Procedure 1, as illustrated by the current method used to control the light-brown apple moth *Epiphyas postvittana* in Australian orchards (Geier 1965), relies on the violent effect of a single, synthetic mortality agent on a pest population, e.g. a broad-spectrum insecticide, and therefore entails potentially all of the disadvantages mentioned already in this connexion. Procedure 1 should be regarded as a palliative, capable of providing temporary relief from injury but basically inadequate to serve as a definitive method of management.

REQUIRED FREQUENCY AND INTENSITY OF HUMAN INTERVENTION	A. LIMITED	B. SATISFACTORY	C. HIGH
MINIMAL	7. Containment induced by self–perpetuating agencies, precariously conditioned Control of olive scale by *Aphytis maculicornis*, U.S.A. (Huffaker et al. 1962)	8. Containment induced by self–perpetuating agencies, dependably conditioned Biological control of spruce sawfly, Canada (Bird and Elgee 1957)	9. Adjustment induced by definitively curtailing the supply of resources Control of pine bark weevil, Australia (Brimblecombe 1945)
INTERMEDIATE	4. Containment induced by self–perpetuating agencies, periodically re-enforced by conditioning interventions Use of insecticides against spruce budworm, Canada (Morris et al. 1963)	5. Containment induced by self–perpetuating agencies requiring re-activation after intermittent recurrence of non–permissive conditions Seasonal control of greenhouse white fly by *Encarsia formosa*, Canada (McLeod 1954)	6. Adjustment induced by periodical interventions to restrict the availability of resources Partial bush clearing against tsetse fly, Africa (Hocking et al. 1963)
MAXIMAL	1. Containment produced by recurrent catastrophic mortality timed arbitrarily and inflicted by man with synthetic devices Chemical control of light-brown apple moth, Australia (Geier 1965)	2. Containment produced by recurrent catastrophic mortality methodically conditioned to optimalize the use of synthetic killing agents "Planned dipping" against cattle tick, Australia (Harley and Wilkinson 1964)	3. Adjustment induced by continual interventions to restrict the availability of resources "Pasture spelling" against cattle tick Australia (Wilkinson 1964)

LONG–TERM RELIABILITY OF PROTECTION

FIGURE 43. Synopsis of procedures used for economic control of pest numbers.

Procedure 2 represents essentially an improvement in which the most unsatisfactory features of procedure 1 have been minimized deliberately by research and development. This is achieved by closely adapting the use of synthetic killing agents to the biology of the pest, and by exploiting to fullest advantage the complementary action of other possible limiting influences (synthetic or naturally-induced) in so-called 'integrated control' (see section 6.1, footnote). As a simple case in point, Harley and Wilkinson (1964) have shown that cattle dipping in acaricide against the cattle tick *Boophilus microplus* is most efficient when repeated at intervals short enough to prevent the surviving ticks from reproducing between dippings.

Procedure 3 involves continually preventing a pest from gaining access to the full supply of material resources available naturally in the environment. Whenever economically feasible, procedure 3 has proved to be highly effective and dependable, as Wilkinson (1964) demonstrated in 'pasture spelling', a methodical rotation of cattle in grazing areas, designed to prevent the build-up of tick populations in northern Australia.

Procedure 4 applies to populations stabilized alternatively by containing and by adjusting mechanisms according to the prevailing weather conditions, etc., and whose numbers reach damaging proportions when released from containment, e.g. *Cardiaspina albitextura* (section 4.29). In such instances, it appears that containment is re-established after appropriate reductions induced either naturally or artificially in the densities of the subject species. A case in point is the lasting control of spruce budworm *Choristoneura fumiferana* achieved over large areas in northern New Brunswick by infrequent, often single, applications of insecticide (see Morris, ed. 1963).

Procedure 5 involves the use of agencies whose containing action, under temporarily permissive environmental conditions, is sufficient to hold pest populations at commercially tolerable densities. The seasonal re-introduction of the parasite *Encarsia formosa* into greenhouses for the control of white fly *Trialeurodes vaporariorum* is a good example.

Procedure 6 differs from procedure 3 only in the lesser frequency and intensity of interventions required to maintain its effective operation. It has been implemented successfully in a variety of instances, notably for the control of tsetse fly *Glossina* spp. To make places unfavourable for adult flies, part of the foliage of shelter plants was removed periodically in critical areas (Hocking *et al.* 1963).

Procedure 7 results in a form of containment which is induced by an agent whose action is not always closely related to the densities of the subject species, and which therefore cannot be depended upon to keep pest numbers constantly within tolerable limits. For instance, Huffaker *et al.* (1962) have indicated that the imported *Aphytis maculicornis* which is normally an effective parasite of olive scale *Parlatoria oleae* in California, could, in certain circumstances, be so reduced in numbers by extreme weather that damaging increases ensued in scale numbers.

Procedure 8 represents ultimate success in biological control, as exemplified by the case of the European spruce sawfly *Diprion hercyniae* in Canada (section 4.28).

Procedure 9 refers to the definitive elimination of a resource whose presence enables a pest to maintain injurious densities. This has been achieved, for instance, by Brimblecombe (1945) for the control of the pine bark weevil *Aesiotes notabilis* which seriously damaged hoop pine plantations in Queensland. Pruning operations were limited to dry periods in winter, thus avoiding the presence of fresh wounds at times when the availability of access into the host plant determines the extent of larval survival.

As each successful method for solving pest problems by strategy 4 must correspond to one of the nine procedures listed, the improvement of any method will proceed ultimately according to steps indicated in the lay-out of the chart. However, the improvement of control can be sought at two levels. The first concerns immediate efficacy. Obviously, this must be pursued as a primary goal regardless of ecological niceties, even though the gain may necessitate discarding a previous procedure whose long-term value was inherently greater. Thus, the progression in desirability indicated by rank in the chart can apply solely to methods whose immediate efficacy is equivalent.

With this proviso, procedures of pest management become more desirable from bottom to top, and from left to right, in the chart. The upward progression is straightforward, because it reflects increased economy of maintenance, following generally greater capital outlay in research and development. The horizontal trend requires some comment. Basically, procedures in column A are the least reliable, because they allow subject populations the most chances of escaping containment. Procedures in column B each represent, in the ecological sequence, the most immediate improvement on their opposite number in column A. For instance, a readily-conceived advance on procedure 4 would be to acquire the means to re-activate immediately (as in procedure 5) those agencies which variable environmental influences render temporarily ineffective.

Procedures in column B are rated 'satisfactory' in long-term reliability. By and large, they are less liable to breakdown following ecological or evolutionary changes in the co-determinants of abundance than are the procedures in column A. They are less secure in this respect than the procedures in column C, because of the probabilistic nature of containment (see sections 3.23, 4.122). But, whereas mechanisms which induce adjustment may prove to be more dependable in the long run, satisfactory containment is usually realized sooner in practice than effective adjustment.

So far, the successful achievement of any procedure of pest management has been brought about more by good fortune than by design. Progress in these matters will remain empirical, or at least dependent on the quasi-intuitive insight of particular workers, for as long as adequate models of the life systems of pests are not available to predict the most feasible pathways to optimal procedures.

6.4 CONCLUSIONS

Our present capabilities to deal with pests adequately are limited in every respect. Objective evaluation of injuriousness, choice of control strategy, and elaboration of procedures to minimize injuriousness are usually impeded by our failure to understand properly the life systems in which damaging densities occur, i.e. by the lack of effective models. Progress in applied ecology of the kind outlined above can serve to improve significantly the control of particular species. But single species are infrequently the only cause of pest problems, e.g. the case of cacao in West Africa. Moreover, restrictive action directed against a specific pest can seldom be so devised as to leave other populations entirely unaffected. For these reasons, the improvements in pest management accruing from life system studies, however comprehensive and penetrating they may be, are limited in turn by the arbitrary bounds of the life system approach. If and when population studies can be broadened to encompass and integrate all of the relevant species involved in pest situations, further advances will be possible, up to a certain point. That limit is set by the nature of ecology. By definition, ecology is concerned essentially with predictable events brought about by the action of recurrent processes – and with their causation by co-determinants of abundance whose attributes are necessarily regarded as constants. This assumption is unrealistic because it fails to consider the evolutionary, i.e. unidirectional and unpredictable, changes which are taking place in the co-determinants of abundance, either spontaneously, or as an effect of man's increasing interference in ecosystems. To free himself finally of pest problems, man would need to develop biological knowledge to an all-embracing level of integration which would give him complete mastery over the existence of other species.

CHAPTER VII

The further development of research on insect populations

In the preceding chapters of this book, we have considered the basic concepts used in the study of insect populations, described in outline the influences involved in the determination of population numbers, and discussed the development of ecological thought and population theories. On the basis of these theories and the results obtained from recent field and laboratory studies, we have attempted to generalize in a straightforward way about the determination of abundance, recognizing that populations together with their environments resemble complex cybernetic systems. We have discussed an approach to the study of natural populations and examined the ecology of pest control. The criterion applied throughout in the acceptance and development of ideas was *usefulness* in the present state of ecological knowledge and understanding. In this short concluding chapter, we shall consider briefly some of the research that is needed to further our understanding of the abundance of insects and a way of thinking about future work.

As most of our readers are aware, insects are the most numerous of all terrestrial animals, both in terms of species and total abundance. Only a small fraction of the total number of insect species are pests. However, more insects are likely to achieve pest status as agricultural development proceeds, especially in those parts of the world where the present standard of primary production is low. On the other hand, there are the far more numerous insect species beneficial in some way to man, e.g. those predators and parasites that contribute towards limitation of the abundance of phytophagous insects and so aid in the preservation of plant and animal life, and saprophytic species, pollinators, etc., which play their part in the natural circulation of matter and energy.

Man has to live in association with insects and he should learn to appreciate fully the fact that they form an important component of the universal web of ecosystems in which he is the dominating species. As part of man's environment, this component requires intelligent management both to restrain troublesome species and to conserve or augment beneficial species. Man has acquired some guiding principles which he can apply profitably to the management of single species. However, much more knowledge is needed to cope effectively with the many pest situations which involve a number of injurious (or potentially injurious) species – and to make the best possible use of beneficial insects. The question is how best to set about obtaining the additional knowledge needed.

In Europe, North America, Japan and Australia, a number of long-term studies on insect life systems are in progress. Almost all of them are concerned, understandably, with recognized pests or other insects which occur at average levels of abundance higher than those at which the majority of insect species exist. These investigations, and the field and laboratory experimentation which they stimulate, will provide a wealth of information on the population dynamics of single species. In addition, efforts are being made to investigate: the fundamentals of predator-prey interactions; the genetics of insect populations; and various new ways of interfering with the behaviour and reproduction of pest species, and with the availability of environmental resources. Before long, similar concentrations of effort will probably be devoted to the incidence of disease in natural populations, and to the influence of host plant physiology and genetics on the abundance of pests. All of this means that fairly rapid progress can be expected in the study of abundant species. However, more than this is needed and some new ground will have to be broken by population ecologists.

It is suggested that the following kinds of investigation should receive increasing attention in the near future. *Firstly*, the majority of insect species remain for long periods, if not indefinitely, at relatively low levels of abundance. An effort should be made to investigate the life systems of a few of these species in different geographic regions, especially life systems that have not been modified greatly by man. Admittedly, the study of such insects is a formidable task because of the difficulties involved in efficient population sampling and in the identification and evaluation of environmental influences. However, granted adequate means, it should be possible in some cases to develop appropriate sampling methods, etc., and to supplement observational work by such experimentation as attempts to increase artificially the numbers of a subject species over limited areas (e.g. by breeding individuals in insectaries) and to study the various environmental responses to the change in numbers. *Secondly*, it would be instructive to investigate concurrently the life systems of 'high-density' and 'low-density' species within particular ecosystems. Such comparisons between insect species which operate at the same consumer level, e.g. plant feeders, are likely to be rewarding in themselves. They have, moreover, the additional value of being first steps in the application of the approach and methods of population ecology to the study of ecosystems as such.

As some workers realize, the time has come to broaden the approach used in population ecology and to consider not only the population dynamics of single species but also the ecosystems which incorporate the particular life systems that they study. This orientation is needed both for the further development of pest management and for obtaining knowledge relevant to the problems of conservation. A few population studies involving groups of species at different consumer levels are already in progress. In Australia, work of this kind is developing on the insect and arachnid faunas of pome fruit orchards; on a complex of scarab beetle and moth species whose larvae infest natural and improved pastures; and on a complex of abundant and relatively uncommon psyllids and their natural enemies which occur on woodland species of *Eucalyptus*. The psyllid investigation is linked with population studies on other woodland insects which occur on the same host trees. Similar intensive work, aimed mainly at pest management, has begun elsewhere, notably in Canada and Japan. In Britain and Holland, the emphasis in population ecology is shifting towards the study of ecosystems in the interests of nature conservation.

A practical approach to the more comprehensive studies advocated is to begin with an abundant species and, after obtaining a working knowledge of its life system, to extend the investigation – firstly to *related* species which obtain their food from the same sources (and share some natural enemies with the original subject species) – and later to *other* species which function at the same consumer level. It would usually be best to begin with phytophagous insects. Thereafter, if it seemed desirable, the emphasis could be shifted to the predators and pathogens of such species. Pioneer studies of this kind would necessarily be limited in scope, but they could be used to pave the way for much more ambitious and comprehensive investigations in which the contributions made by workers on the population ecology of insects would be integrated with those of plant ecologists and workers in other disciplines. It would be of great general value to have at least one intensive numerical study of an ecosystem developed progressively in each country capable of readily financing such a project, either for the purposes of pest management or for nature conservation. Such an investigation could not be entirely compehensive, but systematic studies along carefully-chosen lines could be carried to the level at which sufficient understanding was obtained for much more effective management of ecosystems than is possible at the present time.

The circumstances in which a start can be made in the intensive numerical study of ecosystems are improving steadily, especially in wealthy countries in which agriculture is still a major source of national income. In such countries, the increasing dissatisfaction arising from the defects and dangers of modern chemical insecticides is turning the attention of senior administrators and governments towards alternative methods of pest control. In densely-populated, industrialized countries in which agriculture is relatively unimportant economically, the need to conserve what remains of naturally-evolved ecosystems is being felt increasingly by people in all walks of life. Moreover, the technical means for basic ecological research have been improved greatly by the development of digital computers and other kinds of electronic equipment which can be used increasingly as research tools in the application of ecological programmes, and in techniques of analysis and synthesis. The use of computers in a variety of ways will make possible much more penetrating studies of ecosystems than could be attempted in the past.

The principal prerequisite, however, for the effective investigation and management of ecosystems is man's full appreciation of the fact that, being the dominating and only truly creative species, he must learn much more in the broadest possible way about the consequences of his unceasing but poorly-integrated efforts to improve his environment, and about how best to adjust his activities and population numbers for his own well-being. In other words, if man – a component species – is to advance far in the management of ecosystems, he must acquire more knowledge and understanding of how to manage his own kind.

Bibliography and index of authors

(Abbreviations according to *World List* wherever possible. Italicized page numbers refer to citations in text.)

ADKISSON, P. L., HANNA, R. L., and BAILEY, C. F. (1964) Estimates of the numbers of *Heliothis* larvae per acre in cotton and their relation to the fruiting cycle and yield of the host. *J. econ. Ent.* **57**: 657–63. [*194*]

ALLEE, W. C., EMERSON, A. E., PARK, O., PARK, T., and SCHMIDT, K. P. (1949) *Principles of animal ecology*. Philadelphia and London: W. B. Saunders. [*17*]

ANDREWARTHA, H. G. (1939) The small plague grasshopper (*Austroicetes cruciata* Sauss.). *J. Dep. Agric. S. Aust.* **43**: 99–107. [*40; 41; 42*]

ANDREWARTHA, H. G. (1943) The significance of grasshoppers in some aspects of soil conservation in South Australia and Western Australia. *J. Dep. Agric. S. Aust.* **46**: 314–22. [*42*]

ANDREWARTHA, H. G. (1957) The use of conceptual models in population ecology. *Cold Spring Harb. Symp. quant. Biol.* **22**: 219–36. [*35*]

ANDREWARTHA, H. G. (1959) Self-regulatory mechanisms in animal populations. *Aust. J. Sci.* **22**: 200–5. [*4*]

ANDREWARTHA, H. G. (1961) *Introduction to the study of animal populations.* London: Methuen. [*2; 4; 33; 39*]

ANDREWARTHA, H. G., and BIRCH, L. C. (1954) *The distribution and abundance of animals.* Chicago: University of Chicago Press. [*2; 4; 5; 17; 33; 38; 40; 43; 44; 45; 57*]

ANDREWARTHA, H. G., and BIRCH, L. C. (1960) Some recent contributions to the study of the distribution and abundance of insects. *A. Rev. Ent.* **5**: 219–42. [*33; 39*]

ANDREWARTHA, H. G., and BROWNING, T. O. (1961) An analysis of the idea of 'resources' in animal ecology. *J. theor. Biol.* **1**: 83–97. [*44; 45*]

AUER, C. (1961) Ergebnisse zwölfjähriger quantitativer Untersuchungen der Populationsbewegungen des Grauen Lärchenwicklers *Zeiraphera griseana* Hb. (=*diniana* Guénée) im Oberengadin (1949–60). *Mitt. schweiz. Anst. forstl. VersWes.* **37**: 175–263. [*124; 125; 126; 127; 128; 130; 135*]

BAKKER, K. (1964) Backgrounds of controversies about population theories and their terminologies. *Z. angew. Ent.* **53**: 187–208. [*17; 33; 57*]

BALCH, R. E. (1960) The approach to biological control in forest entomology. *Can. Ent.* **92**: 297–310. [*137*]

BALCH, R. E., and BIRD, F. T. (1944) A disease of the European spruce sawfly *Gilpinia hercyniae* (Htg.), and its place in natural control. *Scient. Agric.* **25**: 65–80. [*137*]

209

BALOGH, H. (1958) *Lebensgemeinschaften der Landtiere.* Berlin: Akademie Verlag. [*32*]

BALTENSWEILER, W. (1958) Zur Kenntnis der Parasiten des Grauen Lärchenwicklers (*Zeiraphera griseana* Hübner) im Oberengadin. *Mitt. schweiz. Anst. forstl. VersWes.* **34**: 399–478. [*124; 127; 131; 132; 133*]

BALTENSWEILER, W. (1964a) *Zeiraphera griseana* Hübner (Lepidoptera: Tortricidae) in the European Alps. A contribution to the problem of cycles. *Can. Ent.* **96**: 792–800. [*124*]

BALTENSWEILER, W. (1964b) Zur Regelung von Insektenpopulationen. *Grüne* No. 26, *1964*: 806–16. [*124; 125; 127; 134*]

BARTLETT, B. R. (1964) Integration of chemical and biological control, pp. 489–511. *In* DEBACH, P. [ed.], *Biological control of insect pests and weeds.* London: Chapman and Hall. [*191*]

BASSAND, D. (1965) Contribution à l'étude de la diapause embryonnaire et de l'embryogénèse de *Zeiraphera griseana* Hübner (=*Z. diniana* Guénée) (Lepidoptera: Tortricidae). *Revue suisse Zool.* **72**: 429–542. [*124*]

BENZ, G. (1962) Untersuchungen über die Pathogenität eines Granulosis-Virus des Grauen Lärchenwicklers *Zeiraphera diniana* (Guénée). *Agron. Glasn.* *1962* (5, 6, 7): 566–74. [*124; 129; 130; 134*]

BIGGER, J. H., and PETTY, H. B. (1953) New control for chinch bugs (*Blissus leucopterus*). *Ext. Circ. Univ. Ill. Coll. Agric.* No. 707. [*195*]

BIRCH, L. C. (1957) The role of weather in determining the distribution and abundance of animals. *Cold Spring Harb. Symp. quant. Biol.* **22**: 203–15. [*42*]

BIRCH, L. C. (1960) The genetic factor in population ecology. *Am. Nat.* **94**: 5–24. [*34; 49*]

BIRCH, L. C. (1962) Stability and instability in natural populations. *N.Z. Sci. Rev.* **20**: 9–14. [*62*]

BIRCH, L. C., and ANDREWARTHA, H. G. (1941) The influence of weather on grasshopper plagues in South Australia. *J. Dep. Agric. S. Aust.* **45**: 95–100. [*41*]

BIRD, F. T., and ELGEE, D. E. (1957) A virus disease and introduced parasites as factors controlling the European spruce sawfly, *Diprion hercyniae* (Htg.), in central New Brunswick. *Can. Ent.* **89**: 371–8. [*137; 201*]

BODENHEIMER, F. S. (1930) Über die Grundlagen einer allgemeinen Epidemiologie der Insektenkalamitäten. *Z. angew. Ent.* **16**: 433–50. [*31*]

BODENHEIMER, F. S. (1938) *Problems of animal ecology.* Oxford: Oxford University Press. [*31; 33*]

BODENHEIMER, F. S., and SWIRSKI, E. (1957) *The Aphidoidea of the Middle East.* Israel: Weizmann Science Press. [*102*]

BONNEMAISON, L. (1951) *Contribution à l'étude des facteurs provoquant l'apparition des formes ailées et sexuées chez les Aphidinae.* Doctoral Thesis: University of Paris. [*16; 102; 103*]

BOVEY, P. (1958) Le problème de la Tordeuse grise du Mélèze *Eucosma griseana* (Hübner) (Lepidoptera: Tortricidae) dans les forêts alpines. *Proc. Int. Congr. Ent. 10. Montreal, 1956.* **4**: 123–31. [*124*]

BOVEY, P., and MAKSYMOV, J. K. (1959) Le problème des races biologiques chez la Tordeuse grise du Mélèze *Zeiraphera griseana* (Hb.). *Vjschr. naturf. Ges. Zürich 1959*: 264–74. [*125*]

BRAZZEL, J. R., and GAINES, J. C. (1957) Cotton yield and quality losses caused by various levels of pink bollworm infestations. *J. econ. Ent.* **50**: 609–13. [*194*]

BRIMBLECOMBE, A. R. (1945) The biology, economic importance and control of the pine bark weevil, *Aesiotes notabilis* Pasc. *Qd. J. agric. Sci.* **2**: 1–88. [*201; 203*]

BURNETT, T. (1949) The effect of temperature on an insect host-parasite population. *Ecology* **30**: 113–34. [*20*]

BURNETT, T. (1951) Effects of temperature and host density on the rate of increase of an insect parasite. *Am. Nat.* **85**: 337–52. [*20*]

BURNETT, T. (1956) Effects of natural temperatures on oviposition of various numbers of an insect parasite. *Ann. ent. Soc. Am.* **49**: 55–59. [*179*]

BURNETT, T. (1958a) A model of host-parasite interaction. *Proc. Int. Congr. Ent. 10. Montreal, 1956.* **2**: 679–86. [*20*]

BURNETT, T. (1958b) Effect of host distribution on the reproduction of *Encarsia formosa* Gahan (Hymenoptera: Chalcidoidea). *Can. Ent.* **90**: 179–91. [*20*]

BURNETT, T. (1960) An insect host-parasite population. *Can. J. Zool.* **38**: 57–75. [*30*]

BUXTON, P. A. (1955) *The natural history of the tsetse flies.* London: Lewis. [*13*]

CANERDAY, T. D., and ARRANT, F. S. (1964) The effect of spider mite populations on yield and quality of cotton. *J. econ. Ent.* **57**: 553–6. [*194*]

CARNE, P. B. (1956) An ecological study of the pasture scarab *Aphodius howitti* Hope. *Aust. J. Zool.* **4**: 259–314. [*22*]

CARNE, P. B. (1962) The characteristics and behaviour of the sawfly *Perga affinis affinis* (Hymenoptera). *Aust. J. Zool.* **10**: 1–34. [*92*]

CARNE, P. B. (1965) Distribution of the eucalypt-defoliating sawfly *Perga affinis affinis* (Hymenoptera). *Aust. J. Zool.* **13**: 593–612. [*92; 94*]

CARNE, P. B. On the population dynamics of the eucalypt-defoliating sawfly *Perga affinis affinis* (Hymenoptera). (*in prep.*). [*92*]

CHAMBERLIN, T. C. (1965) The method of multiple working hypotheses. *Science, N.Y.* **148**: 754–9. [*171*]

CHAPMAN, R. N. (1928) The quantitative analysis of environmental factors. *Ecology* **9**: 111–22. [*21*]

CHITTY, D. (1957) Self-regulation of numbers through changes in viability. *Cold Spring Harb. Symp. quant. Biol.* **22**: 277–80. [*33; 50*]

CHITTY, D. (1960) Population processes in the vole and their relevance to general theory. *Can. J. Zool.* **38**: 99–113. [*33; 49; 50; 52; 57*]

CHITTY, D. (1965) Qualitative changes within fluctuating populations, including genetic variability. *Proc. Int. Congr. Ent. 12. London, 1964*: 384–6. [*53*]

CHORLEY, J. K. (1929) The bionomics of *Glossina morsitans* in the Umniati fly belt, Southern Rhodesia, 1922–23. *Bull. ent. Res.* **20**: 279–301. [*19*]

CHRISTIAN, J. J., and DAVIS, D. E. (1964) Endocrines, behavior, and population. *Science, N.Y.* **146**: 1550–60. [*178*]

CLARK, D. P. (1962) An analysis of dispersal and movement in *Phaulacridium vittatum* (Sjöst.) (Acrididae). *Aust. J. Zool.* **10**: 382–99. [*80; 88*]

CLARK, D. P. A population study of *Phaulacridium vittatum* (Sjöst.) (Acrididae). (*in prep.*). [*80*]

CLARK, L. R. (1947) Ecological observations on the small plague grasshopper, *Austroicetes cruciata* (Sauss.) in the Trangie district, Central Western New South Wales. *Bull. Coun. scient. ind. Res., Melb.* No. 228. [*42*]

CLARK, L. R. (1949) Behaviour of swarm hoppers of the Australian plague locust, *Chortoicetes terminifera* (Walker). *Bull. Coun. scient. ind. Res., Melb.* No. 245. [*55*]

CLARK, L. R. (1953) The ecology of *Chrysomela gemellata* Rossi and *C. hyperici* Forst., and their effect on St. John's wort in the Bright district, Victoria. *Aust. J. Zool.* 1: 1–69. [*21*]

CLARK, L. R. (1962) The general biology of *Cardiaspina albitextura* (Psyllidae) and its abundance in relation to weather and parasitism. *Aust. J. Zool.* 10: 537–86. [*15*; *146*; *147*; *153*; *154*; *155*; *160*; *162*; *164*]

CLARK, L. R. (1963a) Factors affecting the attractiveness of foliage for oviposition by *Cardiaspina albitextura* (Psyllidae). *Aust. J. Zool.* 11: 20–34. [*146*; *155*; *160*; *161*]

CLARK, L. R. (1963b) The influence of population density on the number of eggs laid by females of *Cardiaspina albitextura* (Psyllidae). *Aust. J. Zool.* 11: 190–201. [*146*; *160*; *161*]

CLARK, L. R. (1963c) On the density and distribution of newly-established nymphs of *Cardiaspina albitextura* (Psyllidae) at times of high abundance. *Proc. Linn. Soc. N.S.W.* 88: 67–73. [*146*; *161*]

CLARK, L. R. (1963d) The influence of predation by *Syrphus* sp. on the numbers of *Cardiaspina albitextura* (Psyllidae). *Aust. J. Zool.* 11: 470–87. [*59*; *63*; *146*; *154*; *155*; *160*]

CLARK, L. R. (1964a) The intensity of parasite attack in relation to the abundance of *Cardiaspina albitextura* (Psyllidae). *Aust. J. Zool.* 12: 150–73. [*20*; *146*; *149*; *153*; *160*; *163*]

CLARK, L. R. (1964b) Predation by birds in relation to the population density of *Cardiaspina albitextura* (Psyllidae). *Aust. J. Zool.* 12: 349–61. [*146*; *149*; *151*; *152*; *153*; *155*; *163*]

CLARK, L. R. (1964c) The population dynamics of *Cardiaspina albitextura* (Psyllidae). *Aust. J. Zool.* 12: 362–80. [*146*; *148*; *150*; *156*; *158*]

CLAUSEN, C. P. (1940) *Entomophagous insects*. New York and London: McGraw-Hill. [*19*]

CLEMENTS, F. E. (1916) Plant succession: an analysis of the development of vegetation. *Publ. Carnegie Instn.* No. 242. [*27*]

COAKER, T. H. (1957) Studies of crop loss following insect attack on cotton in East Africa. II. Further experiments in Uganda. *Bull. Ent. Res.* 48: 851–66. [*196*]

COLE, L. C. (1954) The population consequences of life history phenomena. *Q. Rev. Biol.* 29: 103–37. [*16*]

COLLYER, E. (1953a) Biology of some predatory insects and mites associated with the fruit tree red spider mite (*Metatetranychus ulmi* (Koch)) in south-eastern England. IV. The predator-mite relationship. *J. hort. Sci.* 28: 246–59. [*184*]

COLLYER, E. (1953b) The effect of spraying materials on some predatory insects. *Rep. E. Malling Res. Stn. 1952*: 141–5. [*184*]

COMMON, I. F. B. (1954) A study of the ecology of the adult bogong moth *Agrotis infusa* (Boisd.) (Lepidoptera: Noctuidae), with special reference to its behaviour during migration and aestivation. *Aust. J. Zool.* **2**: 223–63. [*23*]

COTTEREL, G. S. (1926) Preliminary study of the life history and habits of *Sahlbergella singularis* Hagl., and *Sahlbergella theobroma* Dist. *Bull. Dep. Agric. Gold Cst.* No. 3. [*188*]

CRISP, D. T. (1959) Hydracarines and nematodes parasitizing *Corixa scotti* (D. and S.), Hemiptera, in Western Ireland. *Ir. Nat. J.* **13**: 88–90. [*20*]

CUNNINGHAM, R. K. (1959) A review of the use of shade and fertilizer in the culture of cocoa. *Tech. Bull. W. Afr. Cocoa Res. Inst.* No. 6. [*185*]

DAHL, F. (1908) Grundsätze und Grundbegriffe der biocönotischen Forschung. *Zool. Anz.* **33**: 349–53. [*28*]

DARWIN, C. (1859) *The origin of species by means of natural selection or the preservation of favoured races in the struggle for life.* London: John Murray. [*26*]

DAVIDSON, J., and ANDREWARTHA, H. G. (1948a) Annual trends in a natural population of *Thrips imaginis* (Thysanoptera). *J. Anim. Ecol.* **17**: 193–9. [*44*]

DAVIDSON, J., and ANDREWARTHA, H. G. (1948b) The influence of rainfall, evaporation and atmospheric temperature on fluctuations in the size of a natural population of *Thrips imaginis* (Thysanoptera). *J. Anim. Ecol.* **17**: 200–22. [*43*]

DEBACH, P., and LANDI, J. (1961) The introduced purple scale parasite, *Aphytis lepidosaphes* Compere, and a method of integrating chemical with biological control. *Hilgardia* **31**: 459–97. [*191*]

DE FLUITER, H. J. (1962) Integrated control of pests in orchards. *Entomophaga* **7**: 199–206. [*191*]

DEMPSTER, J. P. (1961) The analysis of data obtained by regular sampling of an insect population. *J. Anim. Ecol.* **30**: 429–32. [*177*]

DICKSON, R. C. (1949) Factors governing the induction of diapause in the oriental fruit moth. *Ann. ent. Soc. Am.* **42**: 511–37. [*67*]

DODD, A. P. (1936) The control and eradication of prickly pear in Australia. *Bull. ent. Res.* **27**: 503–17. [*48*]

DUNN, J. A. (1960) The natural enemies of the lettuce root aphid, *Pemphigus bursarius* (L.). *Bull. ent. Res.* **51**: 271–8. [*18*]

EDWARDS, R. L. (1964) Some ecological factors affecting the grasshopper populations of Western Canada. *Can. Ent.* **96**: 307–20. [*195*]

ELTON, C. S. (1927) *Animal ecology.* London: Sidgwick and Jackson. [*30; 31; 32*]

ELTON, C. S. (1958) *The ecology of invasions by animals and plants.* London: Methuen. [*183*]

EMBREE, D. G. (1965) The population dynamics of the winter moth in Nova Scotia. *Mem. ent. Soc. Canada* **46**: 1–57. [*176*]

ENGELMANN, M. D. (1961) The role of the soil arthropods in the energetics of an old field community. *Ecol. Monogr.* **31**: 221–38. [*32*]

ENTWISTLE, P. F. (1958) The effect of formicidal spraying on mealybugs. *Rep. W. Afr. Cocoa Res. Inst. 1956–57*: 39–40. [*187*]

FLANDERS, S. E. (1958a) The role of the ant in the biological control of scale insects in California. *Proc. Int. Congr. Ent. 10. Montreal, 1956.* **4**: 579–84. [*20*]

FLANDERS, S. E. (1958b) The *Ephestia-Idechthis* ecosystem for illustrating population dynamics. *Ecology* **39**: 545–7. [*20*]

FLANDERS, S. E., and BADGLEY, M. E. (1963) Prey-predator interactions in self-balanced laboratory populations. *Hilgardia* **35**: 145–83. [*117*; *119*]

FORD, E. B. (1964) *Ecological genetics*. London: Methuen. [*172*]

FRANZ, J. (1950) Über die genetischen Grundlagen des Zusammenbruchs einer Massenvermehrung aus inneren Ursachen. *Z. angew. Ent.* **31**: 228–60. [*33*; *49*]

FRIEDERICHS, K. (1927) Grundsätzliches über die Lebenseinheiten höherer Ordnung und den ökologischen Einheitsfaktor. *Naturwissenschaften* **15**: 153–86. [*28*; *31*; *32*]

GAUSE, G. F. (1932) Ecology of populations. *Q. Rev. Biol.* **7**: 27–46. [*30*]

GAUSE, G. F. (1936) The principles of biocoenology. *Q. Rev. Biol.* **11**: 320–36. [*30*]

GAUSE, G. F. (1937) Experimental populations of microscopic organisms. *Ecology* **18**: 173–9. [*30*; *33*]

GEIER, P. W. (1961) Numerical regulation of populations of the codling moth, *Cydia pomonella* (L.). *Nature, Lond.* **190**: 561–2. [*65*]

GEIER, P. W. (1963a) The life history of codling moth, *Cydia pomonella* (L.) (Lepidoptera: Tortricidae), in the Australian Capital Territory. *Aust. J. Zool.* **11**: 323–67. [*21*; *22*; *65*; *66*; *75*]

GEIER, P. W. (1963b) Wintering and spring emergence of codling moth, *Cydia pomonella* (L.) (Lepidoptera: Tortricidae), in South-eastern Australia. *Aust. J. Zool.* **11**: 431–45. [*65*; *67*]

GEIER, P. W. (1964) Population dynamics of codling moth, *Cydia pomonella* (L.) (Tortricidae), in the Australian Capital Territory. *Aust. J. Zool.* **12**: 381–416. [*65*; *76*; *77*; *78*]

GEIER, P. W. (1965) Conditions of management of two orchard pests, one exotic and the other native to southeastern Australia. *Proc. Int. Congr. Ent. 12. London, 1964*: 598. [*184*; *200*; *201*]

GEIER, P. W. (1966) Management of insect pests. *A. Rev. Ent.* **11**: 471–90. [*200*]

GEIER, P. W., and CLARK, L. R. (1961) An ecological approach to pest control. *Tech. Meet. Int. Un. Conserv. Nat. nat. Resour. 8. Warsaw, 1960*: 10–18. [*170*; *191*]

GEORGE, K. S. (1957) Preliminary investigations on the biology and ecology of the parasites and predators of *Brevicoryne brassicae* (L.). *Bull. ent. Res.* **48**: 619–29. [*102*]

GERIG, L. (1964a) Physiologische Untersuchungen am Grauen Lärchenwickler (*Zeiraphera griseana* Hb. = *diniana* Gn.) während einer Periode der Massenvermehrung. Erste Mitteilung: Biometrische Untersuchungen an Raupen und Puppen. *Z. angew. Ent.* **54**: 119. [*127*]

GERIG, L. (1964b) Physiologische Untersuchungen am Grauen Lärchenwickler (*Zeiraphera griseana* Hb. = *dineana* Gn.) während einer Periode der Massenvermehrung. Zweite Mitteilung: Messung der Atmungsaktivität der Raupen aus verschiedenen Biotopen. *Verh. schweiz. naturf. Ges.* **144**: 143–4. [*127*]

GILMOUR, D., WATERHOUSE, D. F., and MCINTYRE, G. A. (1946) An account of experiments undertaken to determine the natural population

BIBLIOGRAPHY

density of the sheep blowfly *Lucilia cuprina* Wied. *Bull. Coun. scient. ind. Res., Melb.* No. 195. [*173*]

GISIN, H. (1943) Ökologie und Lebensgemeinschaften der Collembolen im schweizerischen Excursionsgebiet Basels. *Revue suisse Zool.* **50**: 131–224. [*32*]

GLASGOW, J. P. (1963) *The distribution and abundance of tsetse.* Oxford: Pergamon Press. [*13; 14; 15; 18; 19; 23*]

GLASGOW, J. P., and DUFFY, B. J. (1961) Traps in field studies of *Glossina pallidipes* Austen. *Bull. ent. Res.* **52**: 795–814. [*22*]

GOLLEY, F. B. (1960) Energy dynamics of a food chain of an old field community. *Ecol. Monogr.* **30**: 187–206. [*32*]

GOODCHILD, A. J. P. (1952) Digestive system of West African cacao capsid bugs. *Proc. zool. Soc. Lond.* **122**: 543–72. [*188*]

GOUDGE, T. A. (1961) *The ascent of life.* London: Allen and Unwin. [*2*]

HAFEZ, M. (1961) Seasonal fluctuations of the population density of the cabbage aphid (*Brevicoryne brassicae* (L.)) in the Netherlands, and the role of its parasite *Aphidius* (*Diaeretiella*) *rapae* (Curtis). *Tijdschr. PlZiekt.* **67**: 445–548. [*102*]

HAIRSTON, N. G. (1959) Species abundance and community organisation. *Ecology* **40**: 404–16. [*32*]

HAMMOND, P. S. (1957) Notes on the progress of pest and disease control in Ghana. *Proc. Cocoa Conf. London, 1957*: 110–18. [*186*]

HARLEY, K. L. S., and WILKINSON, P. R. (1964) A comparison of cattle tick control by 'conventional' acaricidal treatment, planned dipping, and pasture spelling. *Aust. J. agric. Res.* **15**: 841–53. [*201; 202*]

HERRICK, G. W., and HUNGATE, J. W. (1911) The cabbage aphid. *Bull. Cornell Univ. agric. Exp. Stn.* **300**: 715–46. [*102*]

HILL, P. (1956) *The Gold Coast farmer. A preliminary survey.* Accra: Oxford University Press. [*185*]

HOCKING, K. S., LAMERTON, J. F., and LEWIS, E. A. (1963) Tsetse-fly control and eradication. *Bull. Wld. Hlth. Org.* No. 28: 811–23. [*201; 202*]

HOLDAWAY, F. G. (1932) An experimental study of the growth of populations of the 'flour beetle' *Tribolium confusum* Duval, as affected by atmospheric moisture. *Ecol. Monogr.* **2**: 261–304. [*30*]

HOLLING, C. S. (1959) Some characteristics of simple types of predation and parasitism. *Can. Ent.* **91**: 385–98. [*178*]

HOLLING, C. S. (1966) The functional response of invertebrate predators to prey density. *Mem. ent. Soc. Canada* **48**: 1–86. [*178*]

HOWARD, L. O., and FISKE, W. F. (1911) The importation into the United States of the parasites of the gypsy moth and the brown-tail moth. *Bull. Bur. Ent. U.S. Dep. Agric.* No. 91. [*29; 33; 34*]

HUFFAKER, C. B. (1958a) Experimental studies on predation: dispersion factors and predator-prey oscillations. *Hilgardia* **27**: 343–83. [*30; 120; 121*]

HUFFAKER, C. B. (1958b) Concept of balance in nature. *Proc. Int. Congr. Ent. 10. Montreal, 1956.* **2**: 625–36. [*33*]

HUFFAKER, C. B., KENNETT, C. E., and FINNEY, G. L. (1962) Biological control of olive scale, *Parlatoria oleae* (Colvée) in California by imported *Aphytis maculicornis* (Masi) (Hymenoptera: Aphelinidae). *Hilgardia* **32**: 541–636. [*201; 203*]

215

HUFFAKER, C. B., and MESSENGER, P. S. (1964) The concept and significance of natural control, pp. 74–117. *In* DEBACH, P. [ed.], *Biological control of insect pests and weeds*. London: Chapman and Hall. [*57; 63*]

HUFFAKER, C. B., SHEA, K. P., and HERMAN, S. G. (1963) Experimental studies on predation. *Hilgardia* **34**: 305–30. [*117; 122; 123*]

HUGHES, R. D. (1962) A method for estimating the effects of mortality on aphid populations. *J. Anim. Ecol.* **31**: 389–96. [*7; 102*]

HUGHES, R. D. (1963) Population dynamics of the cabbage aphid, *Brevicoryne brassicae* (L.). *J. Anim. Ecol.* **32**:393–424. [*7; 10; 11; 21; 102; 107; 177*]

IVES, W. G. H. (1964) Problems encountered in the development of life tables for insects. *Proc. ent. Soc. Manitoba* **20**: 34–44. [*176*]

JACKSON, C. H. N. (1944) The analysis of a tsetse population II. *Ann. Eugen.* **12**: 176–205. [*15*]

JACKSON, C. H. N. (1949) The biology of the tsetse flies. *Biol. Rev.* **24**: 174–99. [*13; 14*]

JOHNSON, C. G. (1960) A basis for a general system of insect migration and dispersal by flight. *Nature, Lond.* **186**: 348–50. [*23*]

JUDAY, C. (1940) The annual energy budget of an inland lake. *Ecology* **21**: 438–50. [*32*]

KAELIN, A., and AUER, C. (1954) Statistische Methoden zur Untersuchung von Insektenpopulationen, dargestellt am Beispiel des Grauen Lärchenwicklers (*Eucosma griseana* Hb. = *Semasia diniana* Gn.). *Z. angew. Ent.* **36**: 241–82, 423–61. [*124*]

KAY, D., LONGWORTH, J. F., and THRESH, J. M. (1961) The interaction between swollen shoot disease and mirids on cocoa in Nigeria. *Proc. inter-Am. Cacao Conf. 8. Trin. Tobago, 1960*: 224–35. [*186*]

KHO, Y. O., and BRAAK, J. P. (1956) Reduction in the yield and viability of carrot seed in relation to the occurrence of the plant bug *Lygus campestris* L. *Euphytica* **5**: 146–56. [*193*]

KLOMP, H. (1958) On the theories of host-parasite interactions. *Archs. néerl. Zool.* **13**: 134–45. [*33*]

KLOMP, H. (1962) The influence of climate and weather on the mean density level, the fluctuations and the regulation of animal populations. *Archs. néerl. Zool.* **15**: 68–109. [*33*]

KLOMP, H. (1964) Intraspecific competition and the regulation of insect numbers. *A. Rev. Ent.* **9**: 17–40. [*33*]

KLOMP, H., and GRUYS, P. (1965) The analysis of factors affecting reproduction and mortality in a natural population of the pine looper, *Bupalus piniarius* L. *Proc. Int. Congr. Ent. 12. London, 1964*: 369–72. [*135*]

KONTKANEN, P. (1957) On the delimitation of communities in research on animal biocenotics. *Cold Spring Harb. Symp. quant. Biol.* **22**: 373–8. [*32*]

KREBS, J. C. (1964) The lemming cycle at Baker Lake, Northwest Territories, during 1959–62. *Tech. Pap. Arct. Inst. N. Am.* No. 15. [*53*]

KUENEN, D. J. (1958) Some sources of misunderstanding in the theories of regulation of animal numbers. *Archs. néerl. Zool.* **13**: (Suppl. 1): 335–41. [*44*]

LEROUX, E. J., PARADIS, R. O., and HUDON, M. (1963) Major mortality factors in the population dynamics of the eye-spotted bud moth, the pistol casebearer, the fruit-tree leaf roller, and the European corn borer in Quebec. *Mem. ent. Soc. Canada* **32**: 67–82. [*60*; *62*]

LIESERING, R. (1960) Beitrag zum phytopathologischen Wirkungsmechanismus von *Tetranychus urticae* Koch (Tetranychidae, Acari). *Z. PflKrankh. PflPath. PflSchutz* **67**: 524–42. [*193*]

LINDEMAN, R. L. (1942) The trophic-dynamic aspect of ecology. *Ecology* **23**: 399–417. [*32*]

LLOYD, M. (1962) Probability and stochastic processes in ecology. *Rep. Cullowhee Conf. Inst. Stats. N. Carol. St. Coll. 1961.* [*166*]

LONGWORTH, J. F. (1963) The effect of swollen-shoot disease on mature cocoa in Nigeria. *Trop. Agric., Trin.* **40**: 275–83. [*187*]

LOTKA, A. J. (1920) Analytical notes on certain rhythmic relations in organic systems. *Proc. natn. Acad. Sci. U.S.A.* **7**: 410–15. [*30*]

LOTKA, A. J. (1925) *Elements of physical biology.* Baltimore: Williams and Wilkins. [*30*]

MACARTHUR, R. H. (1958) Population ecology of some warblers of northeastern coniferous forests. *Ecology* **39**: 599–619. [*33*]

MACARTHUR, R. H., and MACARTHUR, J. W. (1961) On bird species diversity. *Ecology* **42**: 594–8. [*33*]

MACFADYEN, A. (1952) The small arthropods of a *Mollinia* fen at Cothill. *J. Anim. Ecol.* **21**: 87–117. [*32*]

MACLELLAN, C. R. (1958) Role of woodpeckers in control of the codling moth in Nova Scotia. *Can. Ent.* **90**: 18–22. [*65*]

MACLELLAN, C. R. (1959) Woodpeckers as predators of the codling moth in Nova Scotia. *Can. Ent.* **91**: 673–80. [*65*; *73*]

MACLELLAN, C. R. (1960) Cocooning behavior of overwintering codling moth larvae. *Can. Ent.* **92**: 469–79. [*65*]

MACLELLAN, C. R. (1962) Mortality of codling moth eggs and young larvae in an integrated control orchard. *Can. Ent.* **94**: 655–66. [*65*; *69*; *71*; *72*]

MACLELLAN, C. R. (1963) Predator populations and predation on the codling moth in an integrated control orchard – 1961. *Mem. ent. Soc. Canada* **32**: 41–54. [*65*; *68*; *69*; *71*]

MAKSYMOV, J. K. (1959) Beitrag zur Biologie und Oekologie des Grauen Lärchenwicklers *Zeiraphera griseana* (Hb.) im Engadin. *Mitt. schweiz. Anst. forstl. VersWes.* **35**: 277–315. [*124*; *126*; *127*]

MARKKULA, M. (1953) Biologisch – ökologische Untersuchungen über die Kohlblattlaus, *Brevicoryne brassicae* L. *Annls zool. Soc. zool.-bot. fenn.* **15**: 1–113. [*102*]

MARTIGNONI, M. E. (1957) Contributo alla conoscenza di una granulosi di *Eucosma griseana* (Hübner) quale fattore limitante il pullulamento dell'insetto nella Engadina alta. *Mitt. schweiz. Anst. forstl. VersWes.* **32**: 371–418. [*124*; *129*]

MCFADDEN, J. T. (1963) An example of inaccuracies inherent in interpretation of ecological field data. *Am. Nat.* **97**: 99–116. [*179*]

MCKINLAY, K. S., and GEERING, Q. A. (1957) Studies of crop loss following insect attack on cotton in East Africa. I. – Experiments in Uganda and Tanganyika. *Bull. ent. Res.* **48**: 833–49. [*196*]

MCLEOD, J. H. (1954) Statuses of some introduced parasites and their hosts in British Columbia. *Proc. ent. Soc. Br. Columb.* **50**: 19–27. [*201*]

BIBLIOGRAPHY

MELLANBY, H. (1937) Experimental work on reproduction in the tsetse fly *Glossina palpalis*. *Parasitology* **29**: 131–41. [*14*]

MILLER, C. A. (1959) The interaction of the spruce budworm, *Choristoneura fumiferana* (Clem.), and the parasite *Apanteles fumiferanae* Vier. *Can. Ent.* **91**: 457–77. [*20*]

MILLER, C. A. (1960) The interaction of the spruce budworm, *Choristoneura fumiferana* (Clem.), and the parasite *Glypta fumiferanae* (Vier.). *Can. Ent.* **92**: 839–50. [*20; 178*]

MILLER, C. A. The black-headed budworm in eastern Canada. *Can. Ent.* **98**: 592–613). [*61; 168*]

MILNE, A. (1957a) The natural control of insect populations. *Can. Ent.* **89**: 193–213. [*4; 33; 46; 47*]

MILNE, A. (1957b) Theories of natural control of insect populations. *Cold Spring Harb. Symp. quant. Biol.* **22**: 253–67. [*2; 4; 5; 33; 46; 47; 48*]

MILNE, A. (1962) On a theory of natural control of insect population. *J. theor. Biol.* **3**: 19–50. [*2; 4; 33; 46; 47; 52; 54; 57; 60*]

MIYASHITA, K. (1963) Outbreaks and population fluctuations of insects, with special reference to agricultural insect pests in Japan. *Bull. natn. Inst. agric. Sci., Tokyo. Ser. C*, No. 15: 99–170. [*171*]

MIYASHITA, K., ITÔ, Y., NAKAMURA, K., NAKAMURA, M., and KONDO, M. (1965) Population dynamics of the chestnut gall-wasp, *Dryocosmus kuriphilus* Yasumatsu (Hymenoptera; Cynipidae). III. Five year observation on population fluctuations. *Jap. J. appl. Ent. Zool.* **9**: 42–52. [*183*]

MOEBIUS, K. (1877) Die Auster und die Austernwirtschaft. *Rep. U.S. Fish Comm.*, *1880*: 683–751 (Transl.). [*26; 57*]

MORRIS, R. F. (1955) The development of sampling techniques for forest insect defoliators, with particular reference to the spruce budworm. *Can. J. Zool.* **33**: 225–94. [*173*]

MORRIS, R. F. (1957) The interpretation of mortality data in studies of population dynamics. *Can. Ent.* **89**: 49–69. [*61*]

MORRIS, R. F. (1959) Single factor analysis in population dynamics. *Ecology* **40**: 580–8. [*20; 61; 138; 165; 177*]

MORRIS, R. F. (1960) Sampling insect populations. *A. Rev. Ent.* **5**: 243–64. [*173*]

MORRIS, R. F. [ed.] (1963) The dynamics of epidemic spruce budworm populations. *Mem. ent. Soc. Canada* **31**: 1–332. [*63; 170; 174; 175; 180; 201; 202*]

MORRIS, R. F. (1963) Predictive population equations based on key factors. *Mem. ent. Soc. Canada* **32**: 16–21. [*33; 138; 151; 168; 177*]

MORRIS, R. F. (1964) The value of historical data in population research, with particular reference to *Hyphantria cunea* Drury. *Can. Ent.* **96**: 356–68. [*172*]

MORRIS, R. F. (1965) Contemporaneous mortality factors in population dynamics. *Can. Ent.* **97**: 1173–84. [*167*]

MORRIS, R. F., and MILLER, C. A. (1954) The development of life tables for the spruce budworm. *Can. J. Zool.* **32**: 283–301. [*175*]

MOTT, D. G. (1963) The population model for the unsprayed area, pp. 99–109. *In* MORRIS, R. F. [ed.], The dynamics of epidemic spruce budworm populations. *Mem. ent. Soc. Canada* **31**. [*170*]

NAKAMURA, M., KONDO, M., ITÔ, Y., MIYASHITA, K., and NAKAMURA, K. (1964) Population dynamics of the chestnut gall-wasp *Dryocosmus kuriphilus* Yasumatsu (Hymenoptera: Cynipidae). I. Description of the survey stations and the life histories of the gall-wasp and its parasites. *Jap. J. appl. Ent. Zool.* **8**: 149–58. [*183*]

NEILSON, M. M., and MORRIS, R. F. (1964) The regulation of European spruce sawfly numbers in the Maritime Provinces of Canada from 1937 to 1963. *Can. Ent.* **96**: 773–84. [*137; 138; 139; 140; 142; 143; 144; 145*]

NICHOLSON, A. J. (1927) A new theory of mimicry in insects. *Aust. Zool.* **5**: 10–104. [*34*]

NICHOLSON, A. J. (1933) The balance of animal populations. *J. Anim. Ecol.* **2** (Suppl.): 132–78. [*20; 33; 34; 47; 48; 57; 60; 113; 117; 169*]

NICHOLSON, A. J. (1950) Population oscillations caused by competition for food. *Nature, Lond.* **165**: 476–7. [*30; 108*]

NICHOLSON, A. J. (1954a) Compensatory reactions of populations to stresses, and their evolutionary significance. *Aust. J. Zool.* **2**: 1–8. [*34; 57; 108; 110; 111; 112; 113*]

NICHOLSON, A. J. (1954b) An outline of the dynamics of animal populations. *Aust. J. Zool.* **2**: 9–65. [*3; 33; 34; 35; 36; 37; 38; 47; 54; 57; 60; 61; 63; 108; 109*]

NICHOLSON, A. J. (1957) The self-adjustment of populations to change. *Cold Spring Harb. Symp. quant. Biol.* **22**: 153–72. [*2; 3; 30; 34; 35; 108; 110; 112; 113; 115; 116; 117*]

NICHOLSON, A. J. (1958) Dynamics of insect populations. *A. Rev. Ent.* **3**: 107–36. [*3; 33; 34; 36; 44; 48; 54; 169*]

NICHOLSON, A. J., and BAILEY, V. A. (1935) The balance of animal populations. *Proc. zool. Soc. Lond.* **3**: 551–98. [*20; 113; 117; 178*]

ODUM, E. P., and SMALLEY, A. E. (1959) Comparisons of population energy flow of a herbivorous and a deposit-feeding invertebrate in a salt marsh ecosystem. *Proc. natn. Acad. Sci. U.S.A.* **45**: 617–22. [*32*]

ODUM, H. T. (1957) Trophic structure and productivity of Silver Springs, Florida. *Ecol. Monogr.* **27**: 55–112. [*32*]

ODUM, H. T. (1960) Ecological potential and analogue circuits for the ecosystem. *Am. Scient.* **48**: 1–8. [*32*]

ODUM, H. T., and PINKERTON, R. (1955) Time's speed regulation: the optimum efficiency for maximum power output in physical and biological systems. *Am. Scient.* **43**: 331–43. [*32*]

PARK, T. (1933) Studies in population physiology. II. Factors regulating initial growth of (*Tribolium confusum*) populations. *J. exp. Zool.* **65**: 17–42. [*30*]

PARK, T. (1948) Experimental studies of interspecies competition 1. Competition between populations of the flour beetles *Tribolium confusum* Duval and *Tribolium castaneum* Herbst. *Ecol. Monogr.* **18**: 265–307. [*33*]

PARK, T. (1955) Experimental competition in beetles, with some general implications, pp. 69–82. *In* CRAGG, J. B., and PIRIE, N. W. [ed.], *The numbers of man and animals*. Edinburgh: Oliver and Boyd. [*178*]

PARKER, J. R. (1942) Annual insect-damage appraisal. *J. econ. Ent.* **35**: 1–10. [*193*]

PATTEN, B. C. (1959) An introduction to the cybernetics of the ecosystem: the trophic-dynamic aspect. *Ecology* **40**: 221–31. [*32*]

PEARL, R. (1925) *The biology of population growth.* New York: A. A. Knopf. [*30*]

PETHERBRIDGE, F. R., and WRIGHT, D. W. (1938) The cabbage aphid (*Brevicoryne brassicae* L.). *J. Minist. Agric. Fish.* **45**: 140–8. [*102*]

PEUS, F. (1954) Auflösung der Begriffe 'Biotop' und 'Biozönose'. *Dt. ent. Z.* **1**: 273–308. [*32*]

PHILLIPS, J. (1934, 1935) Succession, development, the climax and the complex organism: an analysis of concepts. *J. Ecol.* **22**: 554–71, **23**: 210–46, 488–508. [*28*]

PICKETT, A. D. (1959) Utilization of native parasites and predators. *J. econ. Ent.* **52**: 1103–5. [*68*; *70*; *71*]

PICKETT, A. D. (1961) The ecological effects of chemical control practices on arthropod populations in apple orchards in Nova Scotia. *Tech. Meet. Int. Un. Conserv. Nat. nat. Resour. 8. Warsaw, 1960*: 19–24. [*191*]

PIMENTEL, D. (1961) On a genetic feed-back mechanism regulating populations of herbivores, parasites and predators. *Am. Nat.* **95**: 65–79. [*33*; *53*]

PLATT, J. R. (1964) Strong inference. *Science, N.Y.* **146**: 347–53. [*171*]

POSNETTE, A. F. (1945) Cacao virus research in West Africa. *Rep. Proc. Cocoa Conf. London, 1945*: 114–17. [*187*]

POSPELOV, V. P. (1926) The influence of temperature on the maturation and general health of *Locusta migratoria*, L. *Bull. ent. Res.* **16**: 363–7. [*14*]

PRESTON, F. W. (1962) The canonical distribution of commonness and rarity. *Ecology* **43**: 186–215, 410–32. [*33*]

RAINEY, R. C. (1964) Meteorology and the migration of desert locusts. *Anti-Locust Mem.* No. 7. [*24*]

RÉGNIER, R., HURPIN, B., and MAILLARD, J. (1953) Peut-on prévoir l'importance et la date des grandes sorties printanières des hannetons? Quand doit-on traiter? *C. r. hebd. Séanc. Acad. Agric. Fr.* **39**: 573–9. [*195*]

RICHARDS, O. W., WALOFF, N., and SPRADBERY, J. P. (1960) The measurement of mortality in an insect population in which recruitment and mortality widely overlap. *Oikos* **11**: 306–10. [*177*]

RIEK, E. F. (1961) The distribution and inter-relationships of *Perga affinis* Kirby and *Perga dorsalis* Leach (Hymenoptera, Symphyta). *Proc. Linn. Soc. N.S.W.* **86**: 237–40. [*92*]

SAILA, S. B., and SHAPPY, R. A. (1963) Random movement and orientation in salmon migration. *J. Conserv.* **28**: 153–66. [*174*]

SAUNDERS, D. S. (1962) Age determination for female tsetse flies and the age composition of samples of *Glossina pallidipes* Aust., *G. palpalis fuscipes* Newst. and *G. brevipalpis* Newst. *Bull. ent. Res.* **53**: 579–95. [*18*]

SCHEERER, M. (1963) Problem-solving. *Scient. Am.* **208**: 118–28. [*171*]

SCHWENKE, W. (1955) Ergebnisse und Aufgaben der ökologischen und biocönologischen Entomologie. *Wanderversamml. dt. Ent. 1954*: 62–80. [*32*]

SEYRIG, A. (1935) Relations entre le sexe de certains Ichneumonides (Hym.) et l'hôte aux dépens duquel ils ont vécu. *Bull. Soc. ent. Fr.* **40**: 67–70. [*15*]

S

HELFORD, V. E. (1911) Physiological animal geography. *J. Morph.* **22**: 551–618. [*27*]

SHELFORD, V. E. (1913) Animal communities in temperate North America as illustrated in the Chicago region. *Bull. geogr. Soc. Chicago* **5**: 1–368. [*27*]

SHELFORD, V. E. (1927) An experimental investigation of the relations of the codling moth to weather and climate. *Bull. Ill. St. nat. Hist. Surv.* **16**: 307–440. [*31*]

SHIYOMI, M., and NAKAMURA, K. (1964) Experimental studies on the distribution of the aphid counts. *Researches Popul. Ecol. Kyoto Univ.* **6**: 79–87. [*173*]

SKELLAM, J. G. (1951) Random dispersal in theoretical populations. *Biometrika* **38**: 196–218. [*173*]

SLOBODKIN, L. B. (1960) Ecological energy relationships at the population level. *Am. Nat.* **94**: 213–36. [*32*]

SLOBODKIN, L. B., and RICHMAN, S. (1961) Calories/gm in species of animals. *Nature, Lond.* **191**: 299. [*32*]

SMITH, F. E. (1961) Density dependence in the Australian thrips. *Ecology* **42**: 403–7. [*44*]

SMITH, H. S. (1935) The role of biotic factors in the determination of population densities. *J. econ. Ent.* **28**: 873–98. [*30; 31; 33; 43*]

SOLOMON, M. E. (1949) The natural control of animal populations. *J. Anim. Ecol.* **18**: 1–35. [*3; 4; 19; 24; 33; 57*]

SOLOMON, M. E. (1957) Dynamics of insect populations. *A. Rev. Ent.* **2**: 121–42. [*24; 33; 57; 60; 61*]

SOLOMON, M. E. (1964) Analysis of processes involved in the natural control of insects, pp. 1–58. *In* CRAGG, J. B. [ed.], *Advances in ecological research Vol. 2*. London and New York: Academic Press. [*33; 172; 180*]

SOUTHWOOD, T. R. E. (1966) *Ecological methods with particular reference to the study of insect populations*. London: Methuen. [*165; 173*]

STERN, V. M., SMITH, R. F., VAN DEN BOSCH, R., and HAGEN, K. S. (1959) The integration of chemical and biological control of the spotted alfalfa aphid. The integrated control concept. *Hilgardia* **29**: 81–101. [*191*]

STRICKLAND, A. H. (1951) The entomology of swollen shoot of cacao. I. The insect species involved, with notes on their biology. *Bull. ent. Res.* **41**: 725–48. [*187*]

STRICKLAND, A. H. (1952) The assessment of insect populations in relation to crop losses. *Trans. Int. Congr. Ent. 9. Amsterdam, 1951*: 611–18. [*194*]

STRICKLAND, A. H. (1956) Problems in estimating insect pest damage to clover seed crops. *Ann. appl. Biol.* **44**: 671–3. [*193*]

STRICKLAND, A. H. (1957) Cabbage aphid assessment and damage in England and Wales, 1946–55. *Pl. Path.* **6**: 1–9. [*194*]

SWEETMAN, H. L. (1938) Physical ecology of the fire brat *Thermobia domestica* (Packard). *Ecol. Monogr.* **8**: 285–311. [*15*]

TAMMES, P. M. L. (1961) Studies of yield losses. II. Injury as a limiting factor of yield. *Tijdschr. PlZiekt.* **67**: 257–63. [*196*]

TANADA, Y. (1963) Epizootiology of infectious diseases, pp. 423–75. *In* STEINHAUS, E. [ed.] *Insect pathology Vol. 2*. New York and London: Academic Press. [*20*]

BIBLIOGRAPHY

TANSLEY, A. G. (1935) The use and abuse of vegetational concepts and terms. *Ecology* 16: 284–307. [*5; 28; 57*]

TAYLOR, D. J. (1954) A summary of the results of capsid research in the Gold Coast. *Tech. Bull. W. Afr. Cacao Res. Inst.* No. 1. [*188*]

TEAL, J. M. (1957) Community metabolism in a temperate cold spring. *Ecol. Monogr.* 27: 283–302. [*32*]

THOMAS, I. (1948) Insect damage assessment. *Agriculture, Lond.* 55: 125–9. [*195*]

THOMPSON, W. R. (1922a) Etude de quelques cas simples de parasitisme cyclique chez les insectes entomophages. *C. r. hebd. Séanc. Acad. Sci., Paris* 174: 1647–9. [*30*]

THOMPSON, W. R. (1922b) Théorie de l'action des parasites entomophages. Accroissement de la proportion d'hôtes parasités dans le parasitisme cyclique. *C. r. hebd. Séanc. Acad. Sci., Paris* 175: 65–68. [*30*]

THOMPSON, W. R. (1923) La théorie mathématique de l'action des parasites entomophages. *Rev. gén. Sci. pur. appl.* 34: 202–10. [*30*]

THOMPSON, W. R. (1939) Biological control and the theories of the interactions of populations. *Parasitology* 31: 299–388. [*33*]

THOMPSON, W. R. (1956) The fundamental theory of natural and biological control. *A. Rev. Ent.* 1: 379–402. [*33; 54*]

THRESH, J. M. (1958) The control of swollen shoot virus in West Africa. *Tech. Bull. W. Afr. Cocoa Res. Inst.* No. 4. [*188*]

THRESH, J. M., and TINSLEY, T. W. (1959) The viruses of cacao. *Tech. Bull. W. Afr. Cocoa Res. Inst.* No. 7. [*187*]

TINSLEY, T. W. (1964) The ecological approach to pest and disease problems of cocoa in West Africa. *Trop. Sci.* 6: 38–46. [*186*]

TISCHLER, W. (1955) *Synökologie der Landtiere.* Stuttgart: Fischer. [*32*]

TROUVELOT, B., and GRISON, P. (1935) Variations de fécondité de *Leptinotarsa decemlineata* Say avec les *Solanum* tubifères consommés par l'insecte. *C. r. hebd. Séanc. Acad. Sci., Paris* 201: 1053–5. [*14*]

URQUHART, F. A. (1960) *The monarch butterfly.* Toronto: University of Toronto Press. [*24*]

UTIDA, S. (1955) Fluctuations in the interacting populations of host and parasite in relation to the biotic potential of the host. *Ecology* 36: 202–6. [*20*]

UTIDA, S. (1957) Population fluctuation, an experimental and theoretical approach. *Cold Spring Harb. Symp. quant. Biol.* 22: 139–51. [*33*]

UVAROV, B. P. (1931) Insects and climate. *Trans R. ent. Soc. Lond.* 79: 1–247. [*31*]

UVAROV, B. P. (1964) Problems of insect ecology in developing countries. *J. appl. Ecol.* 1: 159–68. [*182*]

VAGO, C. (1953) Facteurs alimentaires et activation des viroses latentes chez les insectes. *Int. Congr. Microbiol. 6. Italy, 1953.* 5: 556–64. [*20*]

VAN HOOF, H. A. (1954) Enkele gegevens over de melige koollius (*Brevicoryne brassicae* L.) in het Geestmerambacht, en zijn bestrijdive. *Tijdschr. PlZiekt.* 60: 131–5. [*102*]

VARLEY, G. C. (1947) The natural control of population balance in the knapweed gall-fly (*Urophora jaceana*). *J. Anim. Ecol.* 16: 139–87. [*178*]

BIBLIOGRAPHY

VARLEY, G. C. (1949) Special review: population changes in German forest pests. *J. Anim. Ecol.* **18**: 117–22. [*171*]

VARLEY, G. C. (1963) The interpretation of insect population changes. *Proc. Ceylon Ass. Advmt. Sci. 1962.* **18**: 142–54. [*167; 168*]

VARLEY, G. C., and GRADWELL, G. R. (1960) Key factors in population studies. *J. Anim. Ecol.* **29**: 399–401. [*175*]

VARLEY, G. C., and GRADWELL, G. R. (1963) Predatory insects as density dependent mortality factors. *Proc. Int. Congr. Zool. 16. Washington, 1963.* **1**: 240. [*180*]

VARLEY, G. C., and GRADWELL, G. R. (1965) Interpreting winter moth population changes. *Proc. Int. Congr. Ent. 12. London, 1964*: 377–8. [*180*]

VOELCKER, O. J. (1945) Aims and objects of the West African Cocoa Research Institute. *Rep. Proc. Cocoa Conf. London, 1945*: 109–10. [*188*]

VOLTERRA, V. (1926) Variazioni e fluttuazioni del numero d'individui in specie animali conviventi. *Atti Accad. naz. Lincei Memorie. Cl. di sci. fis. mat. nat.* **2**: 31–112. [*30*]

VERHULST, P. F. (1839) Notice sur la loi que la population suit dans son accroissement. *Corresp. Math. Phys.* **10**: 113–21. [*30*]

WALOFF, N. (1958) Some methods of interpreting trends in field populations. *Proc. Int. Congr. Ent. 10. Montreal, 1956.* **2**: 675–6. [*14*]

WALOFF, N., NORRIS, M. J., and BROADHEAD, E. C. (1948) Fecundity and longevity of *Ephestia elutella* Hübner (Lep. Phycitidae). *Trans. R. ent. Soc. Lond.* **99**: 245–67. [*15*]

WARMING, E. (1909) *An introduction to the study of plant communities.* Oxford: Clarendon Press. [*26; 27*]

WATERS, W. E. (1962) The ecological significance of aggregation in forest insects. *Proc. Int. Congr. Ent. 11. Vienna, 1960.* **2**: 205–10. [*173*]

WATT, K. E. F. (1959) A mathematical model for the effect of densities of attacked and attacking species on the number attacked. *Can. Ent.* **91**: 129–44. [*178*]

WATT, K. E. F. (1961) Mathematical models for use in insect pest control. *Can. Ent.* **93** (Suppl. 19): 1–62. [*167; 174; 175*]

WATT, K. E. F. (1962) Use of mathematics in population ecology. *A. Rev. Ent.* **7**: 243–60. [*167*]

WATT, K. E. F. (1963a) Mathematical models for five agricultural crop pests. *Mem. ent. Soc. Canada* **32**: 83–91. [*62*]

WATT, K. E. F. (1963b) Dynamic programming, 'Look ahead programming', and the strategy of insect pest control. *Can. Ent.* **95**: 525–36. [*171*]

WATT, K. E. F. (1964a) The use of mathematics and computers to determine optimal strategy and tactics for a given insect pest control problem. *Can. Ent.* **96**: 202–20. [*167*]

WATT, K. E. F. (1964b) Density dependence in population fluctuations. *Can. Ent.* **96**: 1147–8. [*180*]

WEIS-FOGH, T. (1956) Biology and physics of locust flight Pt. II. Flight performance of the desert locusts (*Schistocerca gregaria*). *Phil. Trans. R. Soc.* **239**: 459–510. [*24*]

WELCH, H. E. (1963) Nematode infections, pp. 363–92. *In* STEINHAUS, E. [ed.], *Insect Pathology Vol. 2.* New York and London: Academic Press. [*20*]

WELLINGTON, W. G. (1957) Individual differences as a factor in population dynamics: the development of a problem. *Can. J. Zool.* **35**: 293–323. [*50; 51*]

WELLINGTON, W. G. (1960) Qualitative changes in natural populations during changes in abundance. *Can. J. Zool.* **38**: 289–314. [*18; 50; 179*]

WELLINGTON, W. G. (1964) Qualitative changes in populations in unstable environments. *Can. Ent.* **96**: 436–51. [*50*]

WELLINGTON, W. G. (1965) Some maternal influences on progeny quality in the western tent caterpillar *Malacosoma pluviale* (Dyar.). *Can. Ent.* **97**: 1–14. [*172*]

WELLINGTON, W. G., FETTES, J. J., TURNER, K. B., and BELYEA, R. M. (1950) Physical and biological indicators of the development of outbreaks of the spruce budworm, *Choristoneura fumiferana* (Clem.) (Lepidoptera: Tortricidae). *Can. J. Res.* **28**: 308–31. [*195*]

WIGGLESWORTH, V. B. (1950) *The principles of insect physiology.* London: Methuen. [*14*]

WILBERT, H. (1962) Über Festlegung und Einhaltung der mittleren Dichte von Insektenpopulationen. *Z. Morph. Ökol. Tiere* **50**: 576–615. [*33*]

WILKINSON, P. R. (1964) Pasture spelling as a control measure for cattle ticks in southern Queensland. *Aust. J. agric. Res.* **15**: 822–40. [*201; 202*]

WILLIAMS, C. B. (1953) The relative abundance of different species in a wild animal population. *J. Anim. Ecol.* **22**: 14–31. [*33*]

WILLIAMS, E. J. (1959) *Regression analysis.* London and New York: John Wiley and Sons. [*151*]

WILLIAMS, G. (1953) Field observations on the cacao mirids *Sahlbergella singularis* Hagl., and *Distantiella theobroma* (Dist.) in the Gold Coast. Part II. Geographical and habitat distribution. *Bull. ent. Res.* **44**: 427–37. [*188*]

WOODWORTH, C. W. (1908) The theory of the parasitic control of insect pests. *Science, N.Y.* **28**: 227–30. [*34*]

WYNNE-EDWARDS, V. C. (1962) *Animal dispersion in relation to social behaviour.* Edinburgh and London: Oliver and Boyd. [*33; 55*]

ZIMAN, J. M. (1965) Mathematical models and physical toys. *Nature, Lond.* **206**: 1187–92. [*166*]

Index of biological names

Acleris variana, 61, 168
Aesiotes notabilis, 201, 203
alatae, 102ss.
Alternanthera denticulata, 91
Anagasta kuehniella, 117ss.
Anoplognathus sp., 154
ants, 70ss., 152ss.
Anystis agilis, 70
aphid(s), 102ss., 194, 197
Aphodius howitti, 22
Aphytis maculicornis, 201, 203
apple blossom thrips, see Thrips
    imaginis
apples, apple trees, orchards, 64ss.
apterae, 102ss.
archer fishes, 19
Ascogaster quadridentata, 70, 72
Australian plague locust, see
    Chortoicetes terminifera
Austroicetes cruciata, 39ss., 61

bacteria, 20, 117
barley grass, see Hordeum leporinum
bats, 19, 68
Beauveria tenella, 98
bembicine wasps, 19
biennial plants, 104
birds, 19, 22, 68, 73, 83, 95, 137,
    152ss.
black-headed budworm, see Acleris
    variana
Blattisocius tarsalis, 117ss.
Bombyliidae, 19
Boophilus microplus, 201, 202
Brassica oleracea var., 104
Brevicoryne brassicae, see cabbage
    aphid
brussel sprouts, 194

cabbage aphid, 10, 16, 21, 24, 55,
    102ss., 194
cacao, cacao plant, cacao – forest
    association, 184ss.

Cactoblastis cactorum, 48
Calonectria rigidiusculus, 188, 189
Cardiaspina albitextura, 21, 146ss.,
    179, 202
cattle tick, see Boophilus microplus
chameleons, 19
Chloris truncata, 81, 91
Choristoneura fumiferana, 139, 168,
    170, 174, 179, 180, 195, 201, 202
Chortoicetes terminifera, 41, 55
Chrysomela gemellata, 21
chrysopids, 70
Cirsium lanceolatum, 81ss.
clerids, 70
Coccinellidae, 71, 153
codling moth, 21, 22, 64ss., 195
cornborer, 195
cotton boll-weevil, 194
Crematogaster scita, 153
Cydia pomonella, see codling moth
Cymbonotus lawsonianus, 86

Dahlbominus fuscipennis, 137
Danais plexippus, 24
Danthonia spp., 83
desert locust, see Schistocerca
    gregaria
Diaphnocoris sp., 71
Diaretus rapae, 104ss.
Diprion hercyniae, 137ss., 166, 169,
    183, 201, 203
Distantiella theobroma, 188
dragonflies, 19
Drino bohemica, 140
Dryocosmus kuriphilus, 183

earwigs, 76
Echthroplexis psyllae, 153ss.
Encarsia formosa, 201, 202
encyrtid(s), 15, 152, 155
Eotetranychus sexmaculatus, 120ss.
Epiphyas postvittana, 184, 200, 201
epizootics, 128ss., 138

Index of terms
(incorporating concepts, definitions, and examples)

229